EXPLORING CREATION WITH CHEMISTRY

3rd Edition

Kristy Plourde

Solutions and Tests for
Exploring Creation With Chemistry, 3rd Edition

Published by
Apologia Educational Ministries, Inc.
1106 Meridian Plaza, Suite 220/340
Anderson, Indiana 46016
Apologia.com

Exploring Creation With Chemistry, 3rd Edition,
By Kristy Plourde

Printed by Bang Printing, Brainerd, MN

Manufactured in the USA

Second Printing: September 2016

ISBN: 978-1-940110-26-4

Cover: Doug Powell
Book Design: Doug Powell and Andrea Kiser Martin

INSTRUCTIONAL SUPPORT

Did you know that in addition to publishing award-winning curriculum Apologia also offers instructional support? We believe in helping students achieve their full potential, whatever their learning style. When you choose an Apologia curriculum, you are not just selecting a textbook. Every course has been designed with the student's needs in mind.

INDEPENDENT LEARNERS

Apologia textbooks and notebooks are written to the student in a conversational tone so that young people can easily navigate through the curriculum on their own. Apologia curriculum helps students methodically learn, self-check, and master difficult concepts before moving on.

AUDITORY LEARNERS

Sometimes students learn best when they can see and hear what they're studying. **Apologia Audio Books** are the complete text of the course read aloud. Students can follow along with the audio while reading or continue learning when they're away from home by listening in the car.

VISUAL LEARNERS

Sometimes subject matter is easier to comprehend when the topic is animated and presented by a knowledgeable instructor. **Apologia Video Instructional DVDs** enhance the student's education with more than 20 hours of instruction, including on-location video footage, PowerPoint lectures, animated diagrams of difficult concepts, and video presentations of all experiments.

SOCIAL LEARNERS

Some students learn best when they are able to interact with others in an online setting and ask questions of a live instructor. With **Apologia Online Academy**, students can interact in real time with both their classmates and a professional instructor in a structured virtual classroom. Also, we offer recordings of all our live classes on the Apologia Online Academy Video-On-Demand Channel.

At Apologia, we believe in homeschooling. We are here not only to support your endeavors, but also to help you and your student thrive! Find out more at apologia.com.

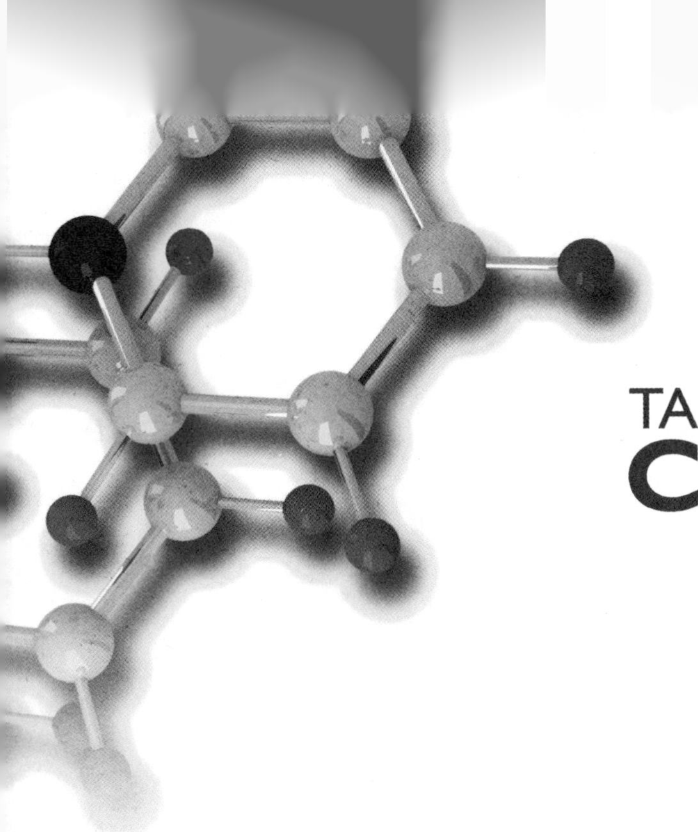

TABLE OF CONTENTS

EXPLORING CREATION WITH
CHEMISTRY
3rd Edition

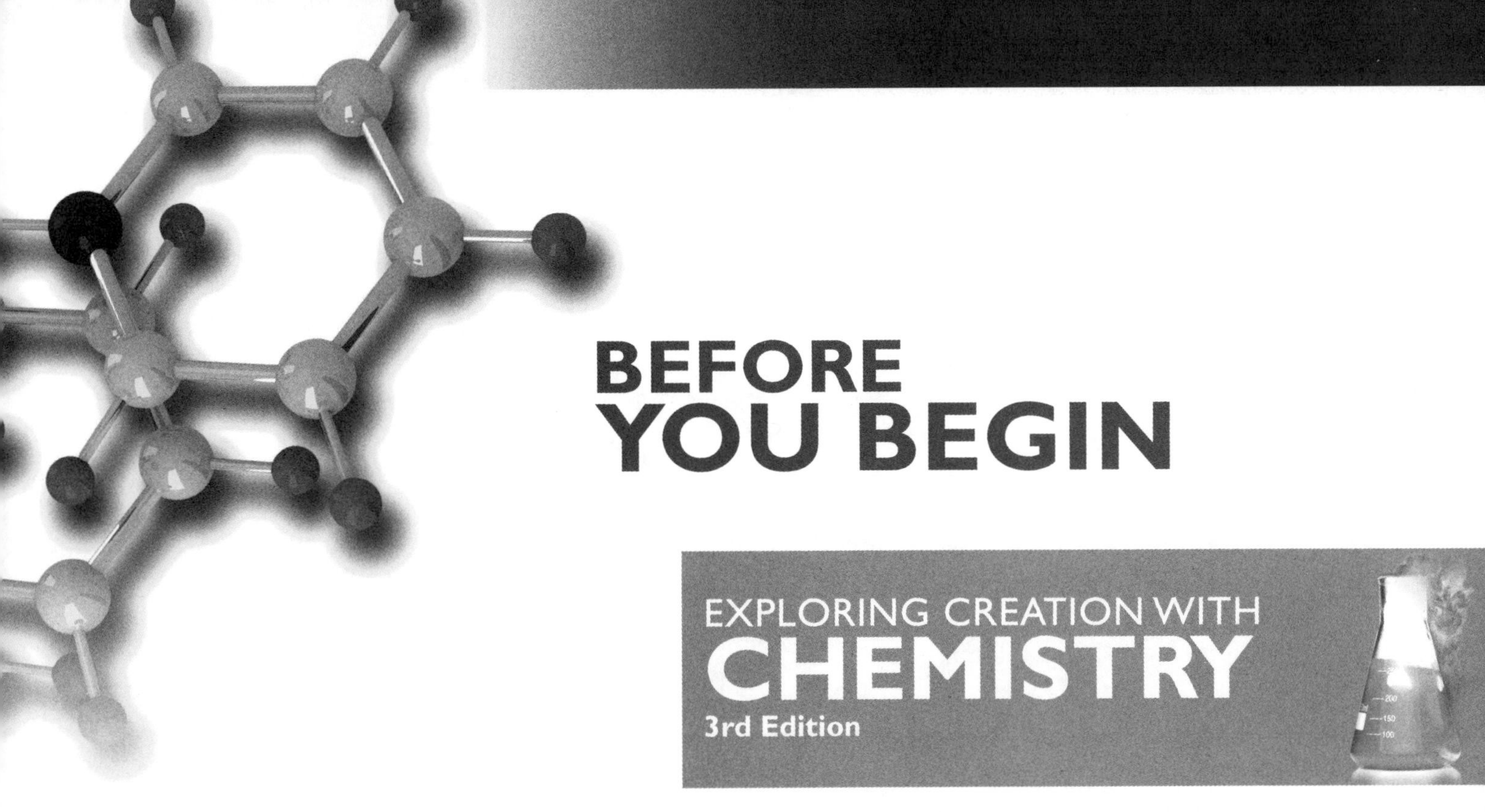

BEFORE YOU BEGIN

Thank you for choosing *Exploring Creation with Chemistry*. This course is designed to meet the needs of the homeschooling parent. We are very sensitive to the fact that most homeschooling parents do not know chemistry very well, if at all. As a result, they consider it nearly impossible to teach to their children. This course has several features that make it ideal for such a parent:

1. The course is written in a conversational style. Unlike many authors, we do not get wrapped up in the desire to write formally. As a result, the text is easy to read, and students feel more like they are *learning*, not just reading.

2. The course is completely self-contained. Each module in the student text includes the text of the lesson, experiments to perform, problems to work, and questions to answer. This Solutions and Tests Manual contains the worked-out solutions to the questions and problems in the student text, tests, worked-out solutions to the tests, and some extra material (example calculations for several experiments, as well as quarterly tests and their worked-out solutions).

3. The chemicals for the experiments are readily available at either the grocery or the hardware store. In addition, nearly all of the experiments can be performed with household equipment such as glasses, measuring cups, spoons, etc. If you wish to perform every experiment contained in the course, however, we suggest that you purchase a set of equipment that we make available for this course. A list of the equipment is included in the Student Notes section of the student text.

4. Most importantly, this course is Christ-centered. In every way possible, we try to make the science of chemistry glorify God. One of the most important things that

you and your student should get out of this course is a deeper appreciation for the wonder of God's creation!

ABOUT THE TEXT

The student text includes three types of exercises that the students are expected to complete: "On Your Own" questions, review questions, and practice problems.

- Students should answer the "**On Your Own**" questions as they read the text. This will cement in their minds the concepts they are trying to learn. Answers are provided at the end of each module in the student text. Students should check their work against the answer key and study it to learn why they missed any questions.

- Students should answer the **review questions** after they complete the entire module. These questions will help them recall the important concepts from the reading. As your students' teacher, you can decide whether or not your students can look at the answers to these questions, which are provided in this Solutions and Tests Manual.

- Students should solve the **practice problems** after completing the module. These problems allow them to review the important quantitative skills from the module. As your students' teacher, you can decide whether or not your students can look at the solutions to these problems, which are provided in this Solutions and Tests Manual.

In addition to the problems, there is also a test for each module. Those tests are in this Solutions and Tests Manual, but a packet of those tests is also included with this book. You can tear the tests out of the packet and give them to your students so that you need not give them this book. You can also purchase additional packets for additional students. You also have our permission to copy the tests out of this book if you would prefer to do that instead of purchasing additional tests for additional students. **We strongly recommend that you administer each test once a student has completed the module and all of the associated exercises. Students should be allowed to have only a calculator, pencil, paper, and a copy of the periodic table of the elements (provided in module 2) while taking the test.**

This book also includes quarterly tests. You can decide whether or not to give these tests to your students. These cumulative tests are probably a good idea if your students are planning to go to college, as they will need to get used to taking such tests. There are 4 quarterly tests, along with their solutions. Each quarterly test covers 4 modules. You have 3 options for administering them: (1) You can give each test individually so that students take 4 quarterly tests. (2) You can combine the first 2 quarterly tests and the second 2 quarterly tests to make 2 semester tests. (3) You can combine all 4 tests to make 1 final exam at the end of the year.

Any information that students must memorize, such as definitions and key facts, is centered in the text and printed in boldface type. Students should know any boldface words (centered or not) for the tests. In addition, students should memorize all definitions presented in the text, as well as all the numbered equations provided in the text, unless otherwise specified. In general, the student exercises such as "On Your Own" questions, review questions, and practice problems are meant as a study guide for the tests. Skills and knowledge necessary to complete them will be required for the tests.

You will notice that every answer or solution contains an underlined section. That is the answer. The rest is simply an explanation of how to get the answer. For questions that require a sentence or paragraph as an answer, students do not need to have *exactly* what is in the solution. The basic message of students' answers, however, have to be the same as the basic message given in the solutions. In the mathematical problems that students must solve, their answers do not need to be *identical* to our answers. They must have the same number of significant figures (you will learn what that means in module 1) as our answers, but they can vary by 1 or 2 digits in the last decimal place. This is to be expected due to rounding errors.

EXPERIMENTS

The experiments in this course are designed to be done as students are reading the text. We recommend that each student keep a notebook of experiments or purchase the Student Notebook that goes with the course. The details of how to perform experiments and keep a lab notebook are discussed in the Student Notes section of the student text.

GRADING

Grading your students is an important part of this course. We recommend that you *correct* the review questions and practice problems, but we do not recommend that you include a student's score in his grade. Instead, we recommend that each student's grade be composed solely of test grades and lab grades. Here is what we suggest you do:

1. Give each student a grade for each lab that is done. This grade should not reflect the accuracy of their results. Rather, it should reflect how well they followed directions, how well they did the calculations and kept track of significant figures, and how well they wrote up the lab in their notebook. If a lab requires calculations, a sample of those calculations is included in this book. That sample will help you determine whether or not your students did the calculations properly and kept track of significant figures.

2. Give each student a grade for each test. In the test solutions, you will see a point value assigned to each problem. If a student answered the problem correctly, he should receive the number of points listed. If a student got a portion of the problem

correct, he should receive a portion of those points. If a student's answer is correct except for the number of significant figures, you should take off one point. The test is set up to add up to 100 points, so your student's percentage grade is the total of the points for the test.

3. The Student Notebook for this course has more details on grading, as well as grade recording charts to help you keep track of your student's grades.

Each student's overall grade in the course should be weighted as follows: 35% lab grade and 65% test grade. If you use the cumulative tests, make them worth twice as much as each module test. If you really feel that you must include the review questions and practice problems in the student's total grade, make the labs worth 35%, the tests worth 55%, and the review questions and practice problems worth 10%. We suggest using a straight 90/80/70/60 scale should be used to calculate the student's letter grade as this is typical for most schools. If you have your own grading system, please feel free to use it.

Finally, we pride ourselves on the fact that this course is user-friendly and reasonably understandable. At the same time, however, *it is not easy*. This is a tough course. We have designed it so that any student who gets a C or better on the tests will be very well prepared for college.

COURSE ADMINISTRATION

The Student Notebook for this course has a complete schedule for your student to follow. If you choose to create your own schedule, we recommend you lay out your calendar to complete each module in 2 weeks. At the end of the 2-week period, give the module test. At the end of 8 weeks, have students use the ninth week to prepare for and take the quarterly test. If you are giving these tests for the purpose of college preparation, we recommend that you give the cumulative tests as 2 semester tests because that is what students will face in college. Based on this schedule, the complete course can be completed in 34–36 weeks. You can add breaks or weeks off at any point to accommodate your family's schedule. Marking the calendar for your students with deadlines will help them understand deadlines and will better prepare them for future courses in college. If a student has difficulty with a particular chapter, you can also add an extra week here or there to give allow additional time on a difficult concept.

MEASUREMENT, UNITS, AND THE SCIENTIFIC METHOD

SOLUTIONS TO THE MODULE 1 REVIEW QUESTIONS

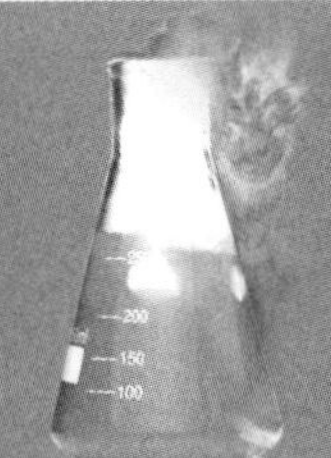

1. Pretty much everything except energy contains matter. Since (c) and (d) are types of energy, then heat (c) and light ray (d) have no matter.

2. Length is measured in meters, mass is measured in grams, time is measured in seconds, and volume is measured in liters.

3. The prefix *milli-* means 0.001 or one-thousandth.

4. All conversion factors, when in the form of a fraction, must equal one.

5. Since a kL is equal to 1,000 L and a mL is equal only to 0.001 L, the glass holding 0.05 kL holds 50 L and the glass holding 12,000 mL holds 12 L. The glass holding 0.05 kL has more liquid in it.

6. The ruler is marked off in 0.1 cm. We can estimate to the next decimal place. Since the end of the ribbon falls between 3.6 cm and 3.7 cm, the best answer is 2.65 cm. Answers from 2.61 to 2.69 should be counted correct as well. (Remember that the measurement started at 1 cm.)

7. Assuming both students reported the proper number of significant figures, the first student was more precise (because that measurement has more places to the right of the decimal), but the second student was more accurate (because that measurement is closer to the correct value).

8. A significant figure is a measured digit that comes from a measuring instrument.

9. a. The last zero is not significant, but the other zero is. There are 5 significant figures.

   b. All of the zeros are significant. Thus, there are 5 significant figures.

   c. None of the zeros in front are significant. There are 2 significant figures.

   d. All digits in front of the multiplication sign of a scientific notation number are significant, so this makes the zero significant. There are 3 significant figures.

10. The student's answer is wrong because the value for combined mass has too few significant figures. By the addition/subtraction rule we should have rounded to the 10ths place.

11. a. With addition problems, the units must match in order to be combined. The answer will have cm as the unit.

    b. With multiplication and/or division, the units will be combined in whatever math operation is present. So grams divided by milliliter will give a unit of grams per milliliter, or g/mL.

12. The answer to 11 b., or g/mL, will be the derived unit.

13. Only one digit in front of the decimal point and only significant figures go in front of the multiplication sign are the 2 rules of scientific notation.

14. Since 0.00 °C = 32.00 °F, both samples are at the same temperature.

SOLUTIONS TO THE PRACTICE PROBLEMS FOR MODULE 1

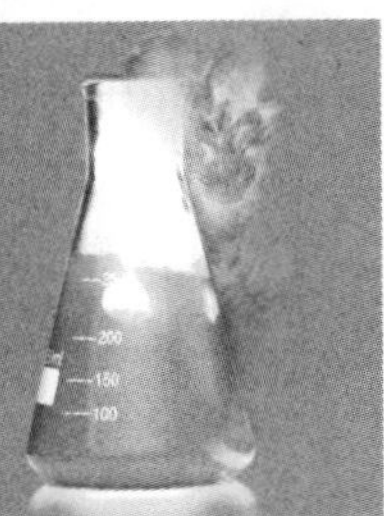

1. $\frac{2.4\ \cancel{mL}}{1} \times \frac{0.001\ L}{1\ \cancel{mL}} = \underline{0.0024\ L}$

The integers in the fractions are exact, and since the 0.001 comes from a definition, it is also exact. The only number that we need to consider when it comes to significant figures is the original measurement. It has 2 significant figures, so our answer can have only 2 significant figures.

2. $\frac{69.00\ \cancel{km}}{1} \times \frac{1{,}000m}{1\ \cancel{km}} = 69{,}000\ m = \underline{6.900 \times 10^4\ m}$

The only number whose significant figures we need to consider here is the original measurement. All of the other numbers are exact. Since the original measurement has 4 significant figures, our answer must have 4. The only way to express the answer with 4 significant figures is to use scientific notation. The decimal place in the scientific notation allows us to make one of the zeros significant. The answer 69,000 should have 4 significant figures, so 6.900×10^4 has 4 significant figures.

3. This is a 2-step conversion, since we know of no relationship between kg and cg.

$\frac{0.091\ \cancel{kg}}{1} \times \frac{1{,}000\ \cancel{g}}{1\ \cancel{kg}} \times \frac{1\ cg}{0.01\ \cancel{g}} = 9{,}100\ cg$

We must first convert kg to g and then convert g to cg. We'll do this on one line: Since the numbers in the conversion relationships are exact, the only number whose significant figures matter is 0.091. It has 2 significant figures, so the answer must have 2. We could also express the answer as $\underline{9.1 \times 10^3\ cg}$, as it would have 2 significant figures as well.

4. This is another 2-step conversion. We must convert mL to L and then L to kL, since there is no direct relationship between mL and kL.

$\frac{69.2\ \cancel{mL}}{1} \times \frac{0.001\ \cancel{L}}{1\ \cancel{ml}} \times \frac{1\ kL}{1{,}000\ \cancel{L}} = \underline{0.0000692\ kL}$

The numbers in the conversion relationships are exact, so the only thing that limits the significant figures is the original measurement. There are 3 significant figures in the original measurement, so the answer must have 3 as well. We could also express the answer as $\underline{6.92 \times 10^{-5}\ \text{kL}}$; it does not matter.

5. The volume of a box is length times width times height:

$$V = 23\ \text{cm} \times 45\ \text{cm} \times 38\ \text{cm} = 39{,}000\ \text{cm}^3$$

All of the numbers have 2 significant figures, so there should be 2 in the final answer as well. The problem asks for the answer in cubic centimeters (cm^3), so we still have to make a conversion:

$$\frac{39{,}000\ \cancel{\text{cm}^3}}{1} \times \left(\frac{0.01\ \text{m}}{1\ \cancel{\text{cm}}}\right)^3 = \frac{39{,}000\ \cancel{\text{cm}^3}}{1} \times \frac{0.000001\ \text{m}^3}{1\ \cancel{\text{cm}^3}} = \underline{0.039\ \text{m}^3}$$

6. This is a simple problem if we recognize that a cubic centimeter, or cc, is the same thing as a mL:

$$\frac{71.0\ \cancel{\text{mL}}}{1} \times \frac{0.001\ \text{L}}{1\ \cancel{\text{mL}}} = \underline{0.0710\ \text{L}}$$

The numbers in the conversion relationship are exact, so the only significant figures that matter are in 71.0 mL. That number has 3 significant figures, so the answer must have 3.

7. a. This number is greater than 1 so the exponent needs to be positive. To get the decimal next to the first digit, we have to move it one place. The answer, then, is $\underline{1.245000 \times 10^1}$.

   b. This is a large number, so the exponent has to be positive. The decimal point needs to be moved 6 places to the left. The answer, then, is $\underline{3.04 \times 10^6}$. Note that the last zeros are not significant.

   c. The exponent will be positive, and the decimal must be moved 3 places to get it next to the first digit. Thus, the answer is $\underline{6.100500 \times 10^3}$. All of the zeros in the original number are significant.

d. This number is small, so the exponent is negative, and the decimal needs be moved 3 places. The answer, then, is $\underline{1.234 \times 10^{-3}}$.

8. a. A positive exponent tells us to make this a big number by moving the decimal 9 places, so the answer is 6,000,000,000. The zeros are not significant, so this number has the same significant figures as the original number.

   b. A negative exponent means to make the number small by moving the decimal 3 places, so the answer is 0.0030450. The last zero must be there, as it is significant in the original number.

   c. A positive exponent tells us to make this a big number by moving the decimal 21 places, so the answer is 1,560,000,000,000,000,000,000. The zeros are not significant, so this number has the same significant figures as the original number.

   d. A negative exponent tells us to make the number small by moving the decimal 7 places, so the answer is 0.000000450000. The last zeros must be there, as they are significant in the original number.

9. We solve this problem by rearranging equation 1.1:

$$°F = \frac{9}{5}(°C) + 32$$

$$°F = \frac{9}{5}(85.6\ °C) + 32 = \underline{186°\ F}$$

So 85.6 °C is the same as 186 °F. Note that since the 9, 5, and 32 in this equation are exact, the only significant figures we need to count are in the original measurement. Since 85.6 °C has 3 significant figures, our answer must have 3.

10. First we convert from K to °C by using a rearranged form of equation 1.2:

$$°C = K - 273.15$$

$$°C = 396 - 273.15 = \underline{123\ °C}$$

Since we are subtracting here, we must follow the rule for addition and subtraction. The number 396 has its last significant figure in the ones place, while 273.15 has its last significant figure in the hundredths place. We can report our answer only to the ones place. This means that the Celsius temperature is 123 °C.

Now we can convert to Fahrenheit:

$$°F = \frac{9}{5}(°C) + 32$$

$$°F = \frac{9}{5}(123°\ C) + 32 = \underline{253\ °F}$$

Since our Celsius temperature had 3 significant figures, and since the other numbers in the equation are exact, the Fahrenheit temperature must have 3 significant figures. Thus, the answer is <u>253 °F</u>.

11. This problem is a direct application of equation 1.1:

$$°C = \frac{5}{9}(°F - 32)$$

$$°C = \frac{5}{9}(-7.0 - 32) = \underline{-22\ °C}$$

Since all of the numbers except –7.0 are exact, the answer must have the same number of significant figures as –7.0 has. The answer is <u>–22 °C</u>.

SAMPLE CALCULATIONS FOR EXPERIMENT 1.3

Length of the book: 10.95 in

Converted to cm:

$$\frac{10.95\ \cancel{in}}{1} \times \frac{2.54\ cm}{1\ \cancel{in}} = 27.81\ cm$$

We can have 4 significant figures because 2.54 cm is exact, as stated in the instructions. Thus, the only number to consider in this conversion is 10.95 in.

Width of the book: 8.54 in

Converted to cm:

$$\frac{8.54\ \cancel{in}}{1} \times \frac{2.54\ cm}{1\ \cancel{in}} = 21.7\ cm$$

Surface area of the book: (10.95 in) (8.54 in) = 93.5 in^2
There are 3 significant figures in the answer because 8.54 has only 3 significant figures.

Measured length of the book in cm: 27.76 cm (Very close to the converted value listed above.)

Measured width of the book in cm: 21.56 cm (Not too far off the converted value listed above.)

Surface area of the book: (27.76 cm) (21.56 cm) = 598.5 cm^2

Surface area converted to in^2:

$$\frac{598.5\ \text{cm}^2}{1} \times \left(\frac{1\ \text{in}}{2.54\ \text{cm}}\right)^2 = \frac{598.5\ \cancel{\text{cm}^2}}{1} \times \frac{1\ \text{in}^2}{6.4516\ \cancel{\text{cm}^2}} = 92.77\ \text{in}^2$$

Note that we have 4 significant figures because the conversion relationship is exact. This value is pretty close to the measured value for the surface area in inches.

SOLUTIONS TO THE EXTRA PRACTICE PROBLEMS FOR MODULE 1

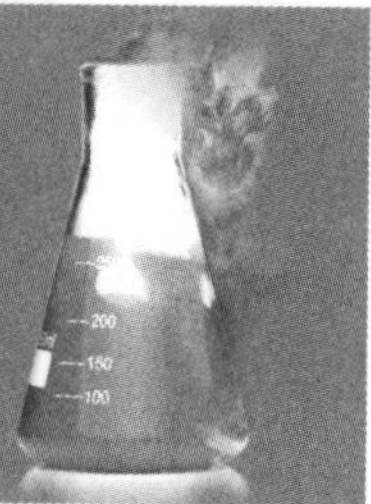

1. Remember, precision is determined by how many decimal places there are. The more decimal places, the more precise the number. Accuracy, on the other hand, tells us how close to the true value a measurement is. The first student is more precise, while the second student is more accurate.

2. $$\frac{403.1\ \cancel{g}}{1} \times \frac{1\ cg}{0.01\ \cancel{g}} = \underline{4.031 \times 10^4\ cg \text{ or } 40{,}310\ cg}$$

3. $$\frac{1355.1\ \cancel{mL}}{1} \times \frac{0.001\ L}{1\ \cancel{mL}} = \underline{1.3551\ L}$$

4. To do this question, we cannot directly convert miles to inches because we have no direct relationship between the 2. Thus, we must first convert to feet. Then we can convert to inches.

$$\frac{26.2\ \cancel{miles}}{1} \times \frac{5.280 \times 10^3\ feet}{1\ \cancel{mile}} = 138{,}000\ feet$$

$$\frac{138{,}000\ \cancel{feet}}{1} \times \frac{12\ inches}{1\ \cancel{foot}} = \underline{1.66 \times 10^6\ inches}$$

5. $$\frac{5{,}000{,}700\ \cancel{mm}}{1} \times \frac{0.001\ \cancel{m}}{1\ \cancel{mm}} \times \frac{1\ km}{1000\ \cancel{m}} = \underline{5.0007\ km}$$

6. First, we need to plug the dimensions into the equation and get the volume:

$$V = (0.12\ m) \times (0.34\ m) \times (0.050\ m) = 0.0020\ m^3$$

Although this *is* the volume of the sphere, it is not the answer because the question asked for the volume in *liters*. Do we know of a way to convert from m^3 to liters? No, because we don't know of a relationship between them. We do know, however, that a mL is the same as a cm^3. Thus, we can convert from m^3 to cm^3, which then is the same as mL. Once we have mL, we can get to liters:

$$\frac{0.0020\ m^3}{1} \times \left(\frac{1\ cm}{0.01\ m}\right)^3 = \frac{0.0020\ \cancel{m^3}}{1} \times \frac{1\ cm^3}{0.000001\ \cancel{m^3}} = 2.0 \times 10^3\ cm^3 = 2.0 \times 10^3\ mL$$

$$\frac{2.0 \times 10^3\ \cancel{mL}}{1} \times \frac{0.001\ liter}{1\ \cancel{mL}} = \underline{2.0\ liters}$$

7.

$$\frac{32.0\ \cancel{in}}{1} \times \frac{2.54\ cm}{1.00\ \cancel{in}} = \underline{81.3\ cm}$$

8.

$$\frac{4200\ \cancel{sec}}{1} \times \frac{1\ \cancel{min}}{60\ \cancel{sec}} \times \frac{1\ hr}{60\ \cancel{min}} = \underline{1.2\ hours}$$

9. a. The decimal point must be moved over 4 places to the left. The last 2 zeros are not significant, so they will not appear in the scientific notation number. This makes the final answer as $\underline{7.08 \times 10^4}$.

   b. The decimal point must be moved over 3 places to get it to the right of the 7. Since the number is small, the exponent is negative. The answer is $\underline{7.840 \times 10^{-3}}$.

10. a. The exponent is negative, so this is a very small number. Move the decimal number to the left 14 times to give <u>0.00000000000009510</u> (that is 13 zeros after the decimal point before the 9).

    b. The exponent is positive, so this is a big number. The exponent also tells us to move the decimal point over 6 places. The answer is <u>9,005,000</u>. Notice how decimal notation does not differentiate between a zero that is measured (the zero in the hundreds place) from a zero that is rounded (the last 2 zeros).

11. a. The 2 zeros to the right of the decimal point are not significant but the last zero is significant. There are <u>4 significant figures</u>.

b. The last zero is not significant as it is not to the right of the decimal point. There are <u>3 significant figures</u>.

c. This is a scientific notation number so all of the digits in front of the multiplication sign must be significant figures. So there are <u>4 significant figures</u>.

12. To Solve this one we rearrange equation 1.1 to solve for °F:

$$°F = \frac{9}{5}\ °C + 32$$

$$°F = \frac{9}{5}(34.5) + 32 = \underline{94.1\ °F}$$

Remember 32 is exact. The starting temperature was 3 significant figures, therefore there are 3 significant figures in the answer.

13. To solve this one, we start with equation 1.1:

$$°C = \frac{5}{9}\ (°F - 32)$$

$$°C = \frac{5}{9}(350.0 - 32) = 176.7\ °C$$

Now that we have the temperature in Celsius, we can convert to Kelvin:

$$K = 176.7\ °C + 273.15 = \underline{449.9\ K}$$

Neither of these numbers is exact, so we must use the rule of addition. The least precise number (176.7) has its last significant figure in the tenths place, so the answer must be reported to the tenths place.

TEST FOR MODULE 1

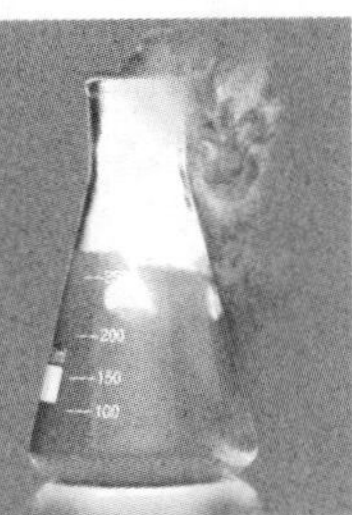

1. (4 pts) Which of the following does not contain matter?
   a. Air
   b. Lightning
   c. A golf ball
   d. A balloon full of air

2. (4 pts) Which of the following is equivalent to the prefix *milli-*?
   a. 0.001
   b. 1/1,000
   c. Both a and b
   d. Neither a nor b

3. (4 pts) Which of the following is equivalent to the prefix *kilo-*?
   a. 1/1,000
   b. 100
   c. 1,000,000
   d. None of the above

4. (4 pts) Which of the following is the correct base metric unit for volume?
   a. Liter
   b. Gallon
   c. Cubic Meter
   d. Milliliter
   e. None of the above

5. (4 pts) Which of the following is the correct base metric unit for mass?
   a. Pound
   b. Gram
   c. Newton
   d. None of the above

6. (4 pts) Which has more mass, a 0.3 g rock or a 30.0 mg rock?
   a. The 0.3 g rock
   b. The 30.0 mg rock
   c. Neither, they are equal in mass.
   d. Cannot solve this problem because grams are not used for mass.

Using the measurements below, answer questions 7 and 8 (Answer using only 1 letter per question, please).

The following numbers are the results of several measurements of a 100.0 yard football field:

a. 113.1 yards
b. 102 yards
c. 1.0×10^2 yards
d. 99.126 yards

7. (4 pts) Which of these numbers represents the most precise measurement?

8. (4 pts) Which of these numbers is the most accurate?

9. (4 pts) What is the volume of the liquid in the following graduated cylinder?

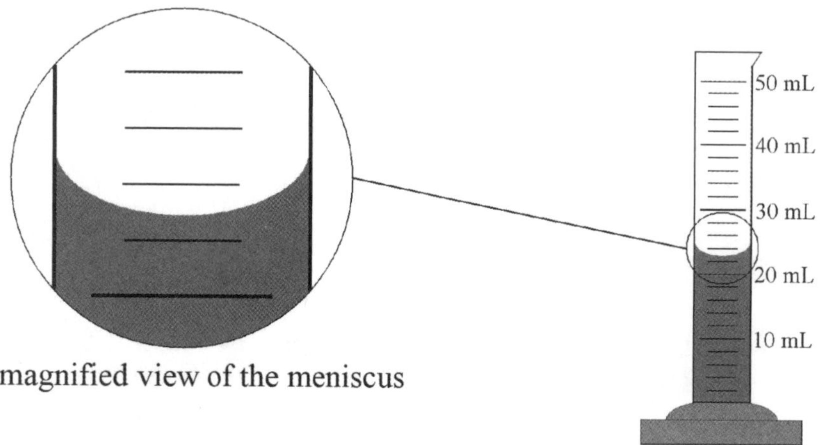

magnified view of the meniscus

10. (4 pts) How many cm are in 16.2 m?
    a. 1.62 cm
    b. 1.62×10^2 cm
    c. 1.62×10^3 cm
    d. 162 cm
    e. None of the above

11. (4 pts) Convert the number 3,478 to scientific notation.
    a. 3.478×10^3
    b. 3.478×10^4
    c. 3.478×10^5
    d. 34.78×10^4
    e. None of the above

12. (4 pts) Convert 0.000345 into scientific notation.
    a. 345×10^4
    b. 345×10^{-6}
    c. 3.45×10^4
    d. 3.45×10^{-4}
    e. None of the above

13. (4 pts) Which of the following is equivalent to 7.9010×10^{-4}?
    a. 0.0007901
    b. 79010
    c. 0.000079010
    d. 0.00079010
    e. None of the above

14. (4 pts) How many significant figures does 0.00150670 have?
    a. 4
    b. 5
    c. 6
    d. 7
    e. 8

15. (4 pts) How many significant figures does 1,500.00 have?
    a. 2
    b. 3
    c. 4
    d. 5
    e. 6

16. (4 pts) How many significant figures will the answer of 134.5×42 have?
    a. 2
    b. 3
    c. 4
    d. 5
    e. 6

17. (4 pts) A chemist wants to add these 2 measurements together: 2.30040×10^6 mL and 7,345.6 mL. What can she report as the correct combined volume?
    a. 2,307,745.6 mL
    b. 2,307,750 mL
    c. 2,307,700 mL
    d. None of the above

18. (4 pts) What is 39 °C in °F?
    a. 102.2 °F
    b. 3.9 °F
    c. 102 °F
    d. 128 °F
    e. None of the above

19. (4 pts) What is 212.0 °C in K?
    a. 485 K
    b. 485.1 K
    c. 485.15 K
    d. 485.2 K
    e. None of the above

Please show your entire work for the following problems.
Remember: **You must have units on all numbers, and your answers must have the correct number of significant figures.**

20. (6 pts) If a football field is 100.0 yards long, how many miles long is it? (1 yard = exactly 3 feet, 1 mile = 5.280×10^3 feet)

21. (6 pts) Convert 100.0 K to both Celsius and Fahrenheit.

22. (4 pts) If 1 gallon = 3.78 L, then how many gallons are equal to 20.0 L?

23. (8 pts) The volume of a sphere is given by the equation

$$V = \frac{4}{3}\pi r^3$$

π = 3.1416, and r is the radius of the sphere. If a sphere's radius is 3.1 m, what is its volume in liters? (Hint: 1 mL = 1 cm^3)

SOLUTIONS TO THE TEST FOR MODULE 1

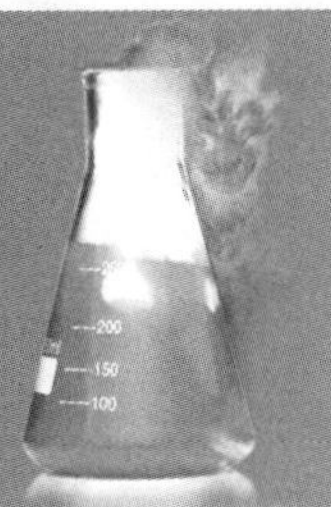

1. (4 pts) b. Lightning

2. (4 pts) c. Both a and b

3. (4 pts) d. None of the above. "Kilo-" means 1,000

4. (4 pts) a. Liter

5. (4 pts) b. Gram

6. (4 pts) a. The 0.3 g rock
   To properly compare these measurements, we need to get them into the same units. We are converting mg to g, although we could just as easily convert g to mg. Since the 30.0 mg rock is really equal to 0.0300, it is the smallest of the 2 masses.

   $$\frac{300\ \cancel{\text{mg}}}{1} \times \frac{0.001\ \text{g}}{1\ \cancel{\text{mg}}} = 0.0300\ \text{g}$$

7. (4 pts) d. 99.126 yards
   Remember, precision is determined by how many decimal places there are. The more decimal places there are, the more precise the number.

8. (4 pts) c. 1.0×10^2 yards
   Accuracy tells us how close to the true value a measurement is. Since a football field is supposed to be 100.0 yards long, (c) is the most accurate.

9. (4 pts) 22.8 mL (any number between 22.6 and 23.2 would be fine)
   It takes 5 dashes to go from 10 to 20 mL. This must mean that each dash is 2 mL.

Since the meniscus is between the first and second dash above the 20 mL mark, the answer is somewhere between 22 and 24 mL. The meniscus looks just slightly below halfway between the 2, so we could estimate that it is a little less than 23 mL. Since we are always to estimate one more decimal place than the scale reads, we could say that the volume is 22.8 mL.(Any number between 22.6 and 23.2 would be fine.)

10. (4 pts) c. $\underline{1.62 \times 10^3 \text{ cm}}$

$$\frac{16.2\ \cancel{\text{m}}}{1} \times \frac{1\text{ cm}}{0.01\ \cancel{\text{m}}} = \underline{1.62 \times 10^3 \text{ cm}}$$

11. (4 pts) a. $\underline{3.478 \times 10^3}$

12. (4 pts) d. $\underline{3.45 \times 10^{-4}}$

13. (4 pts) d. 0.00079010

14. (4 pts) c. 6

15. (4 pts) e. 6

16. (4 pts) a. 2

17. (4 pts) a. 2,307,745.6 mL We must round by addition/subtract rule here. Both numbers that are added together are significant to the 10ths place. Therefore, we must also round our answer to the 10ths place!

18. (4 pts) e. None of the above.
Since 39 °C has two significant figures in it then we need to round the final answer to have two significant figures. Even though the calculator may give 102 °F as the answer, we need to report 1.0×10^2 to show two significant figures.

19. (4 pts) d. 485.2 K

$$K = °C + 273.15 = 212.0\ °C + 273.15 = 485.15\ K$$

Since we are adding, look at the decimal place. The 212.0 has its last significant figure in the tenths place, so the answer can only go to out to the tenths place. 212.0 has 4 significant figures, so the answer needs 4 significant figures. Since the last digit after the tenths place is a five, 485.15 should be rounded up to 485.2 K.

20. (6 pts: 3 pts converting to feet, 3 pts converting to miles, minus 1 pt for incorrect significant figures) 0.05682 miles
To do this problem, we cannot directly convert yards to miles because we have no direct relationship between the 2. Thus, we must first convert to feet. Then we can convert to miles.

$$\frac{100.0\ \cancel{\text{yards}}}{1} \times \frac{3\ \text{feet}}{1\ \cancel{\text{yard}}} = \underline{300.0\ \text{feet}}$$

We need to keep all of the significant figures that were in 100.0, since the relationship between yards and feet is exact. Now we can convert to miles:

$$\frac{300.0\ \cancel{\text{feet}}}{1} \times \frac{1\ \text{mile}}{5.280 \times 10^3\ \cancel{\text{feet}}} = \underline{0.05682\ \text{miles}}$$

21. (6 pts: 3 pts for the answer in °C, 3 pts for the other for the answer in °F, minus 1 pt for incorrect significant figures) –173.2 °C   –279.8 °F

$$°C = K - 273.15 = 100.0 - 273.15 = \underline{-173.2\ °C}$$

Since we are adding, we look at decimal place. The 100.0 has its last significant figure in the tenths place, so the answer can go out only to the tenths place.

$$°F = \frac{9}{5}(°C) + 32$$

$$°F = \frac{9}{5}(-173.2) + 32 = \underline{-279.8°\ F}$$

All numbers in this problem except the temperature in °C are exact. Thus, we keep the same number of significant figures as we had in the original measurement.

22. (4 pts: minus 1 pt for incorrect significant figures) 5.29 gallons

$$\frac{20.0 \cancel{\text{L}}}{1} \times \frac{1 \text{ gallon}}{3.78 \cancel{\text{L}}} = 5.29 \text{ gallon}$$

Both the starting amount and conversion have 3 significant figures, so the final answer is 3 significant figures.

23. (8 pts: 3 pts for the volume in m^3, 3 pts for the conversion to cm^3, and 2 pts for the conversion to liters, minus 1 pt for incorrect significant figures) 1.2×10^5 L This is the hardest problem on the test. First, we need to plug the radius in the equation and get the volume:

$$V = \frac{4}{3} \times (3.1416) \times (3.1 \text{ m})^3 = 1.2 \times 10^2 \text{ m}^3$$

There can be only 2 significant figures in the answer because 3.1 has only 2 significant figures. That's why the number is rounded to 1.2×10^2 m^3, or 120 m^3. Remember, integers are exact, so we do not consider the 4 or the 3 when counting significant figures.

Although this *is* the volume of the sphere, it is not the answer because the question asked for the volume in *liters*. Do we know of a way to convert from m^3 to liters? No, because we don't know of a relationship between them. We do know, however, that a mL is the same as a cm^3. Thus, we can convert from m^3 to cm^3, which then is the same as mL.

$$\frac{1.2 \times 10^2 \text{ m}^3}{1} \times \left(\frac{1 \text{ cm}}{0.01 \text{ m}}\right)^3$$

$$\frac{1.2 \times 10^2 \cancel{\text{m}^3}}{1} \times \frac{1 \text{ cm}^3}{0.000001 \cancel{\text{m}^3}} = 1.2 \times 10^8 \text{ cm}^3 = 1.2 \times 10^8 \text{ mL}$$

Now that we have the volume in mL, we can convert to L:

$$\frac{1.2 \times 10^8 \cancel{\text{mL}}}{1} \times \frac{0.001 \text{ L}}{1 \cancel{\text{mL}}} = 1.2 \times 10^5 \text{ L}$$

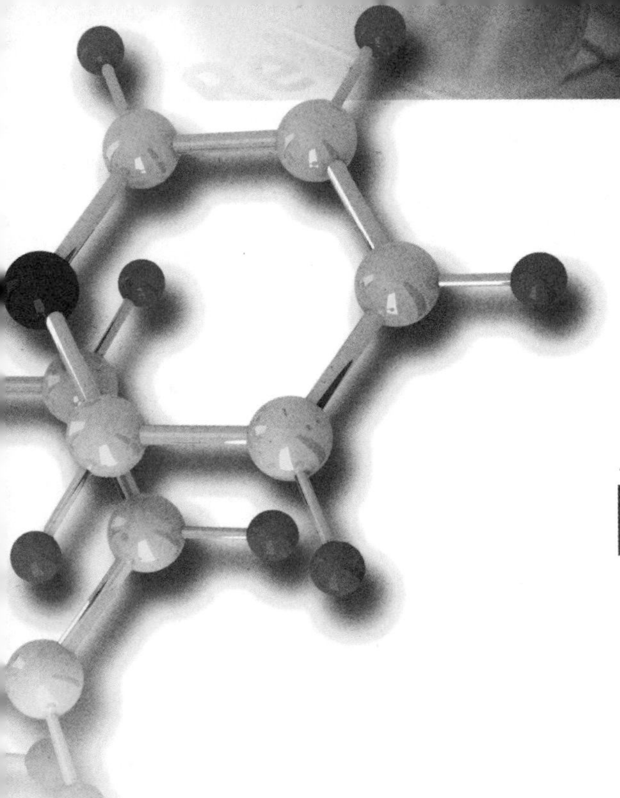

ATOMS AND MOLECULES

SOLUTIONS TO THE MODULE 2 REVIEW QUESTIONS

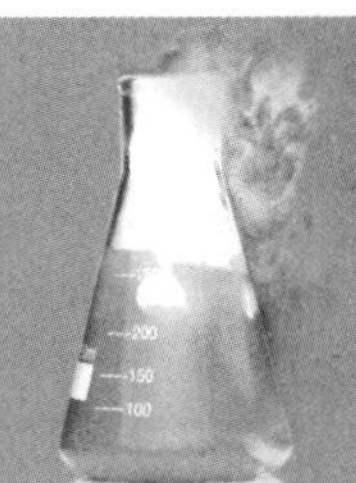

1. The continuous theory of matter states that matter comes in long, continuous sheets. The discontinuous theory, however, assumes that matter comes in little packets and the only reason matter looks continuous is that we cannot magnify it enough to see the little packets of matter.

2. The law of mass conservation and the law of definite proportions were instrumental in the development of Dalton's atomic theory. Dalton predicted the law of multiple proportions.

3. Matter cannot be created or destroyed. Throughout the chemical reaction that occurs in experiment 2.1, the total mass before the reaction must equal the total mass after the reaction. The mass measurement on the scale should not change during the reaction.

4. Dalton's atomic theory assumed 4 things:
   a. All elements are composed of small, indivisible particles called *atoms*.

   b. All atoms of the same element have exactly the same properties.

   c. Atoms of different elements have different properties.

   d. Compounds are formed when atoms are joined together. Since atoms are indivisible, they can join together only in simple, whole-number ratios.

   The assumptions that are wrong are a. and b. Atoms are not truly indivisible, and the mass of the atoms can change within the element.

5. a. Elements are made of identical atoms. All of the atoms within an element are identical.

   b. Compounds are made of identical molecules. All of the molecules within a compound are identical.

   c. An atom is the smallest unit of matter. A molecule is also a unit of matter, but it is formed when atoms join together. A molecule is made up of more than one atom.

   d. Elements are made of identical atoms while compounds are made of identical molecules.

6. Metals are malleable, have luster, and conduct electricity. Nonmetals are brittle, lack luster, and do not conduct electricity.

7. A heavy, jagged line runs down the right side of the chart. If an atom (excluding hydrogen) lies to the left of that line, it is a metal. If it lies to the right of that line, or if it is hydrogen, it is a nonmetal. Hydrogen is the exception.

8. A compound is ionic if, when dissolved in water, it conducts electricity. If it does not conduct electricity, the compound is covalent. Thus, we can perform experiments like experiment 2.2 to determine whether a compound conducts electricity when dissolved in pure water. That will determine whether it is ionic or covalent.

9. If a compound has a metal in it, it must be ionic. If it has no metals, it is covalent.

10. The law of multiple proportions governs why carbon and oxygen can form both CO and CO_2.

11. The way atoms can join together is different between ionic and covalent compounds. In ionic compounds there is only one possible combination of atoms. In covalent compounds, many combinations are possible. Therefore, we need 2 naming systems.

12. Anything that can be separated into its components must be a mixture. Compounds must first be *decomposed* before they can be separated into their component elements.

13. Anything that has a single chemical name is made up of a single atom or molecule. As a result, it must be a pure substance.

14. Nitrogen makes up 78% of the air we breathe.

15. A quantitative measurement is one that is made using a precise and quantifiable

measurement process. A qualitative measurement is descriptive, subjective, or difficult to measure; it is often an estimated measurement or best approximation

16. A change that seems to break a molecule apart is called a chemical change or chemical reaction.

17. The formula should be NaCl. The second letter of an atomic symbol needs to be a lowercase letter.

18. The elements lying along the jagged line are called metalloids or semimetals.

19. A dimensionless quantity is a measurement with no units.

20. Distilled water does not conduct electricity because there are no charged particles in the water that can carry the electricity.

SOLUTIONS TO THE PRACTICE PROBLEMS FOR MODULE 2

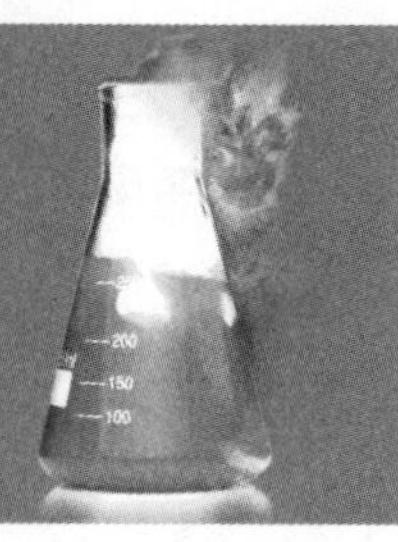

1. Since the chemist starts with 150.0 g of matter, he has to end up with 150.0 g of matter. Since hydrogen and oxygen are the only 2 elements in water, any mass not in the hydrogen must be in the oxygen:

   Total mass = Mass of hydrogen + Mass of oxygen

   Mass of oxygen = Total mass – Mass of hydrogen

   Mass of oxygen = 150.0 g – 16.7 g = 133.3 g

   So the chemist must have made 133.3 g of oxygen during the experiment.

2. The ash, carbon dioxide, and water all came from the combination of wood and oxygen.

   Mass of wood + Mass of oxygen = Mass of water + Mass of ash + Mass of carbon dioxide

   Mass of wood = 3.12 kg + 0.925 kg + 15.14 kg – 3.8 kg = 15.4 kg

   By the law of mass conservation, then, the mass of the wood before the decomposition must have been 15.4 kg. Note: change g to kg for Ash.

3. All elements (except hydrogen) that lie to the left of the jagged line on the chart are metals, while all elements to the right of the jagged line are nonmetals. Thus, Sc and Ra are metals, while Br and P are nonmetals.

4. The chemist starts with 40.0 g + 40.0 g = 80.0 g of matter, so she must end up with 80.0 g of matter. According to the problem, she made 42.6 g of hydrogen peroxide along with leftover hydrogen. Since all 40.0 g must be accounted for, the remaining mass must be in the hydrogen:

   Mass of hydrogen = Total mass – Mass of product

   Mass of hydrogen = 80.0 g – 42.6 g = 37.4 g

By the law of mass conservation, then, 37.4 g of hydrogen were left over. Since we started out with 40.0 g of hydrogen and 37.4 g were left over, only 40.0 g – 37.4 g = 2.6 g were actually used to make hydrogen peroxide. The correct recipe, then, is 2.6 g of hydrogen for every 40.0 g of oxygen.

5. The reaction starts with 100.0 g + 100.0 g = 200.0 g of matter; thus, there must be 200.0 g of matter after everything is finished. According to the problem, these amounts of calcium and nitrogen made 152.5 g of calcium nitride along with left-over nitrogen. Since all 200.0 g must be accounted for, the remaining mass must be in the nitrogen:

$$\text{Mass of nitrogen} = \text{Total mass} - \text{Mass of product}$$

$$\text{Mass of nitrogen} = 200.0\text{ g} - 152.5\text{ g} = 47.5\text{ g}$$

By the law of mass conservation, then, 47.5 g of nitrogen were left over. Since we started out with 100.0 g of nitrogen and 47.5 g were left over, only 100.0 g – 47.5 g = 52.5 g were actually used to make calcium nitride. Thus, the proper recipe for making 152.5 g of calcium nitride is to add 100.0 g of calcium to 52.5 g of nitrogen.

The problem, however, asks us the recipe for making 1.0 kg, or 1.0×10^3 g of calcium nitride. Therefore, we need to determine how much to increase the amount of ingredients in order to make this larger amount:

$$(152.5\text{ g})x = 1.0 \times 10^3\text{ g}$$

$$x = \frac{1.0 \times 10^3\text{ g}}{152.5\text{ g}} = 6.6$$

To make 1.0 kg, then, we just multiply the amount of each component by 6.6:

$$\text{Mass of calcium} = 100.0\text{ g} \times 6.6 = 6.6 \times 10^2\text{ g}$$

$$\text{Mass of nitrogen} = 52.5\text{ g} \times 6.6 = 3.5 \times 10^2\text{ g}$$

We need 6.6×10^2 g of calcium and 3.5×10^2 g of nitrogen to make 1.0 kg of calcium nitride.

6. Put the number of atoms as a subscript *after* each element symbol. If the number is a 1, drop it: $C_{12}H_{24}O_{10}S_2$.

7. To get the total number of atoms in the molecule, we have to realize that each subscript tells us how many of each atom it takes to make the molecule. Thus, the total number of atoms would just be the sum of the subscripts, remembering that if there is no number, we assume it is 1. There are, therefore, 22 atoms in 1 molecule of this compound.

8. Only C_2H_6 and PH_3 are made up entirely of nonmetals, so (a) and (b) are covalent.

9. a. This is a covalent compound, so we have to use prefixes. The prefix for carbon is *di-*. The prefix for hydrogen is *hexa-*, and we change hydrogen's ending to *-ide*. The name is dicarbon hexahydride.

   b. This is a covalent compound so we have to use prefixes. The prefix for phosphorus is *mono-*, but since phosphorus is first in the formula, we will drop the mono. The prefix for hydrogen is *tri-*, so the name is phosphorus trihydride.

   c. This is an ionic compound, so we will name the metal first, followed by the *-ide* name of the nonmetal. So the name of this compound is beryllium sulfide.

   d. This is an ionic compound, so we don't use prefixes: lithium oxide.

10. a. The prefix *tetra-* means 4 and the prefix *hexa-* means 6. The formula is N_4H_6.

    b. *Di-* means 2 and *mono-* means 1. The formula is H_2O.

11. a. Soil is a mixture of many different materials.

    b. Silver is a pure substance.

    c. Nitric acid is a pure substance.

    d. Lemonade is a mixture.

12. a. Since there are many different materials in soil and we can easily see them, this makes soil a heterogeneous mixture.

    b. Silver can be found on the periodic table, making it an element.

    c. Notice that a chemical formula was given for this substance. That makes this a compound.

d. When lemonade is mixed properly, it looks like a pure substance. The sample of lemonade will be the same throughout, making it a homogeneous mixture.

SOLUTIONS TO THE EXTRA PRACTICE PROBLEMS FOR MODULE 2

1. A compound is ionic if, when dissolved in water, it conducts electricity. If it does not conduct electricity, the compound is covalent. Thus, we can perform experiments like experiment 2.2 to determine whether a compound conducts electricity when dissolved in pure water. That will determine whether it is ionic or covalent.

2. If a compound has a metal in it, it must be ionic. If it has no metals, it is covalent. We can tell if a compound is a metal or not based on its position relative to the jagged line on the table. If it is to the left it is a metal, and if it is to the right it is a nonmetal. Hydrogen is an exception and is always a nonmetal.

3. All elements (except hydrogen) that lie to the left of the jagged line on the chart are metals, while all elements to the right of the jagged line are nonmetals. A molecule is covalent only if it has no metals in it. Thus, SO_2 and C_2H_4O are covalent.

4. All elements (except hydrogen) that lie to the left of the jagged line on the chart are metals, while all elements to the right of the jagged line are nonmetals. A molecule is ionic only if it has metals in it. Thus, $RbNO_3$ and Na_2SO_4 are ionic.

5. Since burning is a chemical reaction, the law of mass conservation needs to be obeyed. The mass before burning has to equal the mass after burning. The products (water, ash, and carbon dioxide) add up to 6.40 kg (1.04 kg + 0.308 kg + 5.05 kg), so the reactants must add up to 6.40 kg. The log was 5.13 kg, so that means 6.40 kg – 5.13 kg = 1.27 kg of oxygen were used.

6. The reaction starts with 100.0 g + 100.0 g = 200.0 g of matter; thus, there must be 200.0 g of matter after everything is finished. According to the question, these amounts of calcium and chlorine made 156.5 g of calcium chloride along with leftover calcium. Since all 200.0 g must be accounted for, the remaining mass must be in the calcium:

$$\text{Mass of calcium} = \text{Total mass} - \text{Mass of product}$$

$$\text{Mass of calcium} = 200.0\text{ g} - 156.5\text{ g} = 43.5\text{ g}$$

By the law of mass conservation, then, 43.5 g of calcium were left over. Since we started out with 100.0 g of calcium and 43.5 g were left over, then only 100.0 g – 43.5 g = 56.5 g were actually used to make calcium chloride. The proper recipe for making 156.5 g of calcium chloride is to add 100.0 g of chlorine to 56.5 g of calcium.

The question, however, asks us the recipe for making 1.500 kg, or 1.500×10^3 g of calcium chloride. Therefore, we need to determine how much to increase the amount of ingredients in order to make this larger amount:

$$156.5 \text{ g} \times x = 1.500 \times 10^3 \text{ g}$$

$$x = \frac{1.500 \times 10^3 \cancel{\text{g}}}{156.5 \cancel{\text{g}}} = 9.585$$

To make 1.500 kg, then, we just multiply the amount of each component by 9.585:

$$\text{Mass of chlorine} = 100.0 \text{ g} \times 9.585 = 958.5 \text{ g}$$

$$\text{Mass of calcium} = 56.5 \text{ g} \times 9.585 = 542 \text{ g}$$

We need <u>958.5 g of chlorine and 542 g of calcium to make 1.500 kg of calcium chloride</u>.

7. The reaction starts with 50.0 g + 50.0 g = 100.0 g of matter; thus, there must be 100.0 g of matter after everything is finished. According to the question, these amounts of nitrogen and hydrogen made 60.7 g of ammonia along with leftover hydrogen. Since all 100.0 g must be accounted for, the remaining mass must be in the hydrogen:

$$\text{Mass of hydrogen} = \text{Total mass} - \text{Mass of product}$$

$$\text{Mass of hydrogen} = 100.0 \text{ g} - 60.7 \text{ g} = 39.3 \text{ g}$$

By the law of mass conservation, then, 39.3 g of hydrogen were left over. Since we started out with 50.0 g of hydrogen and 39.3 g were left over, then only 50.0 g – 39.3 g = 10.7 g were used to make ammonia. The proper recipe for making 60.7 g of ammonia is to add 50.0 g of nitrogen to 10.7 g of hydrogen.

The question, however, asks us the recipe for making 150.0 g of ammonia. Therefore, we need to determine how much to increase the amount of ingredients in order to make this larger amount:

$$60.7 \text{ g} \times x = 150.0 \text{ g}$$

$$x = \frac{150.0 \cancel{\text{g}}}{60.7 \cancel{\text{g}}} = 2.47$$

To make 150.0 g, then, we just multiply the amount of each component by 2.47:

Mass of nitrogen = 50.0 g × 2.47 = 124 g

Mass of hydrogen = 10.7 g × 2.47 = 26.4 g

You need 124 g of nitrogen and 26.4 g of hydrogen to make 150.0 g of ammonia. The number actually add to 150.4 because of the rounding done for significant figures.

8. In this question, we already have the recipe for making methane with no leftovers (12.0 g carbon + 4.00 g hydrogen). When the chemist adds 150.0 grams of carbon, he is increasing the amount by:

$$12.0\text{ g} \times x = 150.0\text{ g}$$

$$x = \frac{150.0\text{ g}}{12.0\text{ g}} = 12.5$$

If the chemist added 12.5 times as much carbon, he should also add 12.5 times as much hydrogen:

4.00 g × 12.5 = 50.0 g

However, the chemist added 150.0 g of hydrogen. This means that 100.0 g of hydrogen will not react. 100.0 g of hydrogen will be left over once the methane is made.

9. The reaction starts with 54.0 g + 100.0 g = 154.0 g of matter; thus, there must be 154.0 g of matter after everything is finished. According to the question, these amounts of aluminum and sulfur made 150.3 g of aluminum sulfide along with leftover sulfur. Since all 154.0 g must be accounted for, the remaining mass must be in the sulfur:

Mass of sulfur = Total Mass – Mass of product

Mass of sulfur = 154.0 g – 150.3 g = 3.7 g

By the law of mass conservation, then, 3.7 g of sulfur were left over. Since we started out with 100.0 g of sulfur and 3.7 g were left over, then only 100.0 g – 3.7 g = 96.3 g were used to make aluminum sulfide. The proper recipe for making 150.3 g of aluminum sulfide is to add 54.0 g of aluminum to 96.3 g of sulfur.

The question, however, asks us the recipe for making 150.0 g of aluminum sulfide. Therefore, we need to determine how much to decrease the amount of ingredients in order to make this larger amount:

$$150.3 \text{ g} \times x = 150.0 \text{ g}$$

$$x = \frac{150.0 \text{ g}}{150.3 \text{ g}} = 0.9980$$

To make 150.0 g, then, we just multiply the amount of each component by 0.9980:

$$\text{Mass of aluminum} = 54.0 \text{ g} \times 0.9980 = 53.9 \text{ g}$$

$$\text{Mass of sulfur} = 96.3 \text{ g} \times 0.9980 = 96.1 \text{ g}$$

You need 53.9 g of aluminum and 96.1 g of sulfur to make 150.0 g of aluminum sulfide.

10. a. P_2O_6 b. N_2H_4 c. NO

11. a. This is a covalent compound, so prefixes must be used. The name is sulfur dioxide.

    b. This is an ionic compound, so no prefixes are needed. The name is calcium chloride.

    c. This is a covalent compound, so prefixes are needed. The name is oxygen dichloride.

    d. This is an ionic compound, so no prefixes are needed. The name is sodium sulfide.

12. a. The amount of cereal and milk is different in different parts of the bowl, so this is a heterogeneous mixture.

    b. This is a compound, as it is represented by a single chemical formula that contains more than one type of atom.

    c. This is an element, as it can be found on the periodic table (Cu).

    d. This is a homogeneous mixture, as the amounts of Kool-Aid and water are the same throughout.

TEST FOR MODULE 2

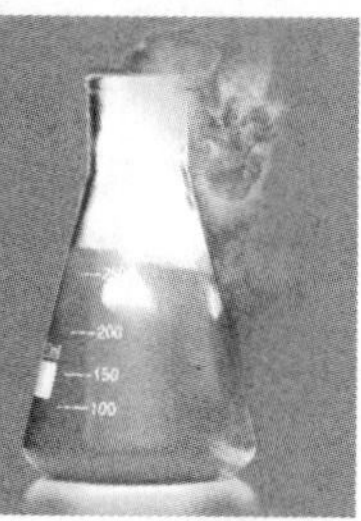

1. (4 pts) The principle that matter cannot be created nor destroyed is called:
   a. The law of mass conservation
   b. The continuous theory of matter
   c. The law of definite proportions
   d. The law of multiple of proportions
   e. None of the above

2. (4 pts) The principle that if elements combine in different proportions, they produce different compounds is called:
   a. The law of mass conservation
   b. The continuous theory of matter
   c. The law of definite proportions
   d. The law of multiple of proportions
   e. None of the above

3. (4 pts) State the law of definite proportions in your own words.

4. (4 pts) A chemist does 2 experiments. In one experiment, he finds that 14.0 g of nitrogen combine with 16.0 g of oxygen to make 30.0 g of a compound he calls compound A. In another experiment, the chemist finds that 48.0 g of oxygen combine with 42.0 g of nitrogen to make 90.0 g of a compound he calls compound B. The chemist states that the law of definite proportions tells him that compound A and compound B are 2 completely different compounds. Why is he wrong?

5. (4 pts) Which of the following is not 1 of Dalton's 4 assumptions in his atomic theory?
   a. All elements are composed of small, indivisible particles called atoms.
   b. All atoms of the same element have the exact same properties.
   c. Atoms of different elements have different properties.
   d. Compounds are formed when atoms are joined together. Since atoms are indivisible, they can join together only in simple, whole number ratios.
   e. All of the above is part of Dalton's atomic theory.

6. (6 pts) A chemist measures the mass of a chunk of wood to be 49.8 g. When the wood is decomposed, 15.0 g of water, and 12.0 g of ash, and some carbon dioxide are produced. How many grams of carbon dioxide were produced?
   a. 76.8 g
   b. 27.0 g
   c. 3.0 g
   d. 22.8 g
   e. None of the above

7. (3 pts) True or False: Manganese, Mn, is a nonmetal.

8. (3 pts) True or False: Xenon, Xe, is a nonmetal.

9. (4 pts) A substance that contains only one type of atom or molecule is a:
   a. Mixture
   b. Pure substance
   c. Physical substance
   d. Chemical substance
   e. None of the above

10. (4 pts) A substance that contains more than one type of individual atom or molecule is a:
    a. Mixture
    b. Pure substance
    c. Physical substance
    d. Chemical substance
    e. None of the above

11. (4 pts) Which of the following is a heterogeneous mixture?
    a. Italian salad dressing
    b. Flat soda
    c. Kool-Aid
    d. Brass
    e. None of the above

12. (4 pts) How can you experimentally determine if a compound is covalent?
    a. If it dissolves in water, then it is covalent.
    b. If it decomposes into its elements, then it is covalent.
    c. If it dissolves in water and then conducts electricity, then it is covalent.
    d. If it will be attracted by a magnet, then it is covalent.
    e. None of the above will prove a compound is covalent.

13. (4 pts) What is an ionic compound?
    a. A compound that will dissolve in water
    b. Two nonmetal atoms bonded together
    c. Two metal atoms bonded together
    d. A metal and a nonmetal atom bonded together
    e. None of the above

14. (4 pts) What type of compound uses the naming system consisting of prefixes like *mono-*, *di-*, and *tri-*?
    a. Ionic
    b. Covalent
    c. Both a and b
    d. Neither a nor b

15. (4 pts) What type of compound uses a naming system that has *-ide* as the ending on the nonmetals?
    a. Ionic
    b. Covalent
    c. Both a and b
    d. Neither a nor b

16. (4 pts) How many total atoms are in this molecule: $C_6H_{12}OH$?
    a. 3
    b. 4
    c. 19
    d. 20
    e. None of the above

17. (4 pts) You are told that a molecule contains a total of 17 atoms. If the formula is $C_5H_{10}Cl_x$, what must x be?
    a. 1
    b. 2
    c. 3
    d. 4
    e. None of the above

18. (4 pts) Which of the following compounds would conduct electricity when dissolved in water? C_3H_6ClF $C_6H_5CH_3$ CS_2 $BaSO_4$
    a. C_3H_6ClF
    b. $C_6H_5CH_3$
    c. CS_2
    d. $BaSO_4$
    e. CS_2 and $BaSO_4$

19. (4 pts) What is the name of N_2O_3?
    a. Nitrogen oxide
    b. Dinitrogen oxide
    c. Nitrogen trioxide
    d. Dinitrogen trioxide
    e. None of the above

20. (4 pts) What is the name of Ca_3N_2?
    a. Tricalcium dinitride
    b. Tricalcium dinitrogen
    c. Calcium nitride
    d. Calcium nitrogen
    e. None of the above

21. (4 pts) What is the chemical formula of sulfur trioxide?

Please provide all of the necessary work for the following problems.

22. (8 pts) In an experiment to determine how to make sulfur trioxide, a chemist combines 32.0 g of sulfur with 50.0 g of oxygen. She finds that she made 80.0 g of sulfur trioxide and had 2.0 g of leftover oxygen. How would the chemist make 100.0 g of sulfur trioxide so that she has no leftovers?

23. (8 pts) To make 44.0 grams of carbon dioxide, you must combine 12.0 g of carbon with 32.0 g of oxygen. If a chemist combines 120.0 g of carbon with 160.0 g of oxygen, how many grams of carbon dioxide will be made? If a substance is left over, indicate whether it is carbon or oxygen, and also determine how many grams are left over.

SOLUTIONS TO THE TEST FOR MODULE 2

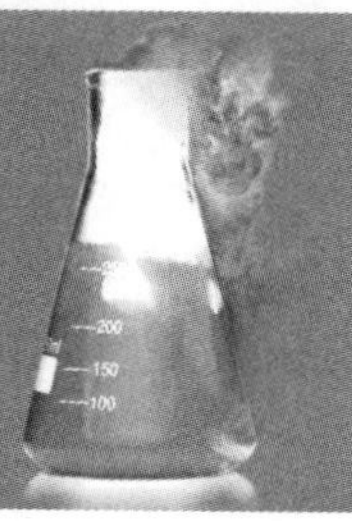

1. (4 pts) a. The law of mass conservation

2. (4 pts) d. The law of multiple proportions

3. (4 pts) A compound is always made up with the same proportion of its elements.

4. (4 pts) Compounds A and B are really the same compound. In order to make 2 different compounds, the elements would have to combine in different *proportions*. Since 48.0 g of oxygen + 42.0 g of nitrogen is just 3 times 16.0 g of oxygen and 14.0 g of nitrogen, the elements have combined in the same proportion, so they make the same compound.

5. (4 pts) e. All of the above is part of Dalton's atomic theory.

6. (6 pts) d. 22.8 g
   The law of mass conservation says that the total mass must always stay constant. Thus, if there was 49.8 g to start with, there must be 49.8 g after the decomposition. The water and ash add up to 27.0 g. Therefore, there must have been 22.8 g of carbon dioxide.

7. (3 pts) False Manganese, Mn, is a metal.

8. (3 pts) True Xenon, Xe, is a nonmetal.

9. (4 pts) b. Pure substance

10. (4 pts) a. Mixture

11. (4 pts) a. Italian salad dressing

12. (4 pts) e. None of the above will prove a compound is covalent.

13. (4 pts) d. A metal and a nonmetal atom bonded together

14. (4 pts) b. Covalent

15. (4 pts) c. Both a and b

16. (4 pts) d. 20
According to the formula there are 6 carbon atoms, 13 hydrogen atoms (12 + 1 hydrogen at the end of the formula), and 1 oxygen atom, giving a total of 20 atoms.

17. (4 pts) b. 2
According to the formula, the molecule has 5 carbon atoms and 10 hydrogen atoms. Thus, there are already 15 atoms. With 17 total atoms, there must be 2 more. Thus $x = 2$.

18. (4 pts) d. $BaSO_4$
Ionic compounds conduct electricity when dissolved in water. Ionic compounds have at least one metal and one nonmetal in them. Thus, BaSO4 will conduct electricity when dissolved in water.

19. (4 pts) d. Dinitrogen trioxide
Covalent compounds use prefixes.

20. (4 pts) c. Calcium nitride
Ionic compounds do not use prefixes.

21. (4 pts) SO_3

22. (8 pts: 4 pts for each mass, minus 1 pt for incorrect significant figures) 40.0 g of sulfur and 60.0 g of oxygen
Since 2.0 g of oxygen were left over, the chemist needed only 48.0 g of oxygen to make 80.0 g of sulfur trioxide. Since there was no leftover sulfur, the chemist

needed all 32.0 g of sulfur. Thus, to make 80.0 g of sulfur trioxide, she needs 32.0 g of sulfur and 48.0 g of oxygen. To make 100.0 g of sulfur trioxide, she simply needs to scale up by 100.0 ÷ 80.0 = 1.25. Thus, she needs 1.25 × 32.0 g = 40.0 g of sulfur and 1.25 × 48.0 g = 60.0 g of oxygen.

23. (8 pts: 4 pts for each mass, minus 1 pt for incorrect significant figures) The chemist will make 2.20×10^2 g of carbon dioxide, and there are 60.0 g of leftover carbon. Based on the recipe given, the chemist has 10 times as much carbon and 5 times as much oxygen. Thus, he can only make 5 times as much carbon dioxide as in the recipe because he will run out of oxygen long before carbon. This means he will make 5 × 44.0 = 2.20×10^2 g of carbon dioxide. This will use up all of the oxygen, but a lot of carbon will be left over. Since he can make only 5 times the amount of carbon dioxide as is in the recipe, he will use only 5 × 12.0 = 60.0 g of carbon. Since he started with 120.0 g of carbon and used only 60.0, there are 60.0 g of leftover carbon.

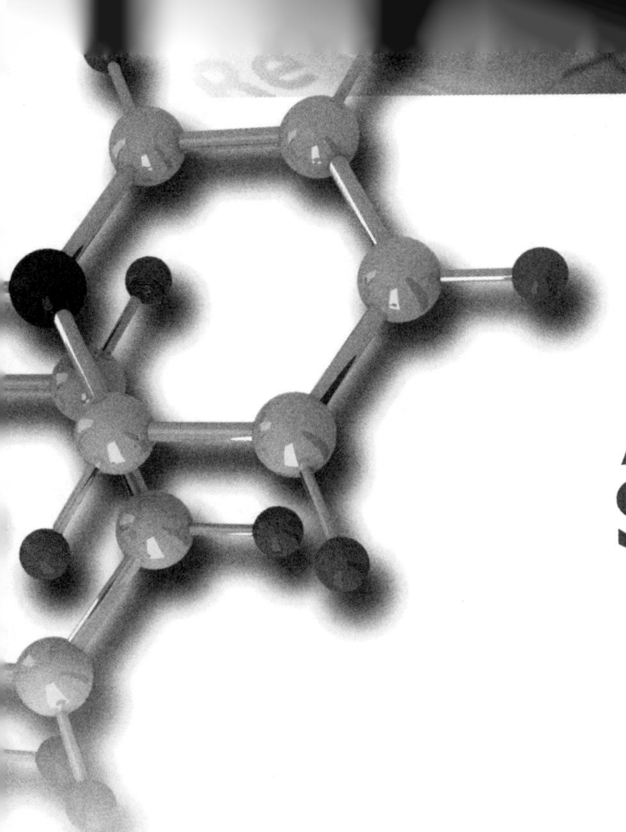

ATOMIC STRUCTURE

SOLUTIONS TO THE MODULE 3 REVIEW QUESTIONS

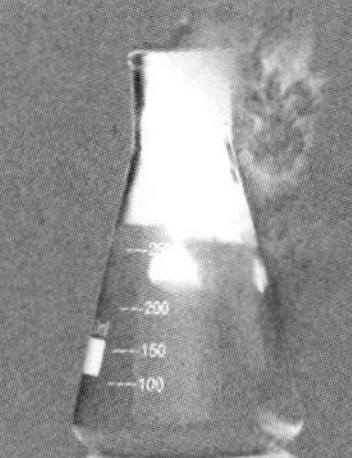

1. Rutherford experimentally determined that the plum pudding model of the atom was incorrect and proposed his own model of the atom, which we call the planetary model. It became the foundation upon which Bohr's model was built.

2. It is called a Crookes tube, and he used it to discover cathode rays, which were later determined to be electrons.

3. Like charges repel each other. Thus, the particles must have the same type of charge.

4. If a substance has an imbalance of charges, it takes on the charge that is more plentiful. Thus, this substance will be negatively charged.

5. Protons and neutrons are tightly packed together in the nucleus of the atom. Electrons are on the outside of the nucleus.

6. The only difference in isotopes is the number of neutrons, so isotopes behave identically in terms of chemistry. It is therefore nearly impossible to separate them.

7. The plum pudding model of the atom had the positive and negative charges equally dispersed throughout the entire atom. The planetary model, on the other hand, concentrated the positive charges at the center of the atom and had the negative charges whirling around the outside in set orbits.

8. For light, since wavelength times frequency equals the constant, c, if wavelength (or frequency) changes, then frequency will need to adjust to keep the product of the 2 equal to c. If wavelength gets longer, then the frequency will get shorter.

9. Remember ROY G. BIV. This is the order of visible light wavelengths from the largest to the smallest. Thus, the orange light bulb has larger wavelengths. When wavelength is large, however, frequency is small; thus, the violet light has the highest frequency. The higher the frequency, the higher the energy, so the violet light also has the highest energy.

10. The wavelengths emitted by the lights are the same, but the brighter bulb emits waves of larger amplitude.

11. When atoms absorb energy, their electrons jump to higher energy orbitals. When they emit light, the electrons are dropping down into lower energy orbitals.

12. The ground state of any substance is its lowest possible energy state. This is important in chemistry because all matter strives to reach its ground state.

13. The neutron is the heaviest, the proton is next, and the electron is the lightest. The proton and neutron differ only slightly in mass, but the proton is 2,000 times heavier than the electron.

14. A physical constant is a measureable quantity in nature that does not change. $c = 3.0 \times 10^8$ m/s or $h = 6.63 \times 10^{-34}$ J/Hz are 2 physical constants introduced in this module.

15. An orbital is a region of space where an electron is most likely to be found.

SOLUTIONS TO THE PRACTICE PROBLEMS FOR MODULE 3

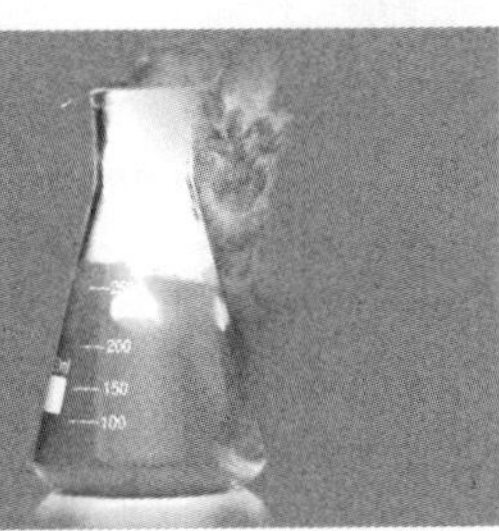

1. a. The periodic table of elements shows that Zr has an atomic number of 40. This means it has <u>40 protons and 40 electrons</u>. Its mass number, according to the problem, is 90. If it has 90 total protons + neutrons, and it has 40 protons, then it has 90 – 40 = <u>50 neutrons</u>.

   b. The periodic table shows that neon (Ne) has an atomic number of 10. This means it has <u>10 protons and 10 electrons</u>. Its mass number, according to the problem, is 22. If it has 22 total protons + neutrons, and it has 10 protons, then it has 22 – 10 = <u>12 neutrons</u>.

   c. The periodic table shows that Ni has an atomic number of 28. This means it has <u>28 protons and 28 electrons</u>. Its mass number, according to the problem, is 58. If it has 58 total protons + neutrons, and it has 28 protons, then it has 58 – 28 = <u>30 neutrons</u>.

   d. The periodic table shows that Rn has an atomic number of 86. This means it has <u>86 protons and 86 electrons</u>. Its mass number, according to the problem, is 222. If it has 222 total protons + neutrons and it has 86 protons, then it has 222 – 86 = <u>136 neutrons</u>.

2. Isotopes have the name number of protons (thus the same atomic number and the same element symbol) but different numbers of neutrons (thus different mass numbers). Therefore <u>^{22}Na, ^{23}Na, and ^{24}Na are isotopes</u>. They all have the same number of protons (11), but they have 11, 12, and 13 neutrons, respectively. Remember, isotope is a relational term. It tells how atoms relate to one another. There is not one "normal" atom with the rest being isotopes. Any atoms that all have the same number of protons but different numbers of neutrons are isotopes.

3. If it has 6 protons and electrons, its atomic number is 6. The symbol that has atomic number 6 is C. The mass number is the number of protons plus the number of neutrons, or 6 + 8 = 14. Thus, the symbol is <u>^{14}C</u>.

4. To solve this, we use equation 3.1:

$$f = \frac{c}{\lambda}$$

But now we have to rearrange it so that we are solving for wavelength:

$$\lambda = \frac{c}{f}$$

Now we can plug in the numbers:

$$\lambda = \frac{3.0 \times 10^{8} \frac{m}{\cancel{s}}}{2.4 \times 10^{14} \frac{1}{\cancel{s}}} = 1.3 \times 10^{-6}\,m$$

The wavelength is <u>1.3×10^{-6} m</u>. Each number in the equation has 2 significant figures, so the answer must have 2 significant figures.

5. This problem is a direct application of equation 3.2:

$$E = h \times f$$

$$E = 6.63 \times 10^{-34} \frac{J}{\cancel{Hz}} \times 9.8 \times 10^{20}\,\cancel{Hz} = 6.5 \times 10^{-13}\,J$$

The energy is <u>6.5×10^{-13} Joules</u>.

6. This problem is a little difficult because the only equation we can use to calculate the energy of light is equation 3.2, and it uses *frequency*, not *wavelength*. To solve this, then, we must first turn the wavelength we've been given into frequency. We can do this with equation 3.1. First, however, we must get units to work out. Since equation 3.1 uses c, and c is in m/s, we need to get our wavelength in meters before we can use equation 3.1.

$$\frac{712\,\cancel{nm}}{1} \times \frac{10^{-9}\,m}{1\,\cancel{nm}} = 7.12 \times 10^{-7}\,m$$

Now we can use equation 3.1:

$$f = \frac{c}{\lambda}$$

$$f = \frac{3.0 \times 10^{8} \frac{\cancel{m}}{s}}{7.12 \times 10^{-7}\,\cancel{m}} = 4.2 \times 10^{14} \frac{1}{s} = 4.2 \times 10^{14}\,Hz$$

Now that we have the frequency, we can use equation 3.2:

$$E = h \times f$$

$$E = 6.63 \times 10^{-34} \frac{J}{\cancel{Hz}} \times 4.2 \times 10^{14}\,\cancel{Hz} = \underline{2.8 \times 10^{-19}\,J}$$

The energy is $\underline{2.8 \times 10^{-19} \text{ Joules}}$.

7. <u>The electron in the 3p orbital has the higher energy</u> because energy level 3 is higher in energy than energy level 2. <u>The electron in the 2s orbital is in a spherical shape, while the 3p orbital is a dumbbell shape.</u>

8. a. To get to element V, we must go through row 1, which has 2 boxes in the s orbital block ($1s^2$). We then go through all of row 2, which has 2 boxes in the s orbital block and 6 boxes in the p orbital block ($2s^2\ 2p^6$). We also go through row 3, which has 2 boxes in the s orbital block and 6 in the p orbital block ($3s^2\ 3p^6$). We then go to the fourth row, where we pass through both boxes in the s orbital block ($4s^2$). Finally, we go through 3 boxes in the d orbital block. Since we subtract 1 from the row number for d orbitals, this gives us $3d^3$. Thus, our final electron configuration is:

   $\underline{1s^2\ 2s^2\ 2p^6\ 3s^2\ 3p^6\ 4s^2\ 3d^3}$

   b. To get to element N, we must go through row 1, which has 2 boxes in the s orbital block ($1s^2$). We then go through row 2, which has 2 boxes in the s orbital block and 3 boxes in the p orbital block ($2s^2\ 2p^3$). Our final electron configuration is:

   $\underline{1s^2\ 2s^2\ 2p^3}$

   c. To get to element Cs, we must go through row 1, which has 2 boxes in the s orbital block ($1s^2$). We then go through all of row 2, which has 2 boxes in the s orbital block and 6 boxes in the p orbital block ($2s^2\ 2p^6$). We also go through row 3, which has 2 boxes in the s orbital block and 6 in the p orbital block ($3s^2\ 3p^6$). We then go to the fourth row, where we pass through both boxes in the s orbital block, all 10 boxes in the d orbital block, and all 6 boxes in the p orbital block. Since we subtract 1 from the row number for d orbitals, this gives us $4s^2\ 3d^{10}\ 4p^6$. As we go through the fifth row, we will pass through 18 boxes ($5s^2\ 4d^{10}\ 5p^6$). Finally, we end up in the first box of the row 6, s orbital block. Thus, our final electron configuration is:

   $\underline{1s^2\ 2s^2\ 2p^6\ 3s^2\ 3p^6\ 4s^2\ 3d^{10}\ 4p^6\ 5s^2\ 4d^{10}\ 5p^6\ 6s^1}$

9. a. The nearest 8A element that has a lower atomic number than Ti is Ar. The only difference between Ti and Ar is that there are 2 boxes in the row 4, s orbital group and 2 boxes in the row 4, d orbital group. Therefore, the abbreviated electron configuration for Ti is:

   $\underline{[Ar]\ 4s^2\ 3d^2}$

b. The nearest 8A element that has a lower atomic number than S is Ne. The only difference between S and Ne is that there are 2 boxes in the row 3, s orbital group, 10 boxes in the row 3, d orbital group, and 4 boxes in the row 3, p orbital group. Thus, the abbreviated electron configuration for S is:

[Ne] $3s^2$ $3p^4$

c. The nearest 8A element that has a lower atomic number than Rb is Kr. The only difference between Rb and Kr is that there is 1 box in the row 5, s orbital group. The abbreviated electron configuration for Rb is:

[Kr] $5s^1$

10. a. There cannot be 7 electrons in the 3p orbitals. The orbital listed as 4d should be 3d.

b. The order that the orbitals were filled is wrong. 3d fills up after 4s.

SOLUTIONS TO THE EXTRA PRACTICE PROBLEMS FOR MODULE 3

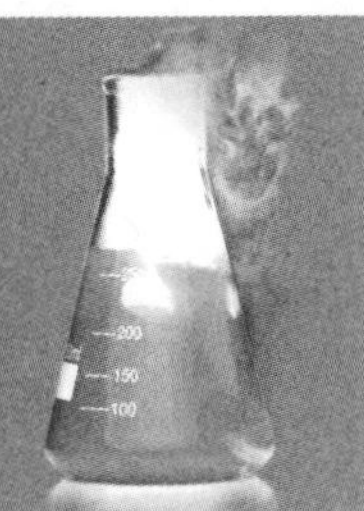

1. a. The periodic table of elements shows that Na has an atomic number of 11. This means it has <u>11 protons and 11 electrons</u>. Its mass number, according to the question, is 23. If it has 23 total protons + neutrons and it has 11 protons, then it has 23 – 11 = <u>12 neutrons</u>.

   b. The periodic table shows that Ar has an atomic number of 18. This means it has <u>18 protons and 18 electrons</u>. Its mass number, according to the question, is 40. If it has 40 total protons + neutrons and it has 18 protons, then it has 40 – 18 = <u>22 neutrons</u>.

   c. The periodic table shows that Fe has an atomic number of 26. This means it has <u>26 protons and 26 electrons</u>. Its mass number, according to the question, is 55. If it has 55 total protons + neutrons and it has 26 protons, then it has 55 – 26 = <u>29 neutrons</u>.

   d. The periodic table shows that Pu has an atomic number of 94. This means it has <u>94 protons and 94 electrons</u>. Its mass number, according to the question, is 238. If it has 238 total protons + neutrons and it has 94 protons, then it has 238 – 94 = <u>144 neutrons</u>.

2. Remember ROY G. BIV. This is the order of visible light wavelengths from the largest to the smallest. Thus, <u>the yellow light bulb has larger wavelengths</u>. When wavelength is large, however, frequency is small; thus, <u>the blue light has the highest frequency</u>. The higher the frequency, the higher the energy, so <u>the blue light also has the highest energy</u>. Since both yellow and blue are lights,they both must travel at the speed of light which means <u>neither has the fastest speed</u>.

3. We are given the fact that 1 nm = 10^{-9} m. Thus, we can first convert to meters:

$$\frac{425 \cancel{\text{nm}}}{1} = \frac{10^{-9}\text{ m}}{1 \cancel{\text{nm}}} = 4.25 \times 10^{-7}\text{ m}$$

Now we can use equation 6.1:

$$f = \frac{c}{\lambda} = \frac{3.0 \times 10^{8} \frac{\cancel{\text{m}}}{\text{sec}}}{4.25 \times 10^{-7} \cancel{\text{m}}} = \underline{7.1 \times 10^{14} \frac{1}{\text{sec}}} \text{ or } \underline{7.1 \text{ x } 10^{14}\text{ Hz}}$$

4. Once again, we use equation 6.1:

$$f = \frac{c}{\lambda}$$

But now we have to rearrange it so that we are solving for wavelength:

$$\lambda = \frac{c}{f}$$

Now we can plug in the numbers:

$$\lambda = \frac{3.0 \times 10^{8} \frac{\text{m}}{\cancel{\text{s}}}}{6.15 \times 10^{14} \frac{1}{\cancel{\text{s}}}} = \underline{4.9 \times 10^{-7} \text{ m}}$$

5.

$$E = h \times f = (6.63 \times 10^{-34} \frac{\text{J}}{\cancel{\text{Hz}}}) \times (7.05 \times 10^{14} \cancel{\text{Hz}}) = \underline{4.67 \times 10^{-19} \text{ J}}$$

6. To get the energy, we start with the frequency:

$$f = \frac{c}{\lambda} = \frac{3.0 \times 10^{8} \frac{\cancel{\text{m}}}{\text{sec}}}{1.95 \times 10^{-7} \cancel{\text{m}}} = \underline{1.5 \times 10^{15} \frac{1}{\text{sec}}}$$

Now we can get the energy :

$$E = h \times f = (6.63 \times 10^{-34} \frac{\text{J}}{\cancel{\text{Hz}}}) \times (1.5 \times 10^{15} \cancel{\text{Hz}}) = \underline{9.9 \times 10^{-19} \text{ J}}$$

7. We will have to start with the frequency:

$$E = h \times f$$

$$f = \frac{E}{h} = \frac{1.50 \times 10^{-18} \cancel{\text{J}}}{6.63 \times 10^{-34} \frac{\cancel{\text{J}}}{\text{Hz}}} = \underline{2.26 \times 10^{15} \text{ Hz}}$$

Now we can get wavelength:

$$\lambda = \frac{3.0 \times 10^{8} \frac{\text{m}}{\cancel{\text{s}}}}{2.26 \times 10^{15} \frac{1}{\cancel{\text{s}}}} = \underline{1.3 \times 10^{-7} \text{m}}$$

8. a. To get to element Sc, we must go through row 1, which has 2 boxes in the s orbital block ($1s^2$). We then go through all of row 2 which has 2 boxes in the s orbital block and 6 boxes in the p orbital block ($2s^22p^6$). We also go through row 3, which has 2 boxes in the s orbital block and 6 in the p orbital block ($3s^23p^6$). We then go to the fourth row where we pass through both boxes in the s orbital block ($4s^2$). Finally, we go through 1 box in the d orbital block. Since we subtract 1 from the row number for d orbitals, this gives us $3d^1$. Thus, our final electron configuration is:

   $1s^2 2s^2 2p^6 3s^2 3p^6 4s^2 3d^1$

   b. To get to element Cl, we must go through row 1, which has 2 boxes in the s orbital block ($1s^2$). We then go through all of row 2 which has 2 boxes in the s orbital block and 6 boxes in the p orbital block ($2s^22p^6$). We also go through both boxes in the s orbital block of row 3, ($3s^2$). Finally, we go through 5 boxes in the p orbital block of row 3, giving us $3p^5$. Thus, our final electron configuration is:

   $1s^2 2s^2 2p^6 3s^2 3p^5$

   c. To get to element Ca, we must go through row 1, which has 2 boxes in the s orbital block ($1s^2$). We then go through all of row 2, which has 2 boxes in the s orbital block and 6 boxes in the p orbital block ($2s^22p^6$). We also go through row 3, which has 2 boxes in the s orbital block and 6 in the p orbital block ($3s^23p^6$). We then go to the fourth row, where we go through the first 2 boxes, giving us $4s^2$. Thus, our final electron configuration is:

   $1s^2 2s^2 2p^6 3s^2 3p^6 4s^2$

9. a. The nearest 8A element that has a lower atomic number than P is Ne. The only difference between P and Ne is that there are 2 boxes in the row 2, s orbital group and 3 boxes in the row 3, p orbital group. Thus, the abbreviated electron configuration for P is:

   [Ne] $3s^2 3p^3$

   b. The nearest 8A element that has a lower atomic number than Mo is Kr. The only difference between Mo and Kr is that there are 2 boxes in the row 5, s orbital group and 4 boxes in the row 4, d orbital group. Thus, the abbreviated electron configuration for Mo is:

   [Kr] $5s^2 4d^4$

c. The nearest 8A element that has a lower atomic number than Ba is Xe. The only difference between Ba and Xe is that there are 2 boxes in the row 6, s orbital group. Thus, the abbreviated electron configuration for Ba is:

   [Xe] $6s^2$

10. a. There are too many electrons in the 2s orbital. There should be only 2 electrons there.

    b. The 3d orbital is not filled. We cannot go on to the next orbital until we fill up the one below.

    c. The 4d orbital should be after the 5s orbital, not before it.

TEST FOR MODULE 3

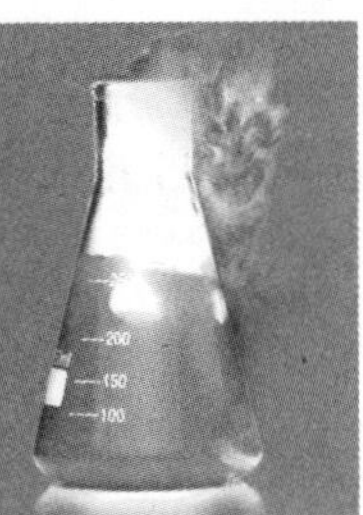

($c = 3.0 \times 10^8$ m/s, *nano-* = 1×10^{-9}, $h = 6.63 \times 10^{-34}$ J/Hz)

1. (4 pts) Two positive charges will ______________.
   a. Attract
   b. Repel
   c. Cancel
   d. Not be affected by one another
   e. None of the above

2. (4 pts) What is the overall charge on an atom that has 42 protons, 43 neutrons, and 41 electrons?
   a. +1
   b. −1
   c. +2
   d. −2
   e. None of the above

3. (4 pts) How many protons are in a ^{141}Ba atom?

4. (4 pts) How many neutrons are in a ^{141}Ba atom?

5. (4 pts) How many electrons are in a ^{141}Ba atom?

6. (4 pts) Crookes's tube experiment confirmed the existence of which atomic particle?
   a. Proton
   b. Neutron
   c. Electron
   d. Nucleus
   e. None of the above

7. (3 pts) True or False: The atomic number tells the mass of an atom's nucleus.

8. (3 pts) True or False: All atoms have an equal number of protons and electrons.

9. (3 pts) True or False: Isotopes have different masses.

10. (4 pts) For ^{23}Na, the number 23 stands for the _______________.
    a. Number of protons and neutrons
    b. Mass number
    c. Both a and b
    d. Neither a nor b

11. (4 pts) Artificially increasing the amount of ^{235}U in order to create an atomic bomb is called _______________.
    a. The Manhattan Project
    b. The plum pudding model
    c. Rutherford's experiment
    d. Isotopic enrichment

12. (4 pts) Rutherford's experiment showed that _______________.
    a. Uranium could be used for an atomic bomb
    b. Electrons existed as part of the atom
    c. Protons existed as part of the atom
    d. As a light wave's frequency increases, the wavelength decreases
    e. None of the above

13. (4 pts) Which is the heaviest: a neutron, a proton, or an electron?

Answer questions 14–16 using 2 lights of equal brightness: a blue and a yellow light.

14. (4 pts) Which light has the longest wavelength?
    a. Blue
    b. Yellow
    c. They are both the same.
    d. Not enough information to answer this question

15. (4 pts) Which light has the least amount of energy?
    a. Blue
    b. Yellow
    c. They are both the same.
    d. Not enough information to answer this question

16. (4 pts) Which light has the greatest amplitude?
    a. Blue
    b. Yellow
    c. They are both the same.
    d. Not enough information to answer this question

17. (4 pts) How many electrons can the s-, p-, and d-orbitals hold, respectively?
    a. 2, 4, and 6
    b. 1, 3, and 5
    c. 2, 6, and 10
    d. 2, 6, and 12
    e. None of the above

18. (3 pts) True or False: All forms of matter try to stay in their lowest possible energy state.

For the following problems, please provide the correct answer and the work needed to complete the problem.

19. (4 pts) What is the element with the following electron configuration? $1s^2 2s^2 2p^5$

20. (4 pts) Write the full electron configuration for Ca.

21. (4 pts) Give abbreviated electron configuration for Cl.

22. (4 pts) Give abbreviated electron configuration for Fr.

23. (8 pts) What is the frequency of light that has a wavelength of 10.0 nm?

24. (8 pts) If the energy of light emitted from an atom is 2.3×10^{-15} Joules, what is its wavelength?

SOLUTIONS TO THE TEST FOR MODULE 3

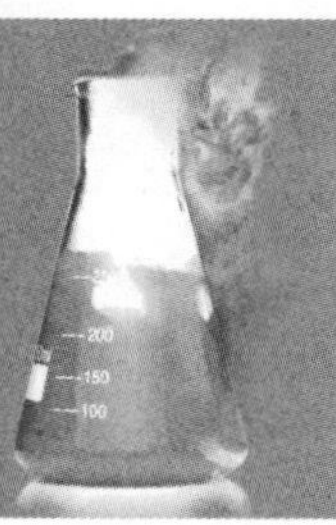

1. (4 pts) b. Repel

2. (4 pts) a. +1

3. (4 pts) 56 protons
   The periodic chart tells us that Ba has an atomic number of 56.

4. (4 pts) 85 neutrons
   The mass number (141) is the sum of protons plus neutrons. If there are 56 protons, then there must be 85 neutrons to make the sum 141.

5. (4 pts) 56 electrons
   Since Ba has no charge and there are 56 protons, it must also have 56 electrons.

6. (4 pts) c. Electron

7. (3 pts) False
   The atomic number does not tell us the mass of an atom's nucleus.

8. (3 pts) True
   All atoms have an equal number of protons and electrons. However, atoms with a charge will have a different number of electrons than protons. These will be discussed in module 4.

9. (3 pts) True
   Isotopes have different masses.

10. (4 pts) c. Both a and b
    The mass number is the sum of protons plus neutrons.

11. (4 pts) d. Isotopic enrichment

12. (4 pts) c. Protons existed as part of the atom.

13. (4 pts) The neutron is the heaviest of the 3.

14. (4 pts) b. Yellow
According to our mnemonic ROY G. BIV, the blue light has a shorter wavelength than the yellow light.

15. (4 pts) b. Yellow
Yellow has the longer wavelength and therefore lower frequency and lower energy.

16. (4 pts) c. They are both the same
Brightness is determined by amplitude; therefore, they have the same amplitude.

17. (4 pts) c. 2, 6, and 10

18. (3 pts) True
All forms of matter try to stay in their lowest possible energy state.

19. (4 pts) Fluorine or F
$1s^2 2s^2 2p^5$ is the electron configuration for Fluorine or F.

20. (4 pts) $1s^2 2s^2 2p^6 3s^2 3p^6 4s^2$
The electron configuration for Ca is $1s^2 2s^2 2p^6 3s^2 3p^6 4s^2$.

21. (4 pts) [Ne] $3s^2 3p^5$
The abbreviated electron configuration for Cl is [Ne] $3s^2 3p^5$.

22. (4 pts) [Rn] $7s^1$
The abbreviated electron configuration for Fr is [Rn] $7s^1$.

23. (8 pts: 4 pts for making the units consistent, and 4 pts for the answer, minus 1 pt for incorrect significant figures) $\underline{3.0 \times 10^{16} \text{ Hz}}$
This is an application of equation 3.1, but the units disagree. The speed of light was given using meters (m/s), but the wavelength is in nm. Thus, we must first convert nm to m:

$$\frac{10.0 \cancel{\text{nm}}}{1} \times \frac{1 \times 10^{-9} \text{ m}}{1 \cancel{\text{nm}}} = 1.00 \times 10^{-8} \text{ m}$$

Now that the units agree, we can use equation 3.1:

$$f = \frac{c}{\lambda} = \frac{3.0 \times 10^{8} \frac{\cancel{\text{m}}}{\text{s}}}{1.00 \times 10^{-8} \cancel{\text{m}}} = 3.0 \times 10^{16} \frac{1}{\text{s}}$$

Since 1/s is the same as Hz, the frequency is $\underline{3.0 \times 10^{16} \text{ Hz}}$.

24. (8 pts: 4 pts for frequency, and 4 pts for wavelength, minus 1 pt for incorrect significant figures) $\underline{8.6 \times 10^{-11} \text{ m}}$
There is no direct relationship between energy and wavelength. However, given the energy, we can get the frequency (equation 3.2), and then we can use equation 3.1 to go from frequency to wavelength.

$$E = h \times f$$

$$2.3 \times 10^{-15} \text{ J} = (6.63 \times 10^{-34} \frac{\text{J}}{\text{Hz}}) \times f$$

$$f = \frac{2.3 \times 10^{-15} \cancel{\text{J}}}{6.63 \times 10^{-34} \frac{\cancel{\text{J}}}{\text{Hz}}} = \underline{3.5 \times 10^{18} \text{ Hz}}$$

Now that we have frequency, we can get wavelength.

$$f = \frac{c}{\lambda}$$

$$3.5 \times 10^{18} \text{ Hz} = \frac{3.0 \times 10^{8} \frac{\text{m}}{\text{s}}}{\lambda}$$

$$\lambda = \frac{3.0 \times 10^{8} \frac{\text{m}}{\cancel{\text{s}}}}{3.5 \times 10^{18} \frac{1}{\cancel{\text{s}}}} = \underline{8.6 \times 10^{-11} \text{ m}}$$

The wavelength is $\underline{8.6 \times 10^{-11}\text{ m}}$.

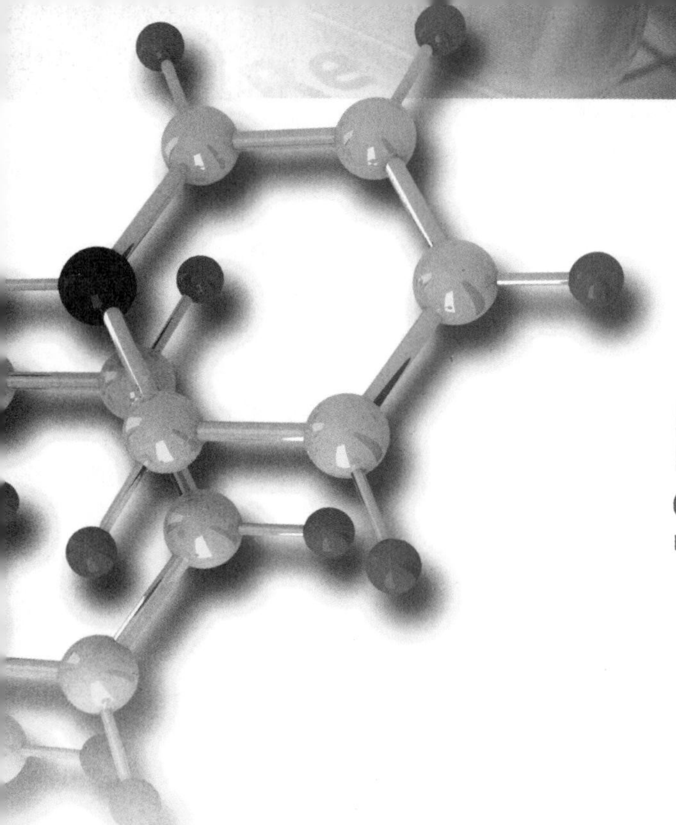

MOLECULAR STRUCTURE

SOLUTIONS TO THE MODULE 4 REVIEW QUESTIONS

1. Valence electrons are those electrons farthest away from the nucleus of an atom. They are important in chemistry because they are responsible for determining the chemical behavior of an atom.

2. The valence electrons in this configuration are the ones in the fifth energy level, since it is the farthest from the nucleus. There are a total of 5 (3 + 2) electrons in the fifth energy level, so there are 5 valence electrons.

3. Since life is based on carbon, it could, in theory, be based on any atom in the same column, since they all have similar chemistry. All compounds in column 4A have 4 valence electrons and can make up to 4 bonds, which makes them ideal central atoms. Thus, life could be based on Si, Ge, Sn, or Pb as well.

4. The noble gases are the elements in group 8A. They are important because they have ideal electron configurations.

5. All atoms strive for 8 valence electrons. Hydrogen, helium, lithium, boron, and beryllium are exceptions.

6. Metals tend to give up electrons to attain the ideal electron configuration, while nonmetals tend to gain electrons for the same purpose.

7. This statement only applies to the columns of the periodic table labeled with the letter A. The columns labeled with the letter B—the transition metals—only have 2 valence electrons.

8. An atom has an equal number of protons and electrons, no electrical charge. Ions have electrical charge because they have an imbalance of protons and electrons.

9. Ionization energy is the amount of energy needed to take an electron away from an atom.

10. Ionization energy, electronegativity, and atomic radius are all periodic properties.

11. Ionization energy and electronegativity increase as we move up a column and to the right along a row on the periodic table. Atomic radius decreases as we move in the same pattern.

12. Ionic compounds form when atoms give and take electrons. Thus, they are composed of ions. Covalent compounds result when atoms share electrons. Thus, no ions are formed.

13. All ionic formulas need to be in the lowest possible ratio. So the equation should be MgO.

14. Nitrogen, oxygen, and ozone protect the earth from the harmful rays of the sun.

15. The homonuclear diatomics are N_2, O_2, Cl_2, F_2, Br_2, I_2, At_2, and H_2.

SOLUTIONS TO THE PRACTICE PROBLEMS FOR MODULE 4

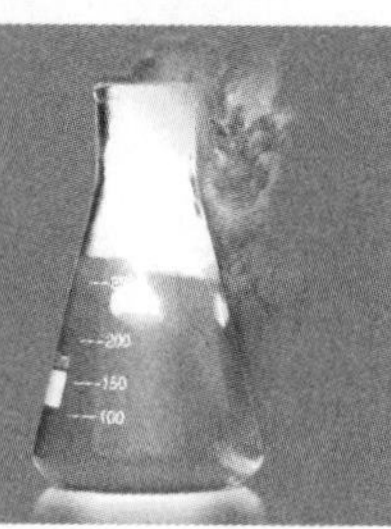

1. a. Ge is in group 4A, so it has 4 valence electrons:

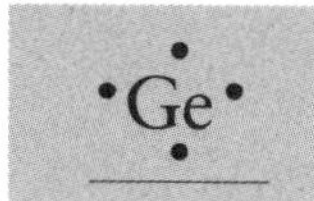

   b. Te is in group 6A, so it has 6 valence electrons:

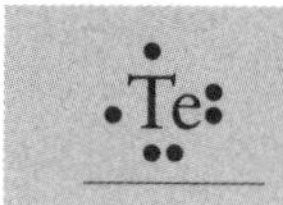

   c. Ba is in group 2A, so it has 2 valence electrons:

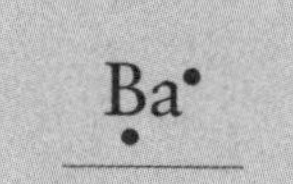

2. a. Al is in group 3A, so it wants a charge of 3+. Sulfur is in group 6A, so sulfide will have a charge of 2–. Ignoring the signs and switching the numbers gives us Al_2S_3.

   b. Iron has a roman numeral of I, which means Fe^{+}. Nitrogen is in group 5A, so nitride will have a charge of 3–. Ignoring the signs and switching the numbers gives us Fe_3N.

   c. Mg is in group 2A, so it wants a charge of 2+. Oxygen is in group 6A, so oxide will have a charge of 2–. The numbers are the same, so we ignore them: MgO.

   d. Cr is an exception because there is a roman numeral in the name. The numeral tells us that Cr wants a charge of 3+. Oxygen is in group 6A, so oxide will have a charge of 2–. Ignoring the signs and switching the numbers gives us Cr_2O_3.

3. Ionization energy decreases as you go down the chart. The atom with the lowest ionization energy will give up its electrons easiest. That would be In.

4. Ionization energy increases as you go from left to right on the chart, so the order is Sr < Sb < I.

5. Electronegativity decreases as you go down the chart, so N has the greatest desire for extra electrons.

6. Atomic radius decreases as you go from left to right on the chart, so the order is Br < Se < As < K.

7. The chemical formula tells us that we have 1 C atom and 4 H atoms to work with:

```
 •
•C•  H•  H•  H•  H•
 •
```

Because C has the most unpaired electrons, it goes in the center and we try to attach the H atoms to it. This is easy since each H atom has a space for an unpaired electron, and the C atom has 4 unpaired electrons. The Lewis structure, then, looks like this:

```
  H
  ••
H:C:H
  ••
  H
```

All atoms have their ideal electron configuration, so we are all set. Now we just have to replace the shared electron pairs with dashes:

```
   H
   |
H—C—H
   |
   H
```

8. The chemical formula tells us that we have 1 P atom and 3 Cl atoms to work with:

```
 •     •     •     •
•P:  :Cl:  :Cl:  :Cl:
 •    ••    ••    ••
```

Because P has the most unpaired electrons, it goes in the center and we try to attach the Cl atoms to it. This is easy since each Cl atom has a space for an unpaired electron, and the P atom has 3 unpaired electrons. The Lewis structure, then, looks like this:

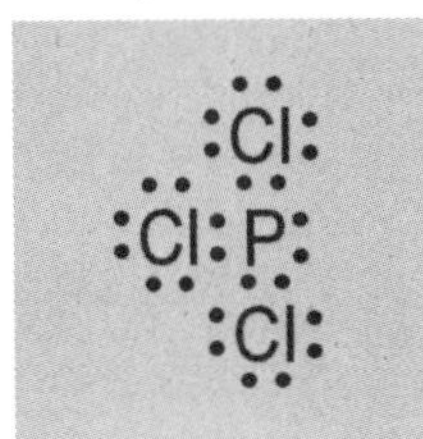

All atoms have their ideal electron configuration, so we are all set. Now we just have to replace the shared electron pairs with dashes:

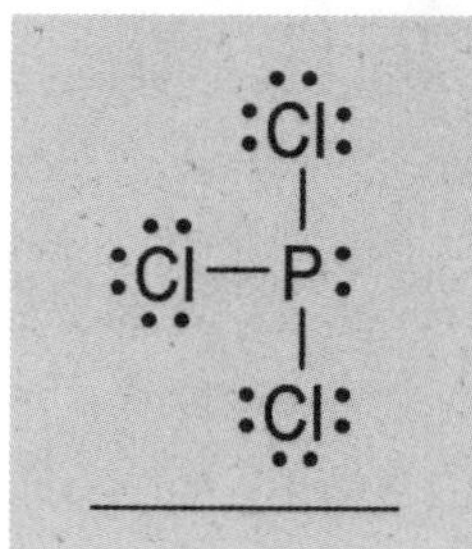

9. The chemical formula tells us that we have 1 F atom, 1 N atom, and 1 O atom to work with:

:F: ·N: ·O:

The N has the most unpaired electrons, so it goes in the middle. We attach the others to it:

:F:N:O:

The F atom now has 8 electrons, so it is all set. The N and O atoms, however, have only 7 each. We will give the O atom 8 by taking the unpaired electron on the N atom and putting it in between the N and O atoms:

:F:N:O: ⟶ :F:N:.O:

We can also give the N atom its 8 by taking the unpaired electron on the oxygen and moving it in between the N and O atoms.

:F:N:.O: ⟶ :F:N::O:

Now all atoms have 8 valence electrons. All we have to do is replace the shared electron pairs with dashes:

:F–N=O:

10. To solve this, we have to determine the Lewis structures of each molecule. They turn out to be:

H–C=C–H (each C also bonded to an H below)   :P≡N: H–H

Based on these 3 Lewis structures, the H_2 molecule will be easiest to break apart because it is held together by a single bond, while the C_2H_4 molecule is held together by a double bond, and the PN molecule is held together by a triple bond.

SOLUTIONS TO THE EXTRA PRACTICE PROBLEMS FOR MODULE 4

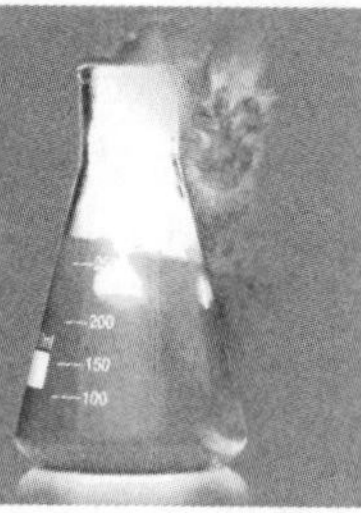

1. a. Sr is in group 2A, so it has 2 valence electrons:

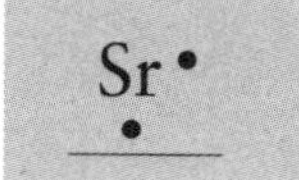

b. Kr is in group 8A, so it has 8 valence electrons:

c. Te is in group 6A, so it has 6 valence electrons:

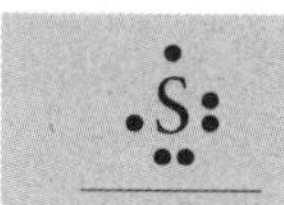

d. Bi is in group 5A, so it has 5 valence electrons:

2. a. Al is in group 3A, so it wants a charge of 3+. Oxygen is in group 6A, so oxide will have a charge of 2–. Ignoring the signs and switching the numbers gives us $\underline{Al_2O_3}$.

b. Ca is in group 2A, so it wants a charge of 2+. Sulfur is in group 6A, so sulfide will have a charge of 2–. Since the charges are equal, we ignore them, giving us $\underline{CaS}$.

c. Be is in group 2A, so it wants a charge of 2+. Carbon is in group 4A, so carbon will have a charge of 4–. Ignoring the signs and switching the numbers gives us Be_4C_2, but that needs to be reduced. The final answer is $\underline{Be_2C}$.

d. K is in group 1A, so it wants a charge of 1+. Nitrogen is in group 5A, so nitride will have a charge of 3–. Ignoring the signs and switching the numbers gives us $\underline{K_3N}$.

3. a. The roman numeral on chromium says that Cr is a 3+ charge. Cl is in Group 7A, so it wants to be a 1– charge. The formula will be $CrCl_3$.

   b. The roman numeral on zinc says that Zn is a 1+ charge. Sulfur is in Group 6A, so it wants to be a 2– charge. The formula will be Zn_2S.

   c. The roman numeral on titanium says that Ti is a +4 charge. P is in group 5A, so it wants to be a 3– charge. The formula will be Ti_3P_4.

4. Ionization energy increases as we go up the chart. So the order is Ra < Sr < Mg.

5. Electronegativity is a measure of an element's desire for electrons. It increases as we move to the right on the chart, so Br has the greatest desire for electrons.

6. Atomic radius increases as we move to the left on the chart. The order is Ar < P < Al < Mg.

7. The chemical formula tells us that we have 1 N atom and 3 F atoms:

   ·N: :F: :F: :F:

   This one is easy to put together, as the N atom has 3 empty spaces and each F atom needs 1 more electron:

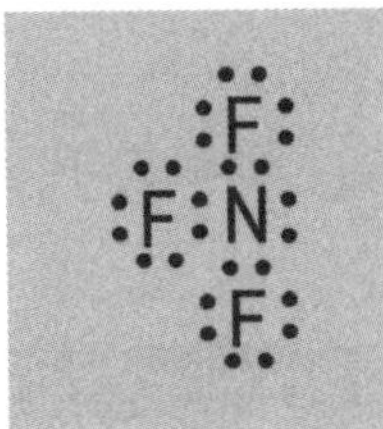

   Now we just replace the shared electron pairs with bonds:

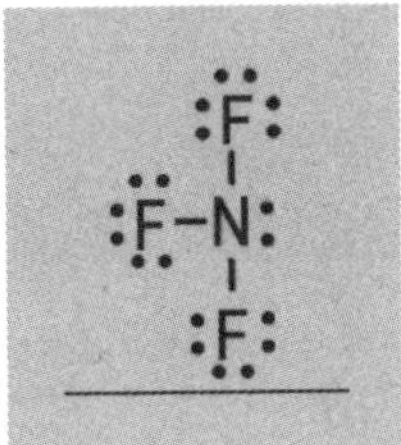

8. The chemical formula says that we have 1 C atom, 2 Cl atoms, and 1 S atom to play with:

   ·C· :Cl: :Cl: ·S:

   The C atom has the most unpaired electrons and therefore goes in the middle:

   :Cl:
   :Cl:C:S:

   The Cl atoms have their ideal electron configurations, but the C and S atoms are each 1 electron short. This can be fixed by taking the unpaired electrons and putting them between the C and S atoms:

   :Cl:
   :Cl:C::S:

   Now we just need to replace the shared electron pairs with bonds:

   :Cl:
   |
   :Cl–C=S:

9. We have 1 Si atom and 2 S atoms to work with in this molecule:

   ·Si· ·S: ·S:

   The Si atom will go in the middle because it has the most unpaired electrons:

   :S:Si:S:

   No atom has its ideal electron configuration yet. However, if we take the unpaired electrons on the S atoms and put them each between the Si atom and the S atom that had the unpaired electron, then the S atom will have its ideal electron configuration. In the same way, if we take the unpaired electrons on the Si atom and put 1 between the Si atom and 1 of the S atoms and the other between the Si atom and the other S atom, the S atoms will have their ideal electron configurations as well:

   :S::Si::S:

Now we can just replace the shared electron pairs with bonds:

:S=Si=S:

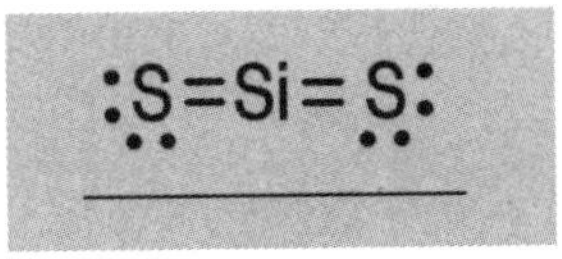

10. In this molecule, we have 1 C atom and 1 S atom, so we might as well link them:

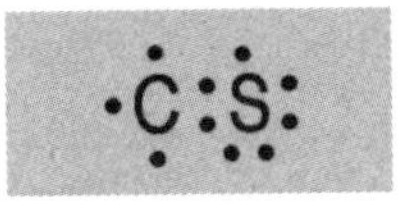

·C:S:

Taking the unpaired electron on the S atom and putting it between the 2 atoms and doing the same with 1 of the unpaired electrons on the C atom gives S its ideal electron configuration:

·C::S:

The C atom still needs 2 more electrons. They must come from the S atom. Thus, we will put 1 of the electron pairs on the S atom between the 2 atoms:

·C:::S:

Now both atoms have their ideal electron configuration. We should go ahead and pair the 2 electrons on the C atom and replace the electron pairs with bonds:

:C≡S:

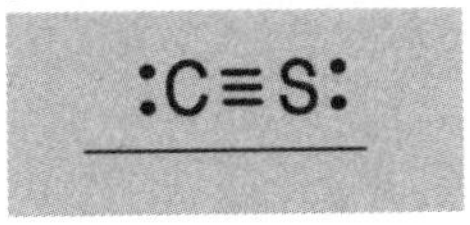

11. The formula tells us that we have 1 S atom and 2 Br atoms:

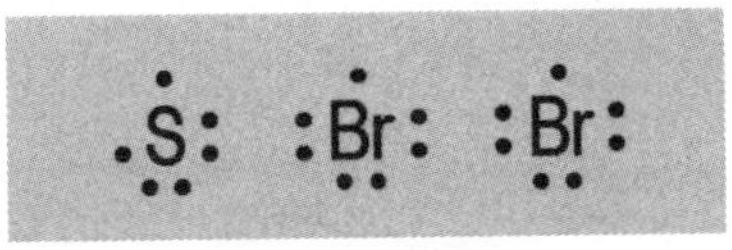

·S: :Br: :Br:

The S atom goes in the middle:

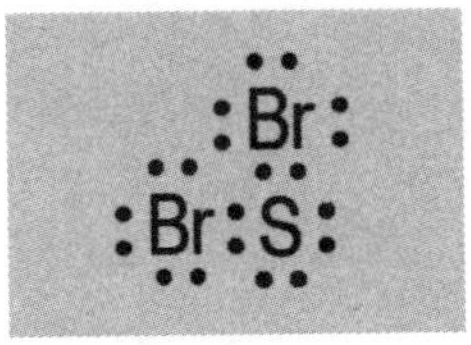

:Br:
:Br:S:

We now just put in the bonds:

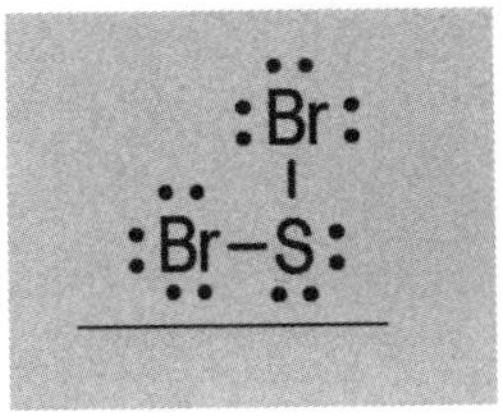

:Br:
|
:Br−S:

12. Based on Lewis structures, the CS molecule would be the hardest to break because it is held together with a triple bond.

TEST FOR MODULE 4

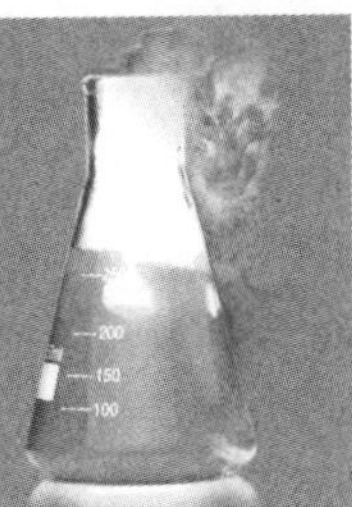

1. (4 pts) The electrons that are located the highest energy level are called ________________.
   a. Ground state electrons
   b. d-orbital electrons
   c. Valence electrons
   d. Excited electrons
   e. None of the above

2. (4 pts) What type of charge do metal ions develop in ionic compounds?
   a. Positive
   b. Negative
   c. Neutral
   d. None of the above

3. (4 pts) What does the octet rule say?
   a. All atoms strive to have 8 electrons.
   b. All atoms strive to have 8 different orbitals.
   c. Almost all atoms strive to have 8 protons.
   d. Almost all atoms strive to have 8 valence electrons.
   e. None of the above

4. (4 pts) The dots in a Lewis structure represent the ______________.
   a. Bonds for each molecule
   b. Entire number of electrons present for each atom
   c. Valence electrons for each atom
   d. Ionic nature of the molecule
   e. None of the above

5. (4 pts) When atoms share electrons to make a molecule, is the compound ionic or covalent?
   a. Ionic compound
   b. Covalent compound

6. (4 pts) What is a molecule made of 2 or more nonmetal atoms?
   a. Ionic compound
   b. Covalent compound

7. (4 pts) What is a molecule made of metal plus nonmetal atoms?
   a. Ionic compound
   b. Covalent compound

8. (4 pts) What is a molecule in which one atom gives its electrons to another atom?
   a. Ionic compound
   b. Covalent compound

9. (4 pts) Zinc and copper are examples of ________________.
   a. Nonmetals
   b. Halogen
   c. Ionic compounds
   d. Metals
   e. None of the above

10. (4 pts) A measure of how easily an atom attracts an electron to itself is called ______________.
   a. Ionization energy
   b. Electronegativity
   c. Periodic property
   d. Covalent nature
   e. None of the above

11. (4 pts) Which periodic property increases from left to right on the periodic table?
   a. Ionization energy
   b. Electronegativity
   c. Both a and b
   d. Neither a nor b

12. (4 pts) Which periodic property increases from top to bottom on the periodic table?
   a. Ionization energy
   b. Electronegativity
   c. Both a and b
   d. Neither a nor b

13. (4 pts) Which gas is responsible for absorbing and protecting us from exposure to the ultraviolet light that comes from the sun?
   a. Nitrogen
   b. Ozone
   c. Oxygen
   d. Argon
   e. None of the above

14. (4 pts) Which of the following atoms gives up its electrons most easily?
   a. Mg
   b. Na
   c. P
   d. S

15. (4 pts) Order the following atoms in terms of increasing electronegativity: Ba, Mg, Ca, Sr

16. (4 pts) Ozone protects us from which harmful type of energy?
    a. Gamma radiation
    b. X-Rays
    c. Microwaves
    d. Ultraviolet light

17. (4 pts) Write the chemical formula for potassium arsenide. (Arsenic is abbreviated As.)

18. (4 pts) Write the chemical formula for iron (III) oxide.

19. (4 pts) What is the name of Mn_2O_3?

20. (4 pts) Draw the Lewis structure for Al.

21. (5 pts) Draw the Lewis structure of Br_2.

22. (5 pts) Draw the Lewis structure of SiO_2.

23. (5 pts) Draw the Lewis structure of OCl_2.

24. (5 pts) Draw the Lewis structure of FSiN. *Note: there are 3 atoms in this molecule.*

SOLUTIONS TO THE TEST FOR MODULE 4

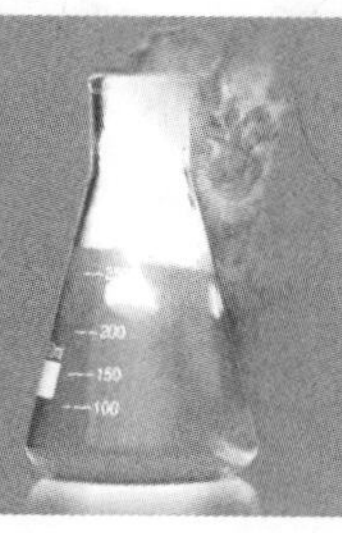

1. (4 pts) c. Valence electrons

2. (4 pts) a. Positive

3. (4 pts) d. Almost all atoms strive to have 8 valence electrons.

4. (4 pts) c. Valence electrons for each atom

5. (4 pts) b. Covalent compound

6. (4 pts) b. Covalent compound

7. (4 pts) a. Ionic compound

8. (4 pts) a. Ionic compound

9. (4 pts) d. Metals

10. (4 pts) b. Electronegativity

11. (4 pts) c. Both a and b

12. (4 pts) d. Neither a nor b

13. (4 pts) b. Ozone

14. (4 pts) b. Na
Na is farthest to the left on the periodic table.

15. (4 pts) Ba < Sr < Ca < Mg
As we go down the periodic table, electronegativity decreases.

16. (4 pts) d. Ultraviolet light

17. (4 pts) K_3As
In ionic compounds, K develops a +1 charge because it is in group 1A. As develops a –3 charge because it is in group 5A. Switching the charges and ignoring the signs gives us: K_3As

18. (4 pts) Fe_2O_3
The roman numeral tells us that Fe develops a +3 charge. O develops a –2 charge because it is in group 6A. Switching the charges and ignoring the signs gives us: Fe_2O_3

19. (4 pts) Manganese (III) oxide
Manganese is a metal, but it can have different positive charges. Oxygen is –2 and as the nonmetal is -oxide, having 3 of oxygen atoms makes an overall –6 charge. This means the overall charge for 2 manganese atoms is +6, so each manganese atom must be +3. This gives the name manganese (III) oxide.

20. (4 pts)

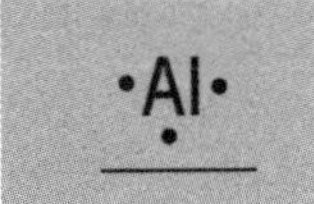

21. (5 pts)

22. (5 pts)

:O=Si=O:

23. (5 pts)

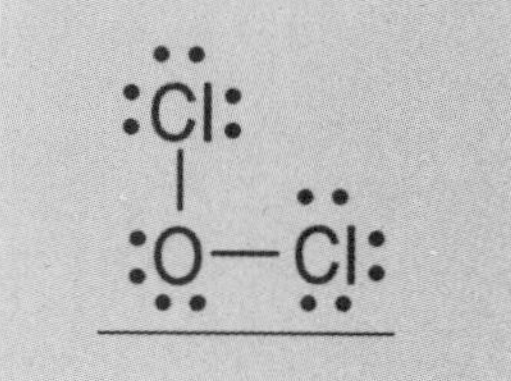

24. (5 pts)

F=Si=N

Another acceptable Lewis Structure is pictured below. This structure is the real molecule that forms. N is less electronegative than F so it is more willing to share electrons. This means the additional bonds are going to form with N instead of F! Please note that the student has not learned this process so points should not be taken off if the first structure is given

F–Si≡N

QUARTER I TEST FOR MOD. 1-4

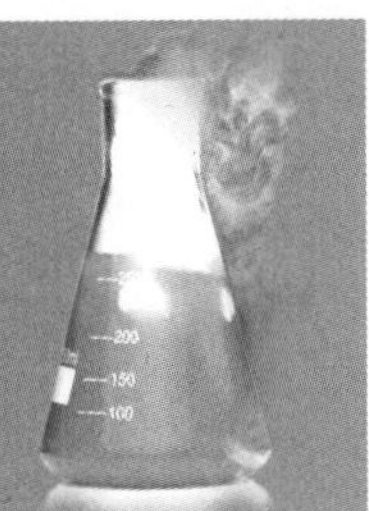

1. (3 pts) Which is longer: a string that measures 0.25 km or a string measuring 101 mm?
   a. 0.25 km string
   b. 101 mm string

2. (3 pts) How long is the black bar in the picture below?

   a. 3.33 cm
   b. 3.43 cm
   c. 2.33 cm
   d. 2.43 cm
   e. 2.50 cm

3. (4 pts) Two students measure the length of a 2.1 meter object. Student A measures the length to be 2.8123 m. Student B measures the length to be 2 m. Which student was more precise?
   a. Student A
   b. Student B

   Which student was more accurate?
   a. Student A
   b. Student B

4. (3 pts) Convert 34.5 kL into L.

5. (3 pts) Convert 0.001400 into scientific notation.

6. (4 pts) Convert 0.00045 kg to mg.

7. (3 pts) How many significant figures does the number 0.0032800 have?
   a. 3
   b. 8
   c. 5
   d. 7
   e. 6

8. (4 pts) Convert 98.6 °F to K. The answer is:
   a. 310.2 K
   b. 508.3 K
   c. 393.0 K
   d. 345.8 K

9. (3 pts) The currently accepted model of the atom involves:
   a. Electrons are restricted to set energy levels but can move among levels.
   b. Electrons that circle the nucleus in orbits
   c. Electron plums that reside in a smear of positively charged protons
   d. Orbitals in which electrons can be at different distances from the nucleus at different times
   e. Answers a and d

10. (3 pts) How can you determine from the periodic table whether a compound is ionic or covalent?

11. (4 pts) Which of the following molecules are covalent? (Select all that apply.)
    a. CO_2 b. $CaBr_2$ c. KCl d. C_3H_8

12. (12 pts) For the following compounds, if the name is given, write its formula. If the formula is given, write its name.
    a. diphosphorus hexaoxide b. PH_3 c. nitrogen dioxide d. CaS

13. (4 pts) Classify the following as an element, compound, homogeneous mixture, or heterogeneous mixture.
    a. A fruitcake
    b. A bottle of CH_4O
    c. A pile of carbon powder
    d. Sugar dissolved in water

14. (3 pts) If a substance has 5 positive charges and 4 negative charges, it is:
    a. Positively charged
    b. Negatively charged
    c. Neutral

15. (6 pts) Give the number of protons, electrons, and neutrons in the following atoms:
    a. ^{39}K b. ^{131}I

16. (6 pts) Give the full electron configurations of the following atoms:
    a. Fe b. P

17. (6 pts) Give the abbreviated electron configurations for the following atoms:
    a. Cl b. Nb

18. (3 pts) What is the fundamental difference between metals and nonmetals?

19. (6 pts) Draw the Lewis structures for the following atoms:
    a. C   b. Cl

20. (4 pts) The abbreviated electron configurations for the F^- ion is (Note: The ion has an extra electron!)
    a. [He] $2s^2 2p^5$
    b. [He] $2s^2 2p^6$
    c. $1s^2 2s^2 2p^5$
    d. [Ne]$2s^2 2p^6$

21. (3 pts) What is the Lewis structure for NH_3?

22. (3 pts) What is the Lewis structure for H_2CO?

23. (3 pts) A chemist measures the mass of a chunk of wood to be 45.4 g. When the wood is burned, 22.0 g of carbon dioxide, 12.0 g of ash, and 15.8 g of water vapor are produced. How many grams of oxygen were used in the burning process?
    a. 79.4 g
    b. 34.0 g
    c. 4.4 g
    d. 23.4 g

24. (4 pts) Given the following information:
    $c = 3.0 \times 10^8$ m/s, 1 nm = 1×10^{-9} m, and h = 6.63×10^{-34} J/Hz

    What is the frequency of orange light (λ = 615 nm)?
    a. 4.9×10^5 Hz
    b. 4.9×10^{14} Hz
    c. 1.9×10^{11} Hz
    d. 1.9×10^2 Hz

SOLUTIONS TO QUARTER 1 TEST FOR MOD. 1-4

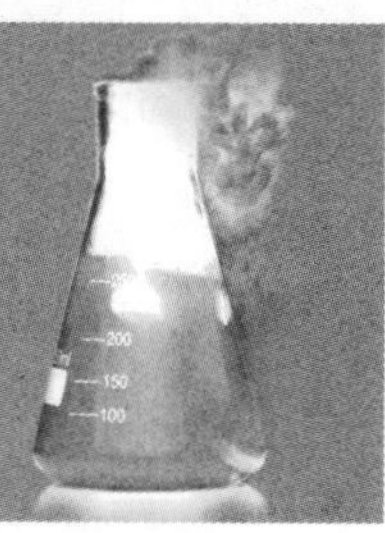

1. (3 pts) a. 0.25 km string
   Since 1 km is equal to 1,000 m and a mm is only equal to 0.001 m, the string measuring 0.25 km is longer.

2. (3 pts) d. 2.43 cm

3. (4 pts) Which student was more precise? a. Student A
   Which student was more accurate? b. Student B

4. (3 pts) 34,500 L or 3.45×10^4 L

$$\frac{34.5\ \cancel{kL}}{1} \times \frac{1000\ L}{1\ \cancel{kL}} = \underline{34{,}500\ L} \text{ or } \underline{3.45 \times 10^4\ L}$$

5. (3 pts) 1.400×10^{-3}

6. (4 pts) 450 mg
   This is a 2-step conversion, since we know of no relationship between kg and mg. Thus, we must first convert kg to g and then convert g to mg. We'll do this on one line:

$$\frac{0.00045\ \cancel{kg}}{1} \times \frac{1000\ \cancel{g}}{1\ \cancel{kg}} \times \frac{1\ mg}{0.001\ \cancel{g}} = \underline{450\ mg}$$

7. (3 pts) c. 5

8. (4 pts) a. 310.2 K
   First we need to convert to °C

$°F = 9/5 \times (°C) + 32$

Rearranging it becomes:

$°C = 5/9 \times (°F - 32) = 5/9 \times (98.6 - 32) = 37.0\ °C$

Then we convert to K:

$K = °C + 273.15 = 37.0 + 273.15 = \underline{310.2\ K}$

9. (3 pts) e. Answers a. and d.
The currently accepted model of the atom involves both quantized energy levels and orbitals in which electrons can be at different distances from the nucleus at different times.

10. (3 pts) If a compound has a metal in it, it must be ionic. If it has no metals, it is covalent. Atoms on the left of the jagged line on the table are metals and atoms to the right are nonmetals.

11. (4 pts: 2 pts for each answer. Take 1 point off for every wrong compound listed.) a. CO_2 and d. C_3H_8 are covalent. All elements (except hydrogen) that lie to the left of the jagged line on the chart are metals, while all elements to the right of the jagged line are nonmetals. A molecule is covalent only if it has no metals in it.

12. (12 pts: 2 pts each) a. P_2O_6 b. phosphorus trihydride c. NO_2 d. calcium sulfide

13. (4 pts: 1 pt each) a. heterogeneous mixture b. compound c. element
d. homogeneous mixture

14. (3 pts) a. Positively charged If a substance has an imbalance of charges, it takes on the charge which the most have. Thus, this substance will be positively charged.

15. (6 pts: 3 pts each)
    a. The periodic table shows that K has an atomic number of 19. This means it has 19 protons and 19 electrons. Its mass number, according to the problem, is 39. If it has 39 total protons + neutrons and it has 19 protons, then it has 39 – 19 = 20 neutrons.

b. The periodic table shows that I has an atomic number of 53. This means it has <u>53 protons and 53 electrons</u>. Its mass number, according to the problem, is 131. If it has 131 total protons + neutrons and it has 53 protons, then it has 131 – 53 = <u>78 neutrons</u>.

16. (6 pts: 3 pts each)

a. <u>$1s^2 2s^2 2p^6 3s^2 3p^6 4s^2 3d^6$</u> To get to element Fe, we must go through row 1, which has 2 boxes in the s orbital block ($1s^2$). We then go through all of row 2, which has 2 boxes in the s orbital block and 6 boxes in the p orbital block ($2s^2 2p^6$). We also go through row 3, which has 2 boxes in the s orbital block and 6 in the p orbital block ($3s^2 3p^6$). We then go to the fourth row where we pass through both boxes in the s orbital block ($4s^2$). Finally, we go through 6 boxes in the d orbital block. Since we subtract 1 from the row number for d orbitals, this gives us $3d^6$. Thus, our final electron configuration is:

<u>$1s^2 2s^2 2p^6 3s^2 3p^6 4s^2 3d^6$</u>

b. <u>$1s^2 2s^2 2p^6 3s^2 3p^3$</u> To get to element P, we must go through row 1, which has 2 boxes in the s orbital block ($1s^2$). We then go through all of row 2, which has 2 boxes in the s orbital block and 6 boxes in the p orbital block ($2s^2 2p^6$). We also go through both boxes in the s orbital block of row 3, ($3s^2$). Finally, we go through 3 boxes in the p orbital block of row 3, giving us $3p^3$. Thus, our final electron configuration is:

<u>$1s^2 2s^2 2p^6 3s^2 3p^3$</u>

17. (6 pts: 3 pts each)

a. <u>[Ne] $3s^2 3p^5$</u> The nearest 8A element that has a lower atomic number than Cl is Ne. The only difference between Cl and Ne is that there are 2 boxes in the row 3, s orbital group and 5 boxes in the row 3, p orbital group. Thus, the abbreviated electron configuration for Cl is:

<u>[Ne] $3s^2 3p^5$</u>

b. <u>[Kr] $5s^2 4d^3$</u> The nearest 8A element that has a lower atomic number than Nb is Kr. The only difference between Nb and Kr is that there are 2 boxes in the row 5, s orbital group and 3 boxes in the row 5, d orbital group. Thus, the abbreviated electron configuration for Nb is:

<u>[Kr] $5s^2 4d^3$</u>

18. (3 pts) Metals tend to give up electrons to attain the ideal electron configuration, while nonmetals tend to gain electrons for the same purpose.

19. (6 pts: 3 pts each)

   a. C is in group 4A, so it has 4 valence electrons:

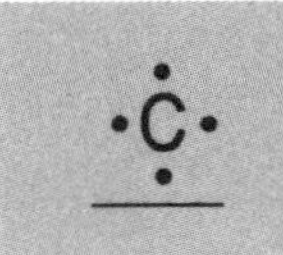

   b. Cl is in group 7A, so it has 7 valence electrons:

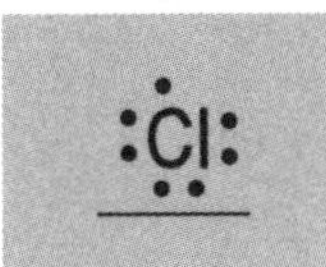

20. (4 pts) b. [He] $2s^2 2p^6$

For a F atom the abbreviated electron configuration would be [He] $2s^2 2p^5$, but since it is the F^- ion, it has gained an additional electron and the abbreviated electron configuration is [He] $2s^2 2p^6$.

21. (3 pts) The chemical formula tells us that we have 1 N atom and 3 H atoms to work with:

•N: H• H• H•

Because N has the most unpaired electrons, it goes in the center and we try to attach the H atoms to it. This is easy since each H atom has a space for an unpaired electron, and the N atom has 3 unpaired electrons. The Lewis structure, then, looks like this:

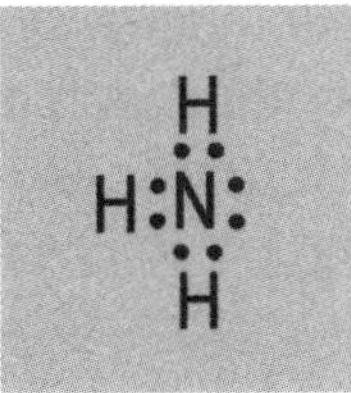

All atoms have their ideal electron configuration, so we are all set. Now we just have to replace the shared electron pairs with dashes:

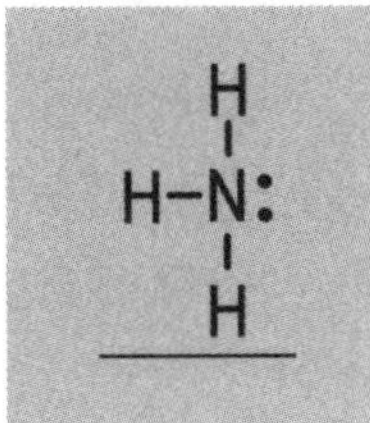

22. (3 pts) The chemical formula tells us that we have 2 H atoms, 1 C atom, and 1 O atom to work with:

```
        •    •
H•  H• •C•  •O:
        •    ••
```

The C atom has the most unpaired electrons, so it goes in the middle. We attach the others to it:

```
  •  •
H:C:O:
  ••  ••
  H
```

The H atoms now have 2 electrons, so they are all set. The C and O, however, have only 7 each. We will give the O 8 by taking the unpaired electron on the C and putting it between the C and the O. We will also give the C its 8 by taking the unpaired electron on the oxygen and moving it between the C and the O:

```
H:C::O:
  ••  ••
  H
```

Now all atoms have 8 valence electrons. All we have to do is replace the shared electron pairs with dashes:

```
H–C=O:
  |  ••
  H
```

23. (3 pts) c. 4.4 g
Total mass produced = 22.0 g of carbon dioxide + 12.0 g of ash + 15.8 g of water vapor = 49.8 g
By the law of mass conservation, the total mass of oxygen and wood reacted = total mass of carbon dioxide, ash, and water produced. Therefore, the mass of oxygen = total mass produced – mass of wood

Mass of oxygen = 49.8 g – 45.4 g = 4.4 g Oxygen

24. (4 pts) b. 4.9×10^{14} Hz
This is an application of equation $c = f\lambda$, but the units disagree. The speed of light was given using meters (m/s), but the wavelength is in nm. Thus, we must first

convert nm to m:

$$\frac{615\ \cancel{\text{nm}}}{1} \times \frac{1 \times 10^{-9}\ \text{m}}{1\ \cancel{\text{nm}}} = 6.15 \times 10^{-7}\ \text{m}$$

Now that the units agree, we can use the equation:

$$f = \frac{c}{\lambda} = \frac{3.0 \times 10^{8}\ \cancel{\text{m}}/\text{s}}{6.15 \times 10^{-7}\ \cancel{\text{m}}} = \underline{4.9 \times 10^{14}\ 1/\text{s}}$$

Since 1/s is the same as Hz, the frequency is $\underline{4.9 \times 10^{14}\ \text{Hz}}$.

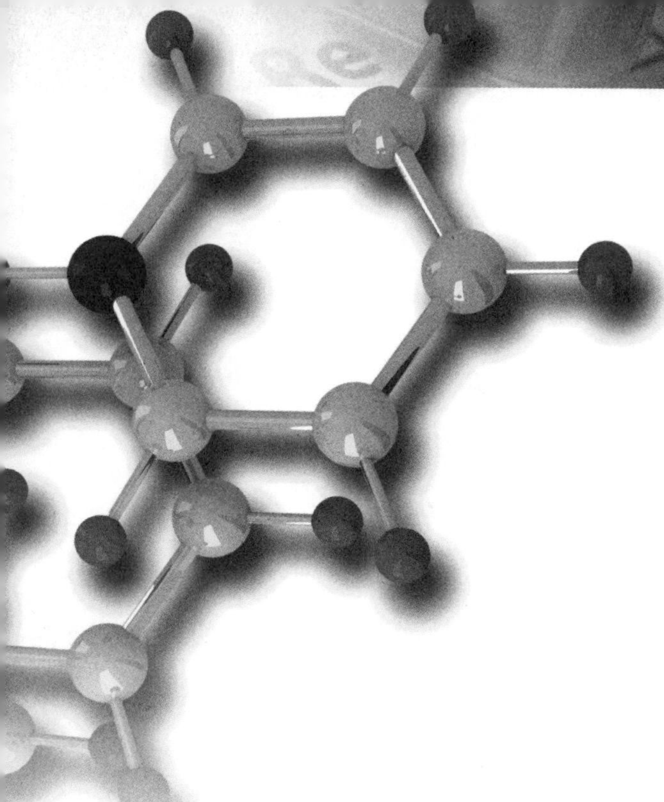

POLYATOMIC IONS AND MOLECULAR GEOMETRY

SOLUTIONS TO THE MODULE 5 REVIEW QUESTIONS

1. All of the ions we have learned about up to this point have consisted of only one atom. The ions we learned about in this module are made up of more than one atom.

2. You should have all of these memorized:

   a. SO_4^{2-}

   b. ClO_2^-

   c. $C_2H_3O_2^-$

   d. This is a question that tests your memory. Sulfide is the name of the ion formed from a single sulfur ion. As we learned in module 4, when a single atom forms a negative ion, the ion's name is the name of the atom with an *-ide* ending. Since sulfur is in group 6A on the chart, it takes on a –2 charge in ionic compounds. Thus, the sulfide ion is S^{2-}.

   e. $Cr_2O_7^{2-}$

   f. PO_4^{3-}

3. These should be memorized:

   a. nitrite

   b. This is also a question to test your memory. This is the oxide ion. You learned in module 4 that when a single atom forms a negative ion, the ion's name is the name of the atom with an -ide ending.

c. chlorate

d. carbonate

e. sulfite

f. chromate

4. VSEPR stands for Valence Shell Electron Pair Repulsion.

5. VSEPR theory states that a molecule will attain whatever shape keeps the valence electrons of the central atom as far apart from one another as possible.

6. Bond angles in a pyramidal molecule are smaller than those in a tetrahedral molecule because the nonbonding electron pair in the pyramidal molecule pushes the bonding electron pairs a little harder than they push on each other. As a result, the bonds are all pushed toward each other a little more than in the tetrahedral molecule, which has no nonbonding electron pairs.

7. Polar covalent bonds are bonds in which the electrons are not shared equally, which causes a partial charge to develop across the molecule. Nonpolar covalent bonds, on the other hand, contain electrons that are shared equally across all bonds. This equal sharing results in the development of no net charge. The sharing cancels out any charge that may develop.

8. Their electronegativities must be the same. After all, if the bond is nonpolar covalent, the electron pair is shared equally. This can happen only if the atoms tug on the electrons with the same strength. Since that strength is determined by electronegativity, the electronegativities must be the same. Do not think that different atoms must have different electronegativities. Electronegativity increases as we go from left to right on the chart, and it decreases as we go down the chart. Thus, if an atom is both to the right of and *below* another atom, those 2 atoms could have the same electronegativity. At and H, for example, have identical electronegativities.

9. Oil and water do not mix because oil is a nonpolar covalent compound and water is a polar covalent compound. These 2 types of compounds cannot mix because one has an electrical charge and the other doesn't.

10. Soap is made up of long molecules that are ionic on one end and nonpolar covalent on the other. Thus, a soap molecule can interact with both charged and uncharged compounds. The ionic end of the molecule can interact with charged compounds such as water. The nonpolar end of the molecule can interact with nonpolar molecules such as the molecules in the stain. Soap can, therefore, couple a reaction between the polar water molecules and the nonpolar stain molecules.

SOLUTIONS TO THE PRACTICE PROBLEMS FOR MODULE 5

1. Ionic compounds are named by simply listing the ions present. In order to get the formula, you must determine the charge of each ion and balance those charges. We learned how to do this in the last module, so the only new thing here is the fact that there are now polyatomic ions to consider.

   a. The name indicates a potassium ion and a sulfite ion. Potassium is abbreviated with a K, and, since it is in group 1A, it has a charge of 1+. We are supposed to have memorized that the sulfate ion is SO_3 and has a charge of 2–. Ignoring the signs and switching the numbers gives us:

   K_2SO_3

   We do not put parentheses around the polyatomic ion because there is only 1 sulfate ion in the molecule.

   b. The name indicates a beryllium ion and a nitrate ion. Beryllium is abbreviated with a Be, and, since it is in group 2A, it has a charge of 2+. We are supposed to have memorized that the nitrate ion is NO_3 and has a charge of 1–. Ignoring the signs and switching the numbers gives us:

   $Be(NO_3)_2$

   c. The name indicates a manganese ion and a carbonate ion. Manganese is abbreviated with a Mn, and, since it has a roman numeral of IV, it has a charge of 4+. We are supposed to have memorized that the carbonate ion is CO_3 and has a charge of 2–. Since the numerical values of the charges are multiples, we must reduce them. This gives us:

   $Mn(CO_3)_2$

   d. The name indicates an aluminum ion and a chromate ion. Aluminum is abbreviated with an Al, and, since it is in group 3A, it has a charge of 3+. We are supposed to have memorized that the chromate ion is CrO_4 and has a charge of 2–. Ignoring the signs and switching the numbers gives us:

   $Al_2(CrO_4)_3$

2. In order to name ionic compounds, we only have to put the names of the ions together.

   a. We see that NH_4 is in parentheses, which means it is a polyatomic ion. We are supposed to have memorized that NH_4^+ is the ammonium ion, and the only other ion is the single-atom oxide ion. Thus, the name is ammonium oxide.

   b. In looking at this molecule, we should notice the NO_2. It tells us the nitrite polyatomic ion is present. The only thing left after that is the rubidium ion. Thus, the name is rubidium nitrite.

   c. We see that PO_4 is in parentheses, which means it is a polyatomic ion. We are supposed to have memorized that PO_4^{3-} is the phosphate ion, and the only other ion is the zinc ion. But zinc is a transition metal, so we need a roman numeral indicating the charge. Here, Zn is a 2+ charge. The name is zinc (II) phosphate.

   d. In looking at this molecule, we should notice the PO_4. It tells us that the phosphate polyatomic ion is present. The cobalt ion is going to need a roman numeral. The name is cobalt (III) phosphate.

3. First, we have to determine the formulas of the molecules involved:
   Calcium nitrate includes Ca^{2+} and NO_3^-. Thus, its formula is $Ca(NO_3)_2$.
   Sodium carbonate includes Na^+ and CO_3^{2-}. Thus, its formula is Na_2CO_3.
   Calcium carbonate includes Ca^{2+} and CO_3^{2-}. Thus, it formula is $CaCO_3$.
   Sodium nitrate includes Na^+ and NO_3^-. Thus, its formula is $NaNO_3$.

4. To determine shapes, we must first draw the Lewis structure:

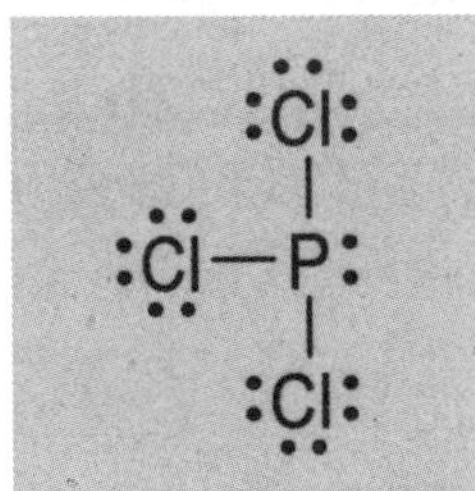

   We see that the central atom has 4 groups of electrons around it. Three of them are bonds, and 1 is a nonbonding pair. Since there are 4 groups, the basic shape is that of a tetrahedron. However, 1 of the legs is missing because it contains a nonbonding pair of electrons. As a result, the molecule's shape is pyramidal with a bond angle of 107°:

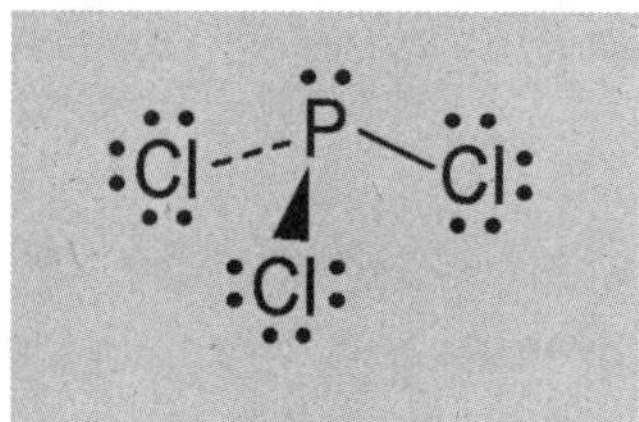

5. To determine shapes, we must first draw the Lewis structure:

H:H

Since there are only 2 atoms here, the molecule is linear with a bond angle of 180°. The picture looks just like the Lewis structure.

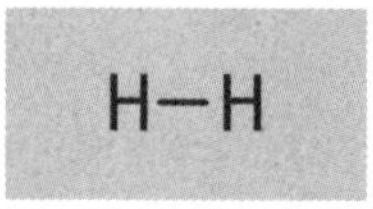

H—H

6. To determine shapes, we must first draw the Lewis structure:

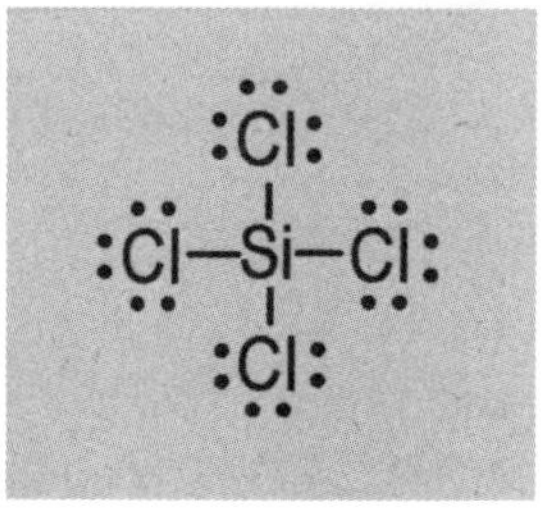

We see that the central atom has 4 groups of electrons around it. Since there are 4 groups, the basic shape is that of a tetrahedron. None of the legs is missing because the molecule contains no nonbonding pairs of electrons. As a result, the molecule's shape is tetrahedral with a bond angle of 109°:

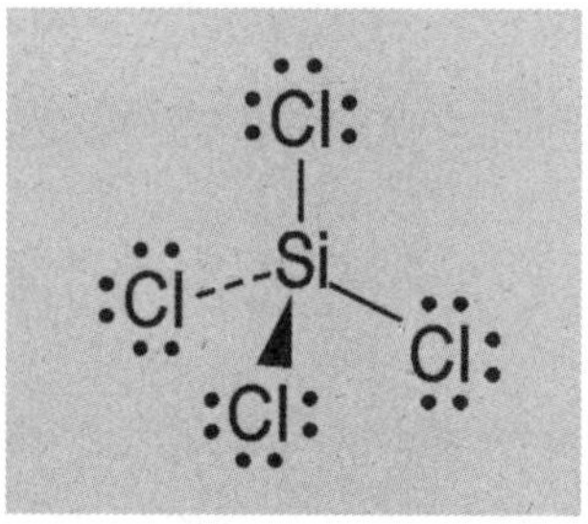

7. To determine shapes, we must first draw the Lewis structure:

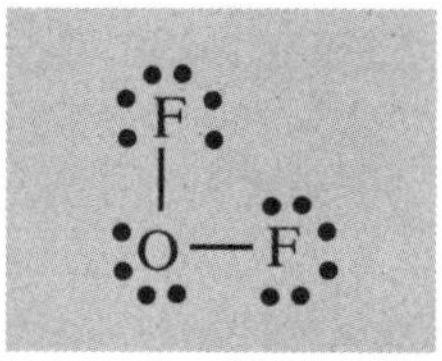

We see that the central atom has 4 groups of electrons around it. Since there are 4 groups, the basic shape is that of a tetrahedron. Two of the legs are missing, however because 2 of the groups are nonbonding pairs of electrons. As a result, the molecule's shape is bent with a bond angle of 105°:

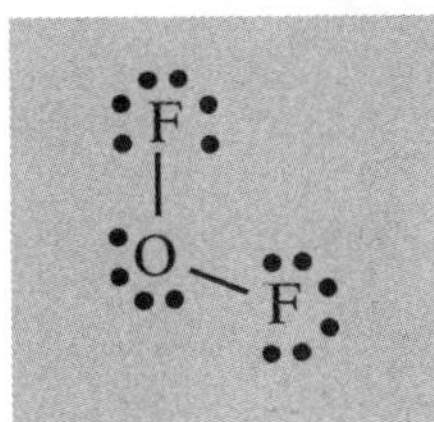

8. To determine shapes, we must first draw the Lewis structure:

   :S=C=S:

   We see that the central atom has 2 groups of electrons around it. Since there are 2 groups, the shape is linear with a bond angle of 180°. The picture looks just like the Lewis structure.

9. a. This compound contains a metal (Mg) and a nonmetal (Cl). It is therefore an ionic compound.

   b. This molecule contains no metals, so it is either nonpolar covalent or polar covalent. To determine which, we must first start with a Lewis structure.

   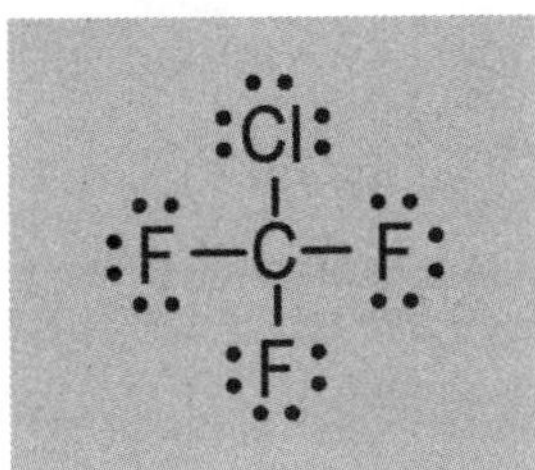

   We then determine its shape. Since the central atom is surrounded by 4 groups of electrons and there are no nonbonding electron pairs on the central atom, the shape is tetrahedral. Now that we know the shape, we can look at the direction that the electrons are being pulled. In this case, both F and Cl are more electronegative than C, so the electrons are all pulled away from the carbon:

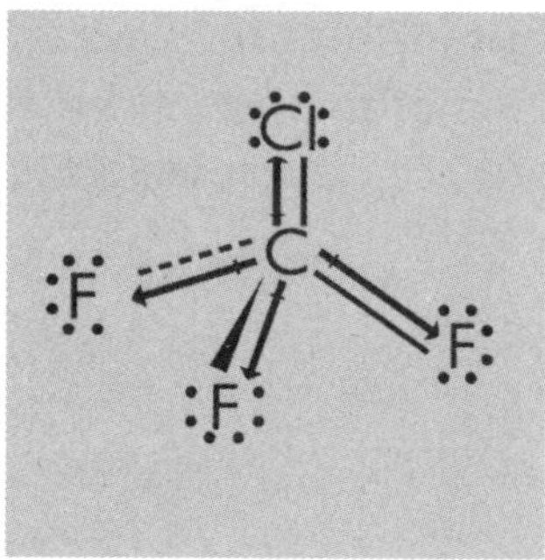

The electrons are all being pulled in opposite directions, but the pulls are not equal. Since F is more electronegative than Cl, it can pull on the electrons harder. Thus, the molecule is polar covalent.

c. We determined the shape of this in a previous problem. We now simply have to determine the direction in which the electrons are being pulled. S is 2 steps to the right of C on the periodic table and only 1 step down. Thus, even though it loses a little electronegativity by being lower than C on the chart, it gains more because it is 2 steps to the right of C. As a result, the electrons are pulled toward the sulfur atoms:

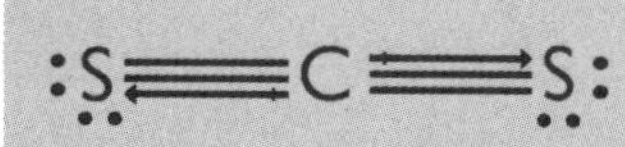

We see from the picture that the electrons are being pulled equally in opposite directions. Thus, the polar bonds cancel each other out and we are left with a nonpolar covalent compound.

d. This is an easy one. There are no polar bonds in this molecule, since the only atoms in it are identical. Since there are no polar bonds, the molecule must be nonpolar covalent.

e. This compound is made of a metal (Sc) and a nonmetal (Cl). That makes this an ionic compound.

f. We determined the shape of this in a previous problem. We now simply have to determine the direction in which the electrons are being pulled. Cl is to the right of P on the periodic table. Thus, the electrons are pulled toward the chlorine atoms:

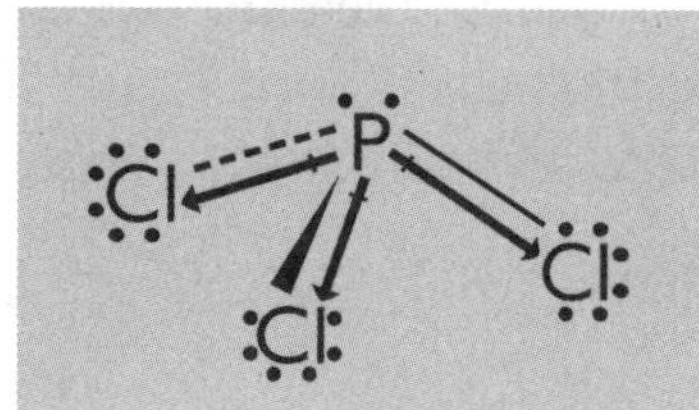

We see from the picture that the electrons are not being pulled in opposite directions, since there is no chlorine pulling straight up. There is simply a pair of nonbonding electrons there. As a result, the polar bonds do not cancel each other out, and the molecule is polar covalent.

10. Water is a polar covalent compound; thus, it has electrical charges. Only other polar covalent compounds or ionic compounds can dissolve in water because they also have electrical charges in them. Nonpolar covalent compounds cannot dissolve in water. We classified all of the compounds in the previous problem, therefore:

$MgCl_2$, CF_3Cl, $ScCl_4$, and PCl_3 will dissolve in water, the other 2 will not.

SOLUTIONS TO THE EXTRA PRACTICE PROBLEMS FOR MODULE 5

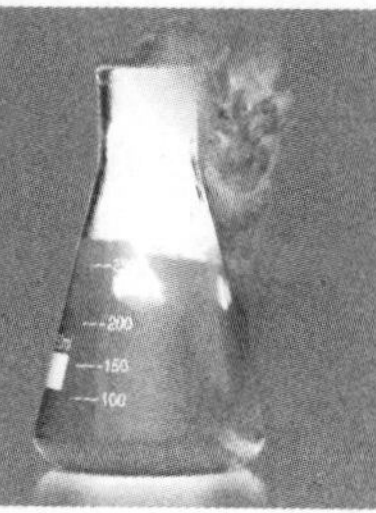

1. Ionic compounds are named by simply listing the ions present. In order to get the formula, we must determine the charge of each ion and balance those charges.

   a. The name indicates a lithium ion and a sulfite ion. Lithium is abbreviated with Li, and, since it is in group 1A, it has a charge of 1+. We are supposed to have memorized that the sulfite ion is SO_3 and has a charge of 2–. Ignoring the signs and switching the numbers gives us:

   $\underline{Li_2SO_3}$

   b. The name indicates an ammonium ion and a phosphate ion. We are supposed to have memorized both of these polyatomic ions. Ammonium ion is NH_4 with a charge of 1+ and the phosphate ion is PO_4 with a charge of 3–. Ignoring the signs and switching the numbers gives us:

   $\underline{(NH_4)_3PO_4}$

   c. The name indicates a calcium ion and a carbonate ion. Calcium is abbreviated with Ca, and, since it is in group 2A, it has a charge of 2+. We are supposed to have memorized that the carbonate ion is CO_3 and has a charge of 2–. Since the numerical values of the charges are the same, we ignore them.

   $\underline{CaCO_3}$

   d. The name indicates an aluminum ion and a dichromate ion. Aluminum is abbreviated with an Al, and, since it is in group 3A, it has a charge of 3+. We are supposed to have memorized that the dichromate ion is Cr_2O_7 and has a charge of 2–. Ignoring the signs and switching the numbers gives us:

   $\underline{Al_2(Cr_2O_7)_3}$

2. To name ionic compounds, we only have to put the names of the ions together.

   a. We are supposed to have memorized that NH_4^+ is the ammonium ion, and the other ion is the ClO_2^- ion. Thus, the name is <u>ammonium chlorite</u>.

b. In looking at this molecule, we should notice the NO_2 is a polyatomic ion, nitrite. The only thing left after that is the manganese ion. Since nitrite is a 1– charge and there are 2 of them, manganese has to have a 2+ charge. This is important because manganese is a transition metal, so a roman numeral reflects its charge. The name is manganese (II) nitrite.

c. Since PO_4 is in parentheses, it is a polyatomic ion. We are supposed to have memorized that PO_4^{3-} is the phosphate ion, and the only other ion is the beryllium ion. The name is beryllium phosphate.

d. In looking at this molecule, we should notice the PO_4. It tells us that the phosphate polyatomic ion is present and the charge is 3–. The only thing left after that is the nickel ion, which is a transition metal that a roman numeral of (III) to match its charge. The name is nickel (III) phosphate.

3. This molecule has only 2 atoms. Thus, it is linear with a bond angle of 180 degrees.

:C≡S:

4. We start with the Lewis structure:

The central atom has 4 groups of electrons around it, and none of them is a nonbonding electron pair. Thus, the shape is tetrahedral with a bond angle of 109 degrees:

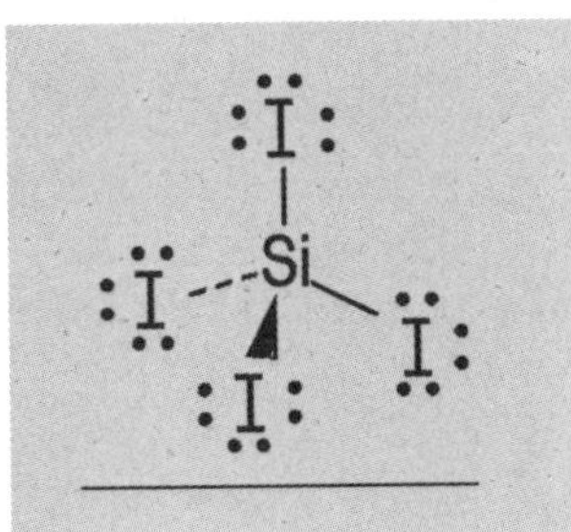

5. We start with the Lewis structure:

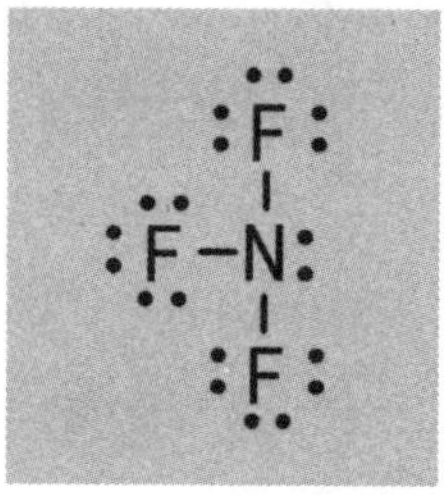

The central atom has 4 groups of electrons around it, so the base geometry is a tetrahedron. However, one "leg" of the tetrahedron is missing because one of the groups is not a bond. Thus, this molecule is <u>pyramidal with a bond angle of 107 degrees</u>:

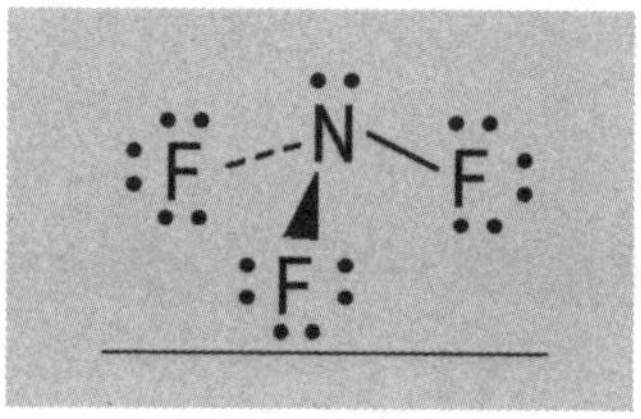

6. We start with the Lewis structure:

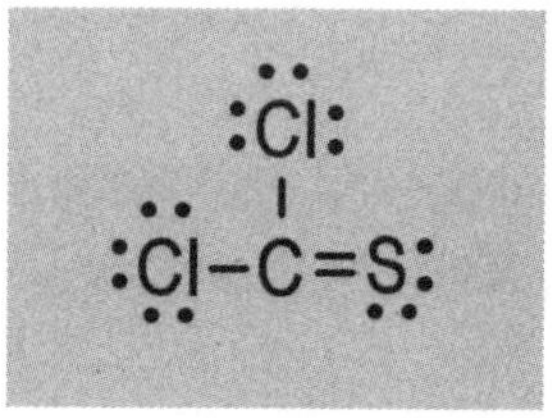

The central atom has 3 groups (3 bonds) around it. One of those bonds is a double bond, but it still counts as only 1 bond. Thus, this molecule is <u>trigonal with a bond angle of 120 degrees</u>.

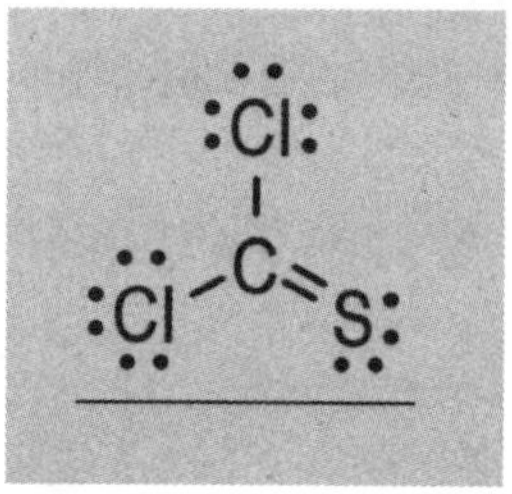

7. We start with the Lewis structure:

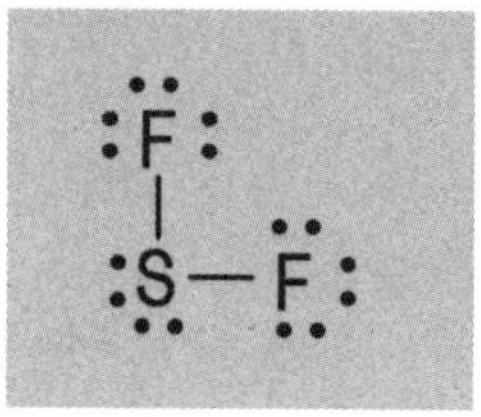

The central atom has 4 groups of electrons around it, so the base geometry is tetrahedral. However, 2 of the "legs" in the tetrahedron are gone, so the resulting structure is bent with a bond angle of 105 degrees:

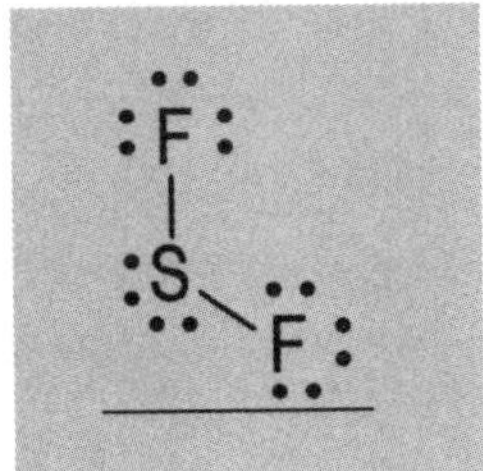

8. To be polar covalent, the molecule must have polar covalent bonds and those bonds cannot cancel each other out. All of the molecules under consideration have polar covalent bonds. However, in the tetrahedral geometry of SiI_4, those bonds cancel. The bonds do not cancel in the other molecules, however, so all of the molecules except SiI_4 are polar covalent, while SiI_4 is nonpolar covalent.

9. a. This molecule has no metals, so it is not ionic. If we determine its geometry, we will find it is tetrahedral. Usually, polar covalent bonds cancel in a tetrahedral geometry. This is only true, however, if the bonds are identical. In this molecule, they are not. Thus, the bonds do not cancel, and the result is a polar covalent molecule.

   b. This molecule has no metals, so it is not ionic. It has polar bonds, but the Lewis structure has only 2 groups of electrons around the central atom. Thus, this molecule is linear, with an S on either side of the C. Since the bonds pull opposite one another, they cancel, making this a nonpolar covalent molecule.

   c. This molecule has a metal (Al), so it is ionic.

   d. This molecule is nonpolar covalent since it has no polar covalent bonds.

   e. This molecule has no metals, so it is not ionic. If we determine its geometry, we will find it is tetrahedral. Since the bonds are all identical in the tetrahedron, they cancel, making this a nonpolar covalent molecule.

   f. This molecule has no metals, so it is not ionic. If we determine its geometry, we will find it is pyramidal. There is no way for the bonds to cancel in a pyramidal structure, so the result is a polar covalent molecule.

10. The ionic and polar covalent molecules should dissolve in water. Thus, we would expect $SiFCl_3$, AlF_3, and PF_3 to dissolve in water.

TEST FOR MODULE 5

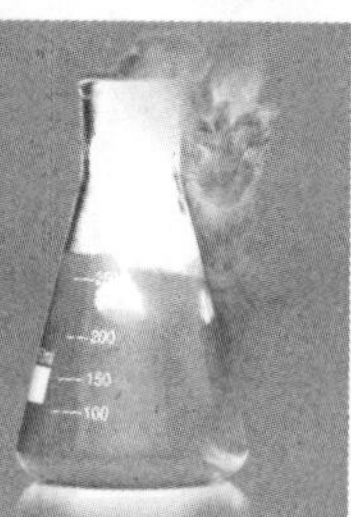

1. (4 pts) How many oxygen atoms are in an $Al_2(CO_3)_3$ molecule?
   a. 3
   b. 6
   c. 9
   d. 12

2. (4 pts) Polyatomic ions are often said to be a cross between covalent compounds and ionic compounds. Why can they be characterized in such a way?

3. (4 pts) In VSEPR theory, which repels other electron groups more strongly:
   a. A bond
   b. A nonbonding electron pair

4. (4 pts) Explain, in your own words, why molecules sometimes attain 3-dimensional shapes rather than just being flat.

5. (4 pts) The only electrons involved in determining the 3-dimensional shape of a molecule are:
   a. The covalent bonds on the central atom
   b. The lone pair valence electrons on the central atom
   c. Both A and B
   d. Neither A nor B

6. (4 pts) The molecular shape that has a 109° bond angle is:
   a. Tetrahedral
   b. Pyramidal
   c. Bent
   d. Linear
   e. None of the above

7. (4 pts) The molecular shape that has a 105° bond angle is:
   a. Tetrahedral
   b. Pyramidal
   c. Bent
   d. Linear
   e. None of the above

8. (4 pts) The molecular shape that has a 90° bond angle is:
   a. Tetrahedral
   b. Pyramidal
   c. Bent
   d. Linear
   e. None of the above

9. (4 pts) A bond that consists of equal sharing of electrons is:
   a. Ionic bond
   b. Polar covalent
   c. Nonpolar covalent
   d. Polyatomic ion
   e. None of the above

10. (4 pts) If a molecule is to be polar covalent:
    a. The molecule must have polar bonds in it.
    b. The polar bonds must be of equal strength.
    c. Both a and b
    d. Neither a nor b

11. (4 pts) If you had a substance that water will not dissolve, then which of the following compounds would you choose to dissolve this substance:
    a. Vegetable oil
    b. Any polar substance
    c. Any ionic substance
    d. None of the above will work.

12. (4 pts) Give the chemical formula for calcium acetate.

13. (4 pts) Give the chemical formula for barium chromate.

14. (4 pts) Give the chemical formula for ammonium carbonate.

15. (4 pts) Give the chemical formulas for each of the following compounds in the reaction that occurs when ammonium chloride reacts with barium nitrate to produce solid barium chloride and ammonium nitrate.

16. (8 pts) Determine the shape of a NHF_2 molecule. Give its bond angles and draw a picture of it.

17. (8 pts) Determine the shape of a CHI_2Cl molecule. Give its bond angles and draw a picture of it.

18. (8 pts) Determine the shape of an I_2O molecule. Give its bond angles and draw a picture of it.

19. (16 pts) Classify the following molecules as ionic, polar covalent, or nonpolar covalent:

a. NHF_2 b. CHI_2Cl c. CF_4 d. KNO_3

SOLUTIONS TO THE TEST FOR MODULE 5

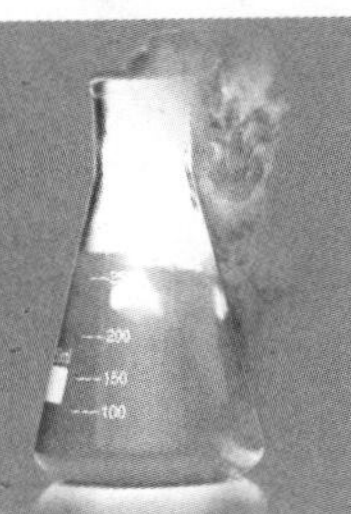

1. (4 pts) c. 9 The CO_3 has 3 oxygen atoms, but it is in a set of parentheses with a 3 as a subscript. This means that there are 3 CO_3 atoms. Thus, there are 3 × 3 = 9 oxygen atoms.

2. (4 pts) Since polyatomic ions have a groups of atoms that share electrons, they are like covalent compounds. However, since they also contain extra electrons or a deficit of electrons, they are also like ionic compounds.

3. (4 pts) b. A nonbonding electron pair
Nonbonding electron pairs repel more strongly than bonds.

4. (4 pts) Molecules do anything they can to get their central atom's valence electron groups far away from each other. They can often get them farther apart if they use all 3 dimensions of space.

5. (4 pts) c. Both a and b

6. (4 pts) a. Tetrahedral

7. (4 pts) c. Bent

8. (4 pts) e. None of the above

9. (4 pts) c. Nonpolar covalent

10. (4 pts) a. The molecule must have polar bonds in it.

11. (4 pts) a. Vegetable oil

12. (4 pts) $Ca(C_2H_3O_2)_2$

13. (4 pts) $BaCrO_4$

14. (4 pts) $(NH_4)_2CO_3$

15. (4 pts) First, we have to determine the formulas of the molecules involved: Ammonium chloride includes NH_4^+ and Cl−. Thus, its formula is NH_4Cl. Barium nitrate includes Ba^{2+} and NO_3^-. Thus, its formula is $Ba(NO_3)_2$. Barium chloride includes Ba^{2+} and Cl−. Thus, its formula is $BaCl_2$. Ammonium nitrate includes NH_4^+ and NO_3^-. Thus, its formula is NH_4NO_3.

16. (8 pts: 4 pts for the shape and bond angle, 4 pts for the picture) Pyramidal, with a bond angle of 107°

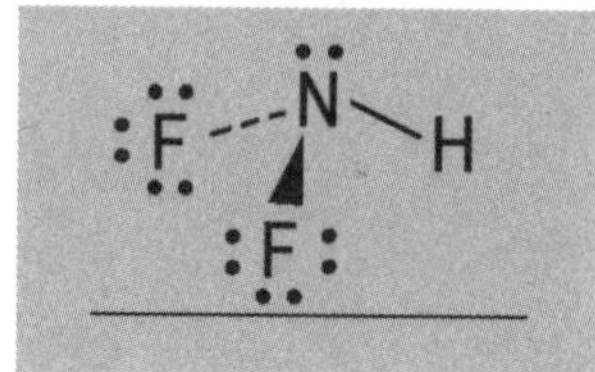

17. (8 pts: 4 pts for the shape and bond angle, 4 pts for the picture) Tetrahedral, with a bond angle of 109°

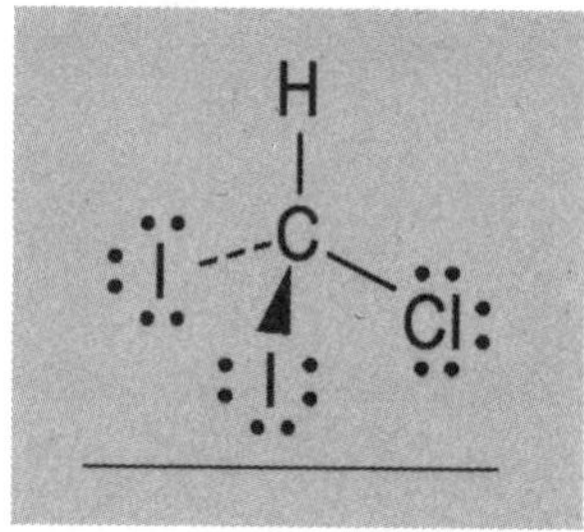

18. (8 pts: 4 pts for the shape and bond angle, 4 pts for the picture) Bent, with a bond angle of 105°

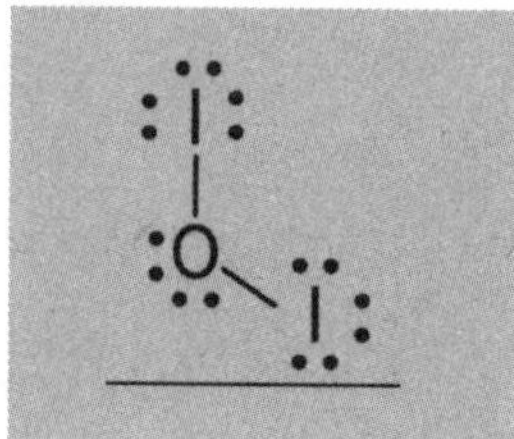

19. (16 pts: 4 pts each)
   a. Polar covalent
   b. Polar covalent
   c. Nonpolar covalent
   d. Ionic

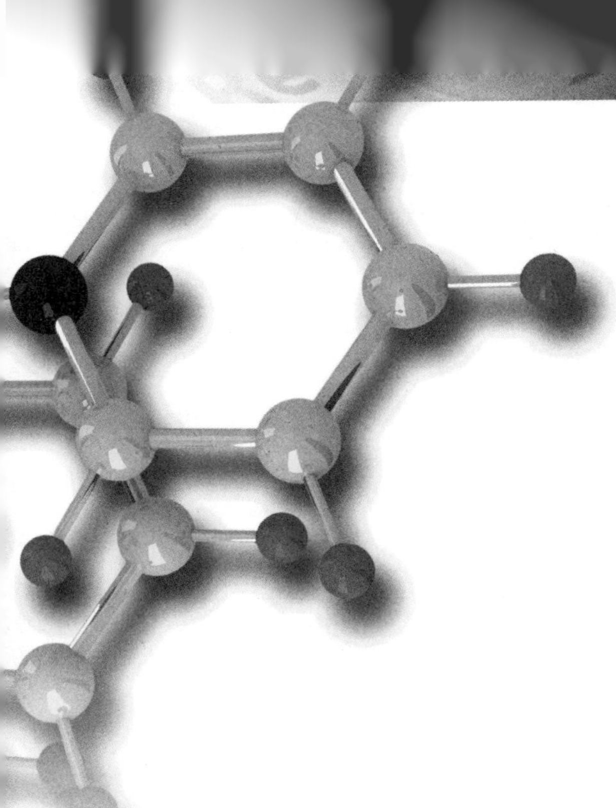

CHANGES IN MATTER AND CHEMICAL REACTIONS

SOLUTIONS TO THE MODULE 6 REVIEW QUESTIONS

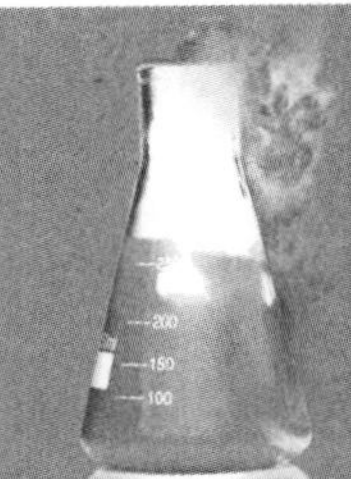

1. A chemical change alters the identity of the substances involved in a change. A physical change does not.

2. Dissolving is a physical change so the identity of the molecules does not change. Chemical reactions change the identity of the molecules to all new molecules.

3. Aluminum reacts with toilet bowl cleaner to produce a nasty gas that is harmful to humans.

4. Since molecules move faster and are farther apart in the gas phase compared to the solid phase, a transition from solid to gas must occur when a substance is heated.

5. The only phase in which molecules move slower and are closer together than in the liquid phase is the solid phase.

6. Water expands when it freezes; thus, its molecules get farther apart. All other natural substances contract when they freeze because their molecules get closer together.

7. This statement is incorrect because it is possible for metals to be liquids and gases.

8. Remember that 1 cc is equal to 1 mL, which means the volume unit used in each density measurement is equivalent. The golden statue would be heavier because the density of gold is greater than that of lead.

9. The student's value for density has far too many significant figures, and it has no units attached. Either of these things would make the student's answer wrong. Without converting, the calculated density should be 0.0671 g/mL.

10. A chemical equation is balanced if each type of atom in the equation is present in the same number on both sides of the arrow.

11. The law of mass conservation requires all equations to be balanced. The law says that matter cannot be created or destroyed; it can only change forms.

12. Measure the mass of a container like an empty beaker. Measure the mass of the same beaker with the liquid in it. Subtract these 2 measurements to find the mass of the liquid.

SOLUTIONS TO THE PRACTICE PROBLEMS FOR MODULE 6

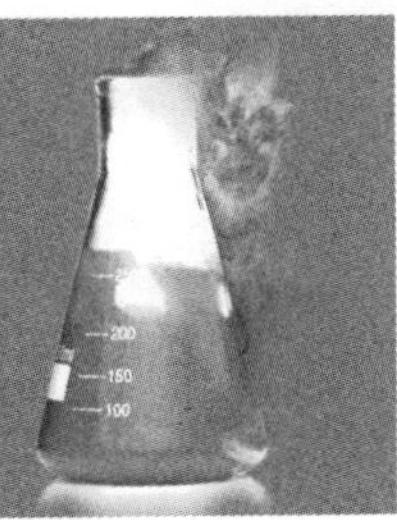

1. a. This is a <u>physical</u> change because the vase's molecules did not change. It is also easily reversible: The vase could be put back together.

   b. This is a <u>chemical</u> change. The molecules in the different ingredients actually react when they are baked to form new molecules. The other way to look at this is you cannot "unbake" a cake.

   c. This is a <u>physical</u> change because the CO_2 is just changing phase.

   d. This is a <u>chemical</u> change. Burning charcoal turns the carbon into CO_2. The other way to look at it is that you cannot "unburn" charcoal.

   e. This is a <u>physical</u> change. Dissolving one substance into another never changes their molecules. Alternatively, you could easily reverse this by boiling off the water to recover the Kool-Aid.

2. We need to use equation 6.1 here, but we must do 2 things. First, we have to get the units to agree. The density is given in grams per mL, but the volume is in L. First, then, we have to convert the volume to mL:

$$\frac{3.45\ \cancel{L}}{1} \times \frac{1\ mL}{0.001\ \cancel{L}} = 3.45 \times 10^3\ mL$$

Now that the units work out, we must also rearrange equation 6.1 to solve for mass:

$$m = \rho \times V$$

$$m = \left(11.4\ \frac{g}{\cancel{mL}}\right)\left(3.45 \times 10^3\ \cancel{mL}\right)$$

$$m = \underline{3.93 \times 10^4\ g}$$

Since each number in the equation has 3 significant figures, the answer must have 3.

3. This problem is like 2, but first we have to convert kg to g to make our units consistent:

$$\frac{45.6\ \cancel{kg}}{1} \times \frac{1{,}000\ g}{1\ \cancel{kg}} = 4.56 \times 10^4\ g$$

Now we can rearrange equation 6.1 to solve for volume:

$$V = \frac{m}{\rho}$$

$$V = \frac{4.56 \times 10^4\ g}{19.3\ \frac{g}{cc}}$$

$$V = \underline{2.36 \times 10^3\ cc}$$

Since the problem did not request any specific units, we can simply leave our answer in cc. Also, since each number in the equation has 3 significant figures, the answer must have 3.

4.

Reactants Side		Products Side		
Ca:	1 × 1 = 1	Ca:	1 × 1 = 1	Balanced with respect to Ca
F:	1 × 2 = 2	F:	1 × 1 = 1	NOT balanced with respect to F
N:	2 × 1 = 2	N	1 × 1 = 1	NOT balanced with respect to N
H:	2 × 4 = 8	H:	1 × 4 = 4	NOT balanced with respect to H
Cl:	2 × 1 = 2	Cl:	1 × 2 = 2	Balanced with respect to Cl

The equation is not balanced.

5. To balance, we must first count the atoms:

Reactants Side		Products Side		
H:	1 × 1 = 1	H:	1 × 2 = 2	NOT balanced with respect to H
Cl:	1 × 1 = 1	Cl:	1 × 2 = 2	NOT balanced with respect to Cl
Zn:	1 × 1 = 1	Zn:	1 × 1 = 1	Balanced with respect to Zn

We can start by balancing the H atoms. There are twice as many on the products side as the reactants side, so we need to double the H atoms on the reactants side:

$$\underline{2HCl\ (aq) + Zn\ (s) \rightarrow ZnCl_2\ (aq) + H_2\ (g)}$$

Counting atoms now gives us:

Reactants Side	Products Side	
H: $2 \times 1 = 2$	H: $1 \times 2 = 2$	Balanced with respect to H
Cl: $2 \times 1 = 2$	I: $1 \times 2 = 2$	Balanced with respect to Cl
Zn: $1 \times 1 = 1$	Zn: $1 \times 1 = 1$	Balanced with respect to Zn

The equation is now balanced.

6. We need to count the atoms on both sides:

Reactants Side	Products Side	
N: $1 \times 1 = 1$	N: $2 \times 1 = 2$	NOT balanced with respect to N
H: $1 \times 4 = 4$	H: $2 \times 4 = 8$	NOT balanced with respect to H
Cl: $1 \times 1 = 1$	Cl: $1 \times 3 = 3$	NOT balanced with respect to Cl
O: $3 + 3 \times 4 = 15$	O: $3 \times 3 + 4 = 13$	NOT balanced with respect to O
Al: $1 \times 2 = 2$	Al: $1 \times 1 = 1$	NOT balanced with respect to Al
S: $3 \times 1 = 3$	S: $1 \times 1 = 1$	NOT balanced with respect to S

Let's start by balancing N with a 2 in front of the first molecule:

$$2NH_4ClO_3 + Al_2(SO_4)_3 \rightarrow Al(ClO_3)_3 + (NH_4)_2SO_4$$

Counting the atoms on both sides:

Reactants Side	Products Side	
N: $2 \times 1 = 2$	N: $2 \times 1 = 2$	Balanced with respect to N
H: $2 \times 4 = 8$	H: $2 \times 4 = 8$	Balanced with respect to H
Cl: $2 \times 1 = 2$	Cl: $1 \times 3 = 3$	NOT balanced with respect to Cl
O: $2 \times 3 + 3 \times 4 = 18$	O: $3 \times 3 + 4 = 13$	NOT balanced with respect to O
Al: $1 \times 2 = 2$	Al: $1 \times 1 = 1$	NOT balanced with respect to Al
S: $3 \times 1 = 3$	S: $1 \times 1 = 1$	NOT balanced with respect to S

To balance the Cl atoms, we will need to change what we just did with N, but that is acceptable as long as it leads us to a balanced equation. To balance 2 Cl atoms on the left with 3 Cl atoms on the right, we will need 6 Cl atoms on both sides. We will put a 6 in front of the first molecule and a 2 in front of the first molecule on the right.

$$6NH_4ClO_3 + Al_2(SO_4)_3 \rightarrow 2Al(ClO_3)_3 + (NH_4)_2SO_4$$

Counting the atoms on both sides:

Reactants Side	Products Side	
N: $6 \times 1 = 6$	N: $2 \times 1 = 2$	NOT balanced with respect to N
H: $6 \times 4 = 24$	H: $2 \times 4 = 8$	NOT balanced with respect to H
Cl: $6 \times 1 = 6$	Cl: $2 \times 3 = 6$	Balanced with respect to Cl
O: $6 \times 3 + 3 \times 4 = 30$	O: $6 \times 3 + 4 = 22$	NOT balanced with respect to O
Al: $1 \times 2 = 2$	Al: $2 \times 1 = 2$	Balanced with respect to Al
S: $3 \times 1 = 3$	S: $1 \times 1 = 1$	NOT balanced with respect to S

Putting a 3 in front of the last molecule will balance out the nitrogen atoms again.

$$6NH_4ClO_3 + Al_2(SO_4)_3 \rightarrow 2Al(ClO_3)_3 + 3(NH_4)_2SO_4$$

Counting the atoms on both sides:

Reactants Side	Products Side	
N: $6 \times 1 = 6$	N: $3 \times 2 = 6$	Balanced with respect to N
H: $6 \times 4 = 24$	H: $3 \times 2 \times 4 = 24$	Balanced with respect to H
Cl: $6 \times 1 = 6$	Cl: $2 \times 3 = 6$	Balanced with respect to Cl
O: $6 \times 3 + 3 \times 4 = 30$	O: $18 + 12 = 30$	Balanced with respect to O
Al: $1 \times 2 = 2$	Al: $2 \times 1 = 2$	Balanced with respect to Al
S: $3 \times 1 = 3$	S: $3 \times 1 = 3$	Balanced with respect to S

The equation is balanced. A quicker approach to balancing this equation would be to balance the polyatomic ions together as 1 ion. This approach will work only when the polyatomic ions stay together throughout the reaction. If any of the polyatomic ions were to break apart, then we would need to balance the equation like we did above.

7. Turning the words into equation form:

$$N_2 + O_2 \rightarrow NO$$

Counting atoms:

Reactants Side	Products Side	
N: $1 \times 2 = 2$	N: $1 \times 1 = 1$	NOT balanced with respect to N
O: $1 \times 2 = 2$	O: $1 \times 1 = 1$	NOT balanced with respect to O

To balance the N atoms, we must double the number of N atoms on the products side:

$$N_2 + O_2 \rightarrow 2NO$$

Counting atoms again:

Reactants Side	Products Side
N: 1 × 2 = 2	N: 2 × 1 = 2 Balanced with respect to N
O: 1 × 2 = 2	O: 2 × 1 = 2 Balanced with respect to O

The equation is now balanced.

8. Turning the words into equation form:

C_7H_{10} (l) + H_2 (g) → C_7H_{16} (l)

Counting atoms:

Reactants Side	Products Side	
C: 1 × 7 = 7	C: 1 × 7 = 7	Balanced with respect to C
H: 1 × 10 + 1 × 2 = 12	H: 1 × 16 = 16	NOT balanced with respect to H

To balance this equation, we must add 6 more H atoms to the reactants side. To do this, we had better not mess with the C_7H_{10} because that will ruin the balance we have for carbon. Thus, we should change the number next to the H_2. Since 10 H atoms come from the C_7H_{10}, we need 6 H atoms to come from H_2. Therefore:

<u>C_7H_{10} (l) + $3H_2$ (g) → C_7H_{16} (l)</u>

Counting atoms again:

Reactants Side	Products Side	
C: 1 × 7 = 7	C: 1 × 7 = 7	Balanced with respect to C
H: 1 × 10 + 3 × 2 = 16	H: 1 × 16 = 16	Balanced with respect to H

9. Counting atoms:

Reactants Side	Products Side	
C: 1 × 7 = 7	C: 1 × 1 = 1	NOT balanced with respect to C
H: 1 × 16 = 16	H: 1 × 2 = 2	NOT balanced with respect to H
O: 1 × 2 = 2	O: 1 × 2 + 1 × 1 = 3	NOT balanced with respect to O

Balancing the C atoms and H atoms at the same time:

C_7H_{16} (l) + O_2 (g) → $7CO_2$ (g) + $8H_2O$ (g)

Counting atoms:

Reactants Side	Products Side	
C: $1 \times 7 = 7$	C: $7 \times 1 = 7$	Balanced with respect to C
H: $1 \times 16 = 16$	H: $8 \times 2 = 16$	Balanced with respect to H
O: $1 \times 2 = 2$	O: $7 \times 2 + 8 \times 1 = 22$	NOT balanced with respect to O

To balance the O atoms, we must multiply the O atoms on the reactants side by 11:

$\underline{C_7H_{16}\ (l) + 11O_2\ (g) \rightarrow 7CO_2\ (g) + 8H_2O\ (g)}$

Counting atoms:

Reactants Side	Products Side	
C: $1 \times 7 = 7$	C: $7 \times 1 = 7$	Balanced with respect to C
H: $1 \times 16 = 16$	H: $8 \times 2 = 16$	Balanced with respect to H
O: $11 \times 2 = 22$	O: $7 \times 2 + 8 \times 1 = 22$	Balanced with respect to O

10. Counting atoms:

Reactants Side	Products Side	
C: $1 \times 1 = 1$	C: $1 \times 12 = 12$	NOT balanced with respect to C
H: $1 \times 2 = 2$	H: $1 \times 24 = 24$	NOT balanced with respect to H
O: $1 \times 2 + 1 \times 1 = 3$	O: $1 \times 12 + 1 \times 2 = 14$	NOT balanced with respect to O

To balance this, we need to leave the O atoms until the end because they appear in all of the substances. We can balance the C atoms and the H atoms in one step:

$12CO_2\ (g) + 12H_2O\ (l) \rightarrow C_{12}H_{24}O_{12}\ (s) + O_2\ (g)$

Counting atoms again:

Reactants Side	Products Side	
C: $12 \times 1 = 12$	C: $1 \times 12 = 12$	Balanced with respect to C
H: $12 \times 2 = 24$	H: $1 \times 24 = 24$	Balanced with respect to H
O: $12 \times 2 + 12 \times 1 = 36$	O: $1 \times 12 + 1 \times 2 = 14$	NOT balanced with respect to O

To balance the O atoms, we can't mess with the $C_{12}H_{24}O_{12}$ because changing its number will throw our C atoms and H atoms off balance. Thus, we must work with the O_2. Since 12 O atoms come from the $C_{12}H_{24}O_{12}$, we need 24 more to come from the O_2. Therefore:

$\underline{12CO_2\ (g) + 12H_2O\ (l) \rightarrow C_{12}H_{24}O_{12}\ (s) + 12O_2\ (g)}$

Counting atoms:

Reactants Side	Products Side	
C: 12 × 1 = 12	C: 1 × 12 = 12	Balanced with respect to C
H: 12 × 2 = 24	H: 1 × 24 = 24	Balanced with respect to H
O: 12 × 2 + 12 × 1 = 36	O: 1 × 12 + 12 × 2 = 36	Balanced with respect to O

SAMPLE CALCULATIONS FOR EXPERIMENT 6.4

Mass of the graduated cylinder: 25 g

Mass of the syrup and the cylinder: 82 g
You can read your mass scale to 1 g, since it is probably marked off in increments of 10 g.

Mass of the syrup: 82 g – 25 g = 57 g
Since both masses have a significant figure in the ones place, the answer can be reported to the ones place.

Density of the syrup:

$$\frac{57\text{ g}}{50.0\text{ mL}} = 1.1\frac{\text{g}}{\text{mL}}$$

Your density might be higher, depending on the syrup used. The answer has 2 significant figures because 57 has 2 significant figures.

Mass of the water and the cylinder: 75 g

Mass of the water: 75 g – 25 g = 5.0×10^1 g
Since both masses have a significant figure in the ones place, the answer can be reported to the ones place. In this case, we had to use scientific notation to indicate that the zero is significant.

Density of the water:

$$\frac{5.0\times10^{1}\ \text{g}}{50.0\ \text{mL}} = 1.0\ \frac{\text{g}}{\text{mL}}$$

The answer has 2 significant figures because 5.0×10^1 has 2 significant figures.

Mass of the oil and the cylinder: 71 g

Mass of the oil: 71 g – 25 g = 46 g
Since both masses have a significant figure in the ones place, the answer can be reported to the ones place.

Density of the oil:

$$\frac{46\ \text{g}}{50.0\ \text{mL}} = 0.92\ \frac{\text{g}}{\text{mL}}$$

The answer has 2 significant figures because 46 has 2 significant figures.

SOLUTIONS TO THE EXTRA PRACTICE PROBLEMS FOR MODULE 6

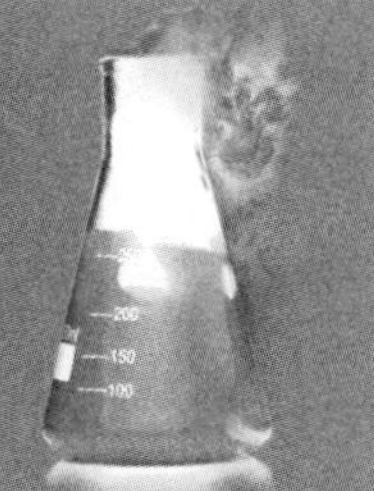

1. The liquid turned into a gas. If it had turned into a solid, the molecules would have slowed down and moved closer together. Even if the liquid was water, the molecules would have still slowed down.

2. With all 3 phases of acetone present in the same container, the phases densities will determine what the inside of the container looks like. Solid acetone is more dense than liquid acetone. Gaseous acetone is the least dense. So in the container, solid acetone will be at the bottom of the liquid acetone. Gaseous acetone will be at the top of the container above the liquid.

3. a. This is a physical change, as all the glass is still glass.

   b. This is a chemical change. It would be impossible to "unbake" bread.

   c. This is a physical change, as all phase changes are physical.

   d. This is a chemical change. It would be impossible to "unburn" the wood log.

4. This is an application of equation 6.1:

$$\rho = \frac{m}{V} \qquad \rho = \frac{23.13\ g}{35.0\ mL} = 0.661\frac{g}{mL}$$

5. To do this question, we must rearrange equation 6.1:

$$\rho = \frac{m}{V} \qquad 2.12 = \frac{g}{mL} = \frac{45\ g}{V}$$

$$V = \frac{45\ g}{2.12\frac{g}{mL}} = 21\ mL$$

6. This is another application of the density equation, but we must first get the units consistent. The volume is in L, while the density is in g/mL. Thus, we need to convert L into mL:

$$\frac{0.67\ \cancel{L}}{1} \times \frac{1\ mL}{0.001\ \cancel{L}} = 670\ mL$$

Now that all units agree, we can use the equation for density to solve for mass.

$$\rho = \frac{m}{V}$$

$$19.3\ \frac{g}{mL} = \frac{m}{670\ mL}$$

$$m = (19.3\ \frac{g}{\cancel{mL}})(670\ \cancel{mL}) = \underline{13{,}000\ g}$$

7. $\underline{2HCl\ (aq) + Ca\ (s) \rightarrow CaCl_2\ (aq) + H_2\ (g)}$

8. $\underline{2HBr\ (aq) + 2Na\ (s) \rightarrow 2NaBr\ (s) + H_2\ (g)}$

9. $\underline{2AgCl\ (aq) + Zn\ (s) \rightarrow ZnCl_2\ (aq) + 2Ag\ (s)}$

10. $\underline{MgCl_2\ (aq) + H_2S\ (aq) \rightarrow MgS\ (s) + 2HCl\ (aq)}$

11. $\underline{18CO_2\ (g) + 16H_2O\ (l) \rightarrow C_{18}H_{32}O_{16}\ (s) + 18O_2\ (g)}$

12. $\underline{2FeCl_3 + 3Na_2CO_3 \rightarrow Fe_2C_3O_9 + 6NaCl}$

13. $\underline{2NH_4Cl + Ba(OH)_2 \rightarrow BaCl_2 + 2NH_3 + 2H_2O}$

TEST FOR MODULE 6

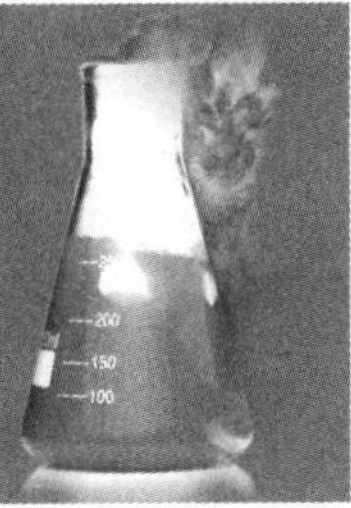

1. (4 pts) What kind of change does a substance undergo without altering the molecules or atoms that are present?
   a. Chemical change
   b. Physical change
   c. Chemical reaction
   d. Pure substance
   e. None of the above

2. (4 pts) What type change affects the type of molecules or atoms in a substance?
   a. Chemical change
   b. Physical change
   c. Qualitative measurement
   d. Quantitative measurement
   e. None of the above

3. (4 pts) When a substance changes from a solid to a liquid, it is called:
   a. A physical change
   b. A phase change
   c. Melting
   d. All of the above

4. (4 pts) Wood burning in a fireplace is a:
   a. Physical change
   b. Chemical change

5. (4 pts) A frozen turkey thawing is a:
   a. Physical change
   b. Chemical change

6. (4 pts) Recall from Biology that photosynthesis is the process in which plants produce their own food. Is photosynthesis a:
   a. Physical change
   b. Chemical change

7. (4 pts) Mowing a lawn is a:
   a. Physical change
   b. Chemical change

8. (4 pts) Ice floats in water. Does frozen HNO_3 float in liquid HNO_3? Explain.
9. (4 pts) True or False: All substances take up the least amount of volume as a solid and the most amount of volume as a gas.

10. (4 pts) Which of the following is true about water:
    a. The liquid is more dense than the solid.
    b. The solid is less dense than the gas.
    c. The gas is more dense than the liquid.
    d. The liquid is less dense than the solid.
    e. None of the above

11. (4 pts) The density of gold is 19.3 grams per mL. A miner finds a gold-colored nugget with a volume of 34.2 mL and mass of 661 grams. Is it really a nugget of gold?

12. (8 pts) A fisherman wants to determine the volume of his lead sinker. If lead's density is 11.4 grams per cc and the sinker has a mass of 0.123 kg, what is the volume of the sinker?

13. (8 pts) Which of the following elements are homonuclear diatomics?
    carbon, nitrogen, fluorine, sodium

14. (2 pts) True or False: The following equation is balanced.
    $2HBr\ (aq) + Ca\ (s) \rightarrow CaBr_2\ (aq) + H_2\ (g)$

15. (4 pts) Balance the following equation:
    $H_2O\ (l) + Na\ (s) \rightarrow NaOH\ (aq) + H_2\ (g)$

16. (10 pts) Under the right conditions, chlorine gas will react with gaseous ethylyne (C_2H_2) to make liquid quadrachloroethane ($C_2H_2Cl_4$). Write the balanced chemical equation.

17. (12 pts) When C_3H_8 reacts with oxygen, it makes carbon dioxide and water. Write the balanced chemical equation.

18. (8 pts) Balance the following equation for the combustion of ethanol:
    $C_2H_6O\ (l) + O_2\ (g) \rightarrow CO_2\ (g) + H_2O\ (g)$

19. (4 pts) How does a balanced chemical equation ensure that mass is conserved during a chemical reaction?

SOLUTIONS TO THE TEST FOR MODULE 6

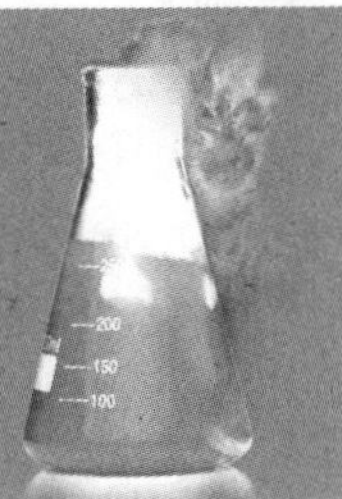

1. (4 pts) b. Physical change

2. (4 pts) a. Chemical change

3. (4 pts) d. All of the above

4. (4 pts) b. Chemical change We can't reverse burning. This is a chemical change.

5. (4 pts) a. Physical change The turkey can be refrozen, so this is a physical change.

6. (4 pts) b. Chemical change Photosynthesis is a chemical change.

7. (4 pts) a. Physical change Just like cutting your hair, this change can be reversed by gluing each blade of grass back together. Thus, this is a physical change.

8. (4 pts) Frozen HNO_3 does not float in liquid HNO_3. Water is one of the few substances which is less dense in its solid phase than its liquid phase. That's why ice floats on water. For the vast majority of other compounds, the solid phase is more dense than the liquid phase, so frozen HNO_3 does not float in liquid HNO_3.

9. (4 pts) False There are substances, like water, where the solid density is less than the liquid density.

10. (4 pts) a. The liquid is more dense than the solid.

11. (4 pts) The nugget is gold! To test whether or not this nugget is gold, we simply compute the density. If the density is 19.3 g/mL, the nugget is gold. If not, the nugget is not gold.

12. (8 pts: 4 pts for converting to get consistent units, and 4 pts for the answer) 10.8 cc
The density is given in g/cc. Remember, this is the same as g/mL, but we will go ahead and use cc. Since density is mass divided by volume, if we know density and mass, we can get volume. Notice, however, that there are conflicting units. The density uses grams (g/cc), but the mass is given in kg. Thus, before we solve the problem, we need to convert from kg to g:

$$\frac{0.123 \cancel{kg}}{1} \times \frac{1000 \text{ g}}{1 \cancel{kg}} = 123 \text{ g}$$

Now that all units agree, we can use the equation for density to solve for volume:

$$\rho = \frac{m}{V} \qquad 11.4 \frac{g}{cc} = \frac{123 \text{ g}}{V}$$

$$V = \frac{123 \text{ g}}{11.4 \frac{g}{cc}} = \underline{10.8 \text{ cc}}$$

13. (8 pts: 4 pts for each answer, minus 2 pts for every wrong element listed)
The 2 homonuclear diatomic elements on this list are nitrogen: N_2 and fluorine: F_2.

14. (2 pts) True The equation is balanced.

15. (4 pts) $2H_2O\ (l) + 2Na\ (s) \rightarrow 2NaOH\ (aq) + H_2\ (g)$

16. (10 pts: 2 pts for the correct element/compounds, 4 pts for the equation, and 4 pts for correctly balancing it) $2Cl_2\ (g) + C_2H_2\ (g) \rightarrow C_2H_2Cl_4\ (l)$

17. (12 pts: 4 pts for the correct element/compounds, 4 pts for the equation, and 4 pts for correctly balancing it) $C_3H_8 + 5O_2 \rightarrow 3CO_2 + 4H_2O$

18. (8 pts) $C_2H_6O\ (l) + 3O_2\ (g) \rightarrow 2CO_2\ (g) + 3H_2O\ (g)$

19. (4 pts) If a chemical equation is balanced, then the same number of atoms appear on both sides. This would mean the mass is the same whether we are talking about reactants or products. That's another way of stating the law of mass conservation.

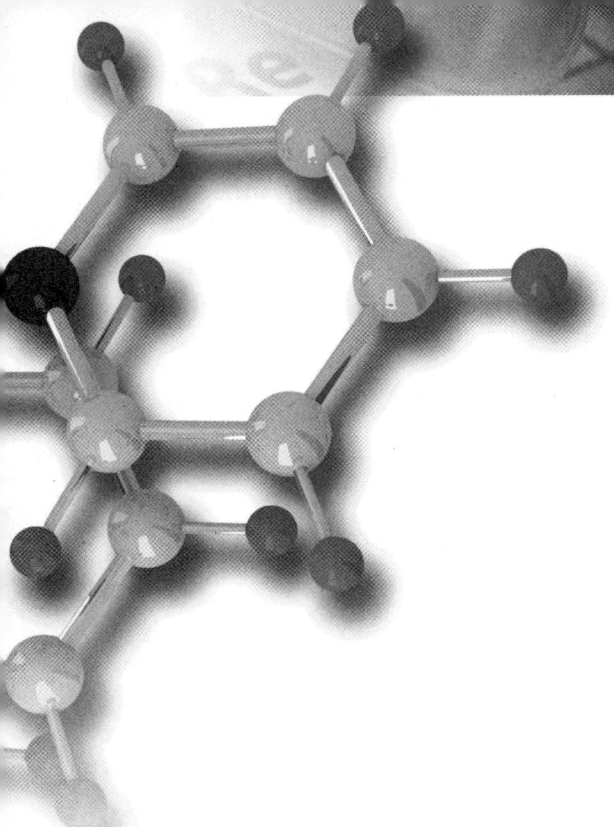

DESCRIBING CHEMICAL REACTIONS

SOLUTIONS TO THE MODULE 7 REVIEW QUESTIONS

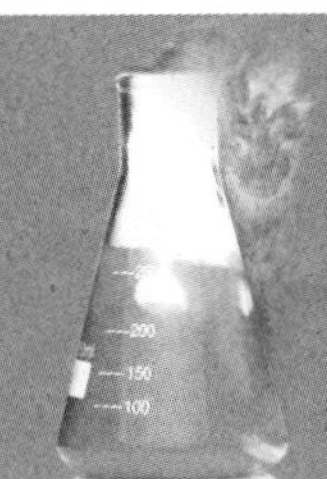

1. Elements cannot undergo decomposition reactions because elements have nothing to decompose into.

2. a. This equation represents a complete combustion reaction because O_2 is added, while CO_2 and H_2O are produced.

   b. This equation represents a formation reaction because 2 elements come together to produce 1 compound.

   c. None of these

   d. None of these

   e. This equation represents a decomposition reaction because a single compound is breaking down into its elements.

3. The only equation that does not represent a formation reaction is (a). The equation for (b) is a formation equation because it starts with 2 reactants and makes only 1 in the end. Remember, reactions do not have to start with elements in order to be formation equations; we just assume they do when we write them ourselves.

4. The only equation that does not represent a combustion reaction is (b). The equation in (b) is a decomposition equation. Even though it produces CO_2 and H_2O, it does not have O_2 as a reactant, so it is not combustion.

5. Complete combustion produces carbon dioxide and water. Incomplete combustion produces either carbon monoxide and water or carbon and water.

6. A catalytic converter converts some of the carbon monoxide produced in an automobile to carbon dioxide, a nonpoisonous gas.

7. According to the periodic table, 100 H atoms would have a mass of 100 × 1.01 = 101 amu, 4 S atoms would have a mass of 4 × 32.1 = 128.4 amu, and 1 La atom has a mass of 138.9 amu. Thus, 1 La atom has the most mass.

8. All of the samples contain 1 mole.

9. Avogadro's number is 6.02×10^{23} atoms/mole, and it represents the number of things that are contained in 1 mole.

10. The equation can be interpreted in molecules or moles. Two molecules of C_3H_8O plus 9 molecules of oxygen gas produces 6 molecules of carbon dioxide and 8 molecules of water. Or 2 moles of C_3H_8O plus 9 moles of oxygen gas produces 6 moles of carbon dioxide and 8 moles of water.

SOLUTIONS TO THE PRACTICE PROBLEMS FOR MODULE 7

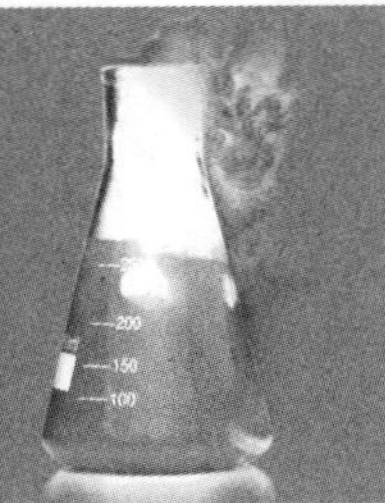

1. The compound has Rb, N, and O in it. Remember, N and O are homonuclear diatomics!

   $RbNO_3 \rightarrow Rb + N_2 + O_2$

   The Rb atoms are already balanced. To balance the N atoms and O atoms without disturbing the Rb atoms, we will have to use fractions:

   $RbNO_3 \rightarrow Rb + \frac{1}{2}N_2 + \frac{3}{2}O_2$

   Eliminating the fractions:

   $2 \times [RbNO_3] \rightarrow 2 \times [Rb + \frac{1}{2}N_2 + \frac{3}{2}O_2]$

   $\underline{2RbNO_3 \rightarrow 2Rb + N_2 + 3O_2}$

2. The compound is made up of Na, H, S, and O. H and O are homonuclear diatomics, thus:

   $Na + H_2 + S + O_2 \rightarrow NaHSO_4$

   The Na atoms and S atoms are already balanced. To balance the H atoms without disturbing the others, we will use a fraction. The O atoms are easy to balance:

   $Na + \frac{1}{2}H_2 + S + 2O_2 \rightarrow NaHSO_4$

   Eliminating the fraction:

   $2 \times [Na + \frac{1}{2}H_2 + S + 2O_2] \rightarrow 2 \times [NaHSO_4]$

   $\underline{2Na + H_2 + 2S + 4O_2 \rightarrow 2NaHSO_4}$

3. A complete combustion reaction involves adding oxygen while producing carbon dioxide and water:

   $C_8H_{18} + O_2 \rightarrow CO_2 + H_2O$

We can also add phase symbols here because we were told that the gasoline was evaporated; thus, we know it is a gas. We also know that oxygen and carbon dioxide are both gases. Finally, combustion is usually hot enough to turn water into a gas, therefore:

$$C_8H_{18}\ (g) + O_2\ (g) \rightarrow CO_2\ (g) + H_2O\ (g)$$

Now all we have to do is balance the equation. Balancing the C atoms and H atoms is easy:

$$C_8H_{18}\ (g) + O_2\ (g) \rightarrow 8CO_2\ (g) + 9H_2O\ (g)$$

To balance the O atoms without disturbing the balance of the C atoms and H atoms, we use a fraction:

$$C_8H_{18}\ (g) + \frac{25}{2}O_2\ (g) \rightarrow 8CO_2\ (g) + 9H_2O\ (g)$$

To continue, we need to eliminate the fraction:

$$2 \times [C_8H_{18}\ (g) + \frac{25}{2}O_2\ (g)] \rightarrow 2 \times [8CO_2\ (g) + 9H_2O\ (g)]$$

$$\underline{2C_8H_{18}\ (g) + 25O_2\ (g) \rightarrow 16CO_2\ (g) + 18H_2O\ (g)}$$

4. An Ar atom has a mass of 39.9 amu according to the periodic table. All we have to do is convert this to grams:

$$\frac{39.9\ \cancel{amu}}{1} \times \frac{1.66 \times 10^{-24}\ g}{1.00\ \cancel{amu}} = \underline{6.62 \times 10^{-23} g}$$

An Ar atom has a mass of $\underline{6.62 \times 10^{-23}\ g}$.

5. Aluminum dichromate has the formula of $Al_2(Cr_2O_7)_3$ which has 2 Al atoms (27.0 amu each), 6 Cr atoms (52.0 amu each), and 21 O atoms (16.0 amu each):

$$\text{Mass of } Al_2(Cr_2O_7)_3 = 2 \times 27.0\ amu + 6 \times 52.0\ amu + 21 \times 16.0\ amu = 702.0\ amu$$

Remember, since we are adding here, we look at decimal place. Each mass is reported to the tenths place, so the answer can be reported to the tenths place. Since we can only relate amu to g, we need to do a 2-step conversion:

$$\frac{702.0\ \cancel{amu}}{1} \times \frac{1.66 \times 10^{-24}\ \cancel{g}}{1.00\ \cancel{amu}} \times \frac{1\ kg}{1{,}000\ \cancel{g}} = \underline{1.17 \times 10^{-24}\ kg}$$

The conversation factor for relating grams and amu, 1.66×10^{-24} g = 1 amu, is a rounded value so we must consider it in determining significant figures. Therefore, we must round our answer to 3 significant figures.

An $Al_2(Cr_2O_7)_3$ molecule has a mass of $\underline{1.17 \times 10^{-24} \text{ kg.}}$

6. The periodic table tells us that 1 Au atom has a mass of 197.0 amu. Therefore:

   197.0 grams Au = 1 mole Au

   This is the conversion relationship we need to convert kilograms into grams of Au and then into moles of Au:

   $$\frac{2.56 \cancel{\text{kg}}}{1} \times \frac{1000 \cancel{\text{g}}}{1 \cancel{\text{kg}}} \times \frac{1 \text{ mole Au}}{197.0 \cancel{\text{g Au}}} = \underline{13.0 \text{ moles Au}}$$

   There are 13.0 moles of Au in this sample.

7. The molecular mass of $NaHCO_3$ is:

   $1 \times 23.0 \text{ amu} + 1 \times 1.01 \text{ amu} + 1 \times 12.0 \text{ amu} + 3 \times 16.0 \text{ amu} = 84.0 \text{ amu}$

   Using the rule of addition and subtraction, we can only report our answer to the tenths place because the least precise numbers in the problem (23.0, 12.0, and 16.0) have their last significant figure in the tenths place. This means:

   84.0 g $NaHCO_3$ = 1 mole $NaHCO_3$

   Now we do the grams to moles conversion:

   $$\frac{125 \cancel{\text{g NaHCO}_3}}{1} \times \frac{1 \text{ mole NaHCO}_3}{84.0 \cancel{\text{g NaHCO}_3}} = \underline{1.49 \text{ moles NaHCO}_3}$$

   There are 1.49 moles of $NaHCO_3$ in this sample.

8. The formula for copper (II) chloride is $CuCl_2$. We still need to determine the molecular mass of $CuCl_2$ first, however:

   Mass of $CuCl_2$ = $1 \times 63.5 \text{ amu} + 2 \times 35.5 \text{ amu} = 134.5 \text{ amu}$

   This means:

   134.5 grams $CuCl_2$ = 1 mole $CuCl_2$

Now we can do our conversion:

$$\frac{0.344 \text{ ~~moles CuCl~~}}{1} \times \frac{134.5 \text{ g } CuCl_2}{1 \text{ ~~mole } CuCl_2\text{~~}} = \underline{46.3 \text{ g } CuCl_2}$$

This sample has a mass of 46.3 g $CuCl_2$.

9. Once again, this is just a conversion problem. We first look at the periodic table to determine the relationship between grams and moles:

$$183.8 \text{ g W} = 1 \text{ mole W}$$

Now we use this relationship in a conversion:

$$\frac{457 \text{ ~~g W~~}}{1} \times \frac{1 \text{ mole W}}{183.8 \text{ ~~g W~~}} = \underline{2.49 \text{ mole W}}$$

Moles can be converted into atoms by using Avagadro's number.

$$\frac{2.49 \text{ ~~mole W~~}}{1} \times \frac{6.02 \times 10^{23} \text{ atoms W}}{1 \text{ ~~mole W~~}} = \underline{1.50 \times 10^{24} \text{ atoms W}}$$

This sample has 1.50×10^{24} atoms in it.

10. To solve this problem, we must first find the balanced chemical equation for this reaction. According to the problem, the reaction is the decomposition of dinitrogen pentaoxide:

$$N_2O_5 \rightarrow N_2 + O_2$$

Balancing the equation gives us:

$$2N_2O_5 \rightarrow 2N_2 + 5O_2$$

The chemical equation, then, tells us:

$$2 \text{ moles } N_2O_5 = 5 \text{ moles } O_2$$

Now all we have to do is use this fact in a conversion:

$$\frac{1.2 \text{ ~~moles } N_2O_5\text{~~}}{1} \times \frac{5 \text{ moles } O_2}{2 \text{ ~~mole } N_2O_5\text{~~}} = \underline{3.0 \text{ moles } O_2}$$

Thus, 3.0 moles of oxygen will be formed.

SAMPLE CALCULATIONS FOR EXPERIMENT 7.1

Number of drops to get 10.0 mL: 251

mL per drop:

$$\frac{10.0 \text{ mL}}{251 \text{ drops}} = 0.0398 \frac{\text{mL}}{\text{drop}}$$

Diameter of the circle: 12.75 cm

The volume of 1 drop is 0.0398 mL. To get the mass in 1 drop, we just multiply that by the density of the solution, which was given:

$$0.0398 \cancel{\text{mL}} \times 100 \frac{\text{g}}{\cancel{\text{mL}}} = 0.0398 \text{ g}$$

That's the mass of the solution, but only a fraction of that is sodium stearate:

$$\text{Mass of sodium sterate added} = 0.0398 \text{ g} \times 0.000125 = 4.98 \times 10^{-6} \text{g}$$

Now we need to convert to moles. First, we need to know the mass of a sodium stearate molecule:

$$1 \times 23.0 \text{ amu} + 18 \times 12.0 \text{ amu} + 35 \times 1.01 \text{ amu} + 2 \times 16.0 \text{ amu} = 306.4 \text{ amu}$$

This means:

$$1 \text{ mole } NaC_{18}H_{35}O_2 = 306.4 \text{ g } NaC_{18}H_{35}O_2$$

We can use that to convert to moles:

$$\frac{4.98 \times 10^{-6} \cancel{\text{g } NaC_{18}H_{35}O_2}}{1} \times \frac{1 \text{ mole } NaC_{18}H_{35}O_2}{306.4 \cancel{\text{g } NaC_{18}H_{35}O_2}} = 1.63 \times 10^{-8} \text{ moles } NaC_{18}H_{35}O_2$$

Since a mole contains 6.02×10^{23} molecules, we can determine the number of molecules:

$$\text{Number of molecules} = (1.63 \times 10^{-8} \cancel{\text{moles}}) \times (6.02 \times 10^{23} \frac{\text{molecules}}{\cancel{\text{mole}}}) = 9.81 \times 10^{15} \text{ molecules}$$

Now we need to know the area of the circle:

$$A = \pi r^2 = (3.1416) \times (6.375\ \text{cm})^2 = 127.7\ \text{cm}^2$$

Now we can calculate the area per molecule:

$$\frac{127.7\ \text{cm}^2}{9.81 \times 10^{15}} = 1.30 \times 10^{-14}\ \text{cm}^2$$

The width is roughly the square root of that, or <u>1.14×10^{-7} cm</u>.

SOLUTIONS TO THE EXTRA PRACTICE PROBLEMS FOR MODULE 7

1. $4CoS_2 + 11O_2 \rightarrow 2Co_2O_3 + 8SO_2$

2. Since H and O are homonuclear diatomics, we must have H_2 and O_2 as reactants:

   $$C + H_2 + O_2 \rightarrow C_2H_4O$$

   Now we balance:

   $$4C + 4H_2 + O_2 \rightarrow 2C_2H_4O$$

3. We will assume that this is complete combustion, which involves adding oxygen and producing carbon dioxide and water:

   $$C_{16}H_{34} + O_2 \rightarrow CO_2 + H_2O$$

   Now we have to balance:

   $$2C_{16}H_{34} + 49O_2 \rightarrow 32CO_2 + 34H_2O$$

4. To find the mass in kilograms, we will first need to find the mass of 1 Hg atom. This is found on the periodic table: 1 Hg atom = 200.6 amu. We will need to convert the amu into grams and then convert into kg.

   $$\frac{200.6 \text{ amu}}{1} \times \frac{1.66 \times 10^{-24} \text{ g}}{1.00 \text{ amu}} \times \frac{1 \text{ kg}}{1000 \text{ g}} = 3.33 \times 10^{-25} \text{ kg}$$

   The conversation factor for relating grams and amu, 1.66×10^{-24} g = 1 amu, is a rounded value so we must consider it in determining significant figures. Therefore, we must round our answer to 3 significant figures.

   The mass of a single mercury atom (Hg) is 3.33×10^{-25} kg.

5. This molecule has 2 Li atoms (6.94 amu), 1 C (12.0 amu), and 3 O atoms (16.0 amu). The molecular mass, then, is:

$$\text{Mass of } Li_2CO_3 = 2 \times 6.94 \text{ amu} + 12.0 \text{ amu} + 3 \times 16.0 \text{ amu} = 73.9 \text{ amu}$$

Converting to grams:

$$\frac{73.9 \cancel{\text{amu}}}{1} \times \frac{1.66 \times 10^{-24} \text{ g}}{1.00 \cancel{\text{amu}}} = \underline{1.23 \times 10^{-22} \text{ g}}$$

The mass is $\underline{1.23 \times 10^{-22} \text{ g}}$.

6. This molecule has 2 H atoms (1.01 amu), 1 C (12.0 amu), and 3 O atoms (16.0 amu). The molecular mass, then, is:

$$\text{Mass of } H_2CO_3 = 2 \times 1.01 \text{ amu} + 12.0 \text{ amu} + 3 \times 16.0 \text{ amu} = 62.0 \text{ amu}$$

This tells us that:

$$62.0 \text{ grams } H_2CO_3 = 1 \text{ mole } H_2CO_3$$

This is the conversion relationship we need for converting grams into moles:

$$\frac{1250 \cancel{\text{g } H_2CO_3}}{1} \times \frac{1 \text{ mole } H_2CO_3}{62.0 \cancel{\text{g } H_2CO_3}} = \underline{20.2 \text{ moles } H_2CO_3}$$

7. This is just another conversion question, but this time we are converting moles into grams. We need to determine the molecular mass of $CaCl_2$ first, however:

$$\text{Mass of } CaCl_2 = 1 \times 40.1 \text{ amu} + 2 \times 35.5 \text{ amu} = 111.1 \text{ amu}$$

This means:

$$111.1 \text{ grams } CaCl_2 = 1 \text{ mole } CaCl_2$$

Now we can do our conversion:

$$\frac{0.344 \cancel{\text{moles } CaCl_2}}{1} \times \frac{111.1 \text{ g } CaCl_2}{1 \cancel{\text{mole } CaCl_2}} = \underline{38.2 \text{ g } CaCl_2}$$

8. We start by determining the formula of the molecule. Potassium ion is K^+ and chloride is Cl^-, so the formula has to be KCl. Now to find the mass of a KCl molecule:

$$\text{Mass of KCl} = 1 \times 39.1 \text{ amu} + 1 \times 35.5 \text{ amu} = 74.6 \text{ amu}$$

This tells us that:

$$74.6 \text{ grams KCl} = 1 \text{ mole KCl}$$

This is the conversion relationship we need for converting grams into moles:

$$\frac{25.0 \cancel{\text{g KCl}}}{1} \times \frac{1 \text{ mole KCl}}{74.6 \cancel{\text{g KCl}}} = \underline{0.335 \text{ moles KCl}}$$

9. We start by determining the formula of the molecule. The name says we have 1 carbon atom and 2 oxygen atoms, so the formula is CO_2. Now we need to find the mass of a CO_2 molecule:

$$\text{Mass of } CO_2 = 1 \times 12.0 \text{ amu} + 2 \times 16.0 \text{ amu} = 44.0 \text{ amu}$$

This means:

$$44.0 \text{ grams } CO_2 = 1 \text{ mole } CO_2$$

Now we can do our conversion:

$$\frac{9.02 \cancel{\text{moles } CO_2}}{1} \times \frac{44.0 \text{ g } CO_2}{1 \cancel{\text{mole } CO_2}} = \underline{397 \text{ g } CO_2}$$

10. To find the number of atoms from a gram measurement, we will need to convert to moles first, then we will convert to atoms. First, we need to find out how many grams are in 1 mole. This will come from the periodic table as 1 mole Cu = 63.5 grams.

$$\frac{100.0 \cancel{\text{g}} \text{ Cu}}{1} \times \frac{1 \text{ mole Cu}}{63.5 \cancel{\text{g}} \text{ Cu}} = \underline{1.57 \text{ moles Cu}}$$

Technically, this could be the final answer as the unit mole does tell us how many atoms there are. So if you stopped here, your answer is correct. However, you could also go one step farther by using Avogadro's number to convert to atoms.

$$\frac{1.57 \cancel{\text{moles}} \text{ Cu}}{1} \times \frac{6.02 \times 10^{23} \text{ atoms}}{1 \cancel{\text{mole}}} = \underline{9.45 \times 10^{23} \text{ atoms Cu}}$$

11. To find the number of molecules from a kilogram measurement, we will need to convert to grams, then to moles, and then convert to molecules. First, we need to find the formula for nickel (IV) bromide. The (IV) is the charge on nickel, so the ion is Ni^{+4}. Bromide is Br^-, so the formula will be $NiBr_4$. Now we need to convert the kilograms into grams. 1.78 kg = 1780 grams.
Next, we need to find out how many grams are in 1 mole.

$$\text{Mass of } NiBr_4 = 58.7 \text{ amu} + 4 \times 79.9 \text{ amu} = 378.3 \text{ amu}$$

This means:

$$378.3 \text{ grams } NiBr_4 = 1 \text{ mole } NiBr_4$$

$$\frac{1780 \text{ g } NiBr_4}{1} \times \frac{1 \text{ mole } NiBr_4}{378.3 \text{ g } NiBr_4} = 4.71 \text{ moles } NiBr_4$$

Technically, this could be the final answer as the unit mole does tell us how many molecules there are. So if you stopped here then your answer is correct. However, you could also go one step farther by using Avogadro's number to convert to molecules.

$$\frac{4.71 \text{ moles } NiBr_4}{1} \times \frac{6.02 \times 10^{23} \text{ molecules}}{1 \text{ mole}} = 2.84 \times 10^{24} \text{ molecules } NiBr_4$$

12. We start by determining the formula of the molecule. Ammonium is NH_4^+. Phosphate is PO_4^{3-}. We need to balance for charge so we need 3 ammonium ions with a charge of +1 to cancel the -3 charge from the phosphate. This gives us the formula for ammonium phosphate of $(NH_4)_3PO_4$.

Next write the balanced decomposition reaction.

$$3N_2 + 6H_2 + P + 2O_2 \rightarrow (NH_4)_3PO_4$$

The balanced chemical reaction tells us that it takes 3 moles of N to produce 1 mole of $(NH_4)_3PO_4$. That allows us to convert from N to $(NH_4)_3PO_4$.

$$\frac{15 \text{ moles } (NH_4)_3PO_4}{1} \times \frac{3 \text{ moles N}}{1 \text{ mole } (NH_4)_3PO_4} = 45 \text{ moles N}$$

13. To do this, we first must come up with a balanced chemical equation. We will assume that this is complete combustion, which involved adding oxygen and producing carbon dioxide and water:

$$C_3H_8 + O_2 \rightarrow CO_2 + H_2O$$

Now we have to balance the equation:

$$C_3H_8 + 5O_2 \rightarrow 3CO_2 + 4H_2O$$

This tells us:

$$1 \text{ mole } C_3H_8 = 3 \text{ moles } CO_2$$

This allows us to convert from moles of C_3H_8 to moles of CO_2:

$$\frac{13.2 \cancel{\text{ moles } C_3H_8}}{1} \times \frac{3 \text{ moles } CO_2}{1 \cancel{\text{ mole } C_3H_8}} = \underline{39.6 \text{ moles } CO_2}$$

TEST FOR MODULE 7

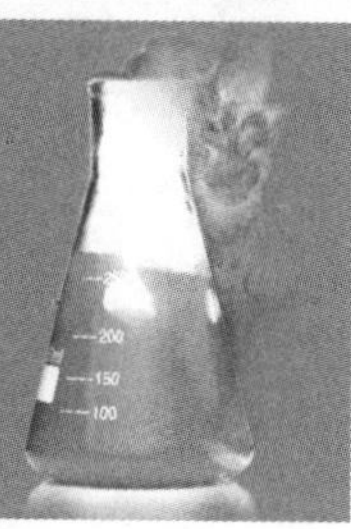

(1.00 amu = 1.66×10^{-24} g)

1. (4 pts) Classify the reaction: $2H_2CO_3$ (aq) → 2C (s) + $3O_2$ (g) + $2H_2$ (g)
   a. Formation
   b. Decomposition
   c. Combustion
   d. None of the above

2. (4 pts) Classify the reaction: 2AgCl (aq) + Ca (s) → $CaCl_2$ (aq) + 2Ag (s)
   a. Formation
   b. Decomposition
   c. Combustion
   d. None of the above

3. (4 pts) Classify the reaction: $2C_2H_2 + 5O_2 \rightarrow 4CO_2 + 2H_2O$
   a. Formation
   b. Decomposition
   c. Combustion
   d. None of the above

4. (4 pts) Classify the reaction: Br_2 (g) + C (s) + H_2 (g) → CH_2Br_2 (l)
   a. Formation
   b. Decomposition
   c. Combustion
   d. None of the above

5. (4 pts) What is the mass of a Pr atom in kg?
   a. 1.40×10^{-22} kg
   b. 2.34×10^{-25} kg
   c. 2.34×10^{-22} kg
   d. 2.34×10^{25} kg
   e. None of the above

6. (4 pts) What is the mass of an $HClO_4$ molecule in amu?
   a. 84.5 amu
   b. 100.5 amu
   c. 201.0 amu
   d. 136.0 amu
   e. None of the above

7. (6 pts) How many moles are in 34.5 g of $NaBrO_3$?
   a. 0.290 moles
   b. 0.229 moles
   c. 3.44 moles
   d. 4.36 moles
   e. None of the above

8. (4 pts) If you are given the number of moles of a substance and asked to convert to grams, you should:
   a. Divide by the mass of 1 mole of that substance.
   b. Multiply by the mass of 1 mole of that substance.
   c. Add the mass of 1 mole of that substance.
   d. Subtract the mass of 1 mole of that substance.
   e. Look for more information before solving the problem.

9. (8 pts) A chemist wants to make 5.0 moles of $(NH_4)_3PO_4$ in a formation reaction starting with the constituent elements. How many moles of hydrogen gas are needed?
   a. 12 moles
   b. 24 moles
   c. 6 moles
   d. 2 moles
   e. None of the above

10. (8 pts) Which sample has more atoms in it: 150.0 g of gold (Au), or 10.0 g of lithium?
    a. Au
    b. Li
    c. They are both the same.
    d. There is not enough information to solve this problem.

11. (4 pts) True or False: The coefficients in a balanced chemical equation indicate how many moles and grams of each molecule are needed for the reaction.

12. (6 pts) Write the chemical equation for the formation of PH_2Br.

13. (6 pts) Write the chemical equation for the decomposition of Na_2CrO_4.

14. (8 pts) Write the chemical equation for the complete combustion of liquid $C_{10}H_{22}$. Include phase symbols in your answer.

15. (8 pts) If a chemist has 12.3 moles of $N_2H_4O_3$, what is the mass of the sample?

16. (8 pts) If a chemist has 0.45 moles of K_2CO_3 and causes it to decompose into its constituent elements, how many moles of oxygen will form?

17. (4 pts) If a fireplace or furnace has poor airflow, what should you be concerned about?

18. (6 pts) A chemist has 1 mole of an unknown molecule. The mass of this sample is 111.1 grams. After doing some tests, the chemist determines that the molecule has 2 chlorine atoms in it and 1 other atom she cannot identify. In other words, the molecule's formula is XCl_2, where X is unknown. Based on the mass of the sample, what is atom X?

SOLUTIONS TO THE TEST FOR MODULE 7

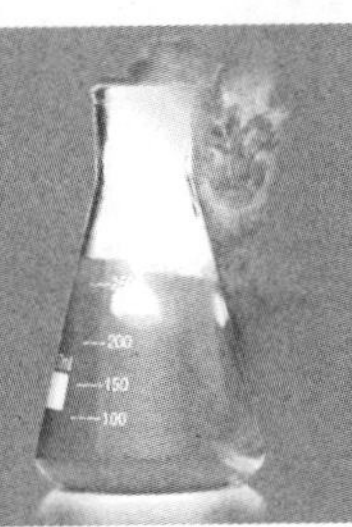

1. (4 pts) b. Decomposition A single compound is breaking down into its elements.

2. (4 pts) d. None of the above

3. (4 pts) c. Combustion
Oxygen is being added, and CO_2 and H_2O are being produced.

4. (4 pts) a. Formation
Elements are forming a single compound.

5. (4 pts) b. 2.34×10^{-25} kg
According to the periodic table, Pr has a mass of 140.9 amu. We just need to convert it to kg. However, the relationship we were given is between amu and grams. Thus, we need to do a 2-step conversion.

$$\frac{140.9\ \cancel{\text{amu}}}{1} \times \frac{1.66 \times 10^{-24}\ \cancel{\text{g}}}{1.00\ \cancel{\text{amu}}} \times \frac{1\ \text{kg}}{1{,}000\ \cancel{\text{g}}} = \underline{2.34 \times 10^{-25}\ \text{kg}}$$

6. (4 pts) b. 100.5 amu
To get the mass of a molecule, we just add the masses of all atoms in the molecule:

$$1.01\ \text{amu} + 35.5\ \text{amu} + 4 \times 16.0\ \text{amu} = \underline{100.5\ \text{amu}}$$

Since we are adding here, we look at decimal place. The 2 least precise numbers (35.5 and 16.0) each have their last significant figure in the tenths place, so the answer must be reported to the tenths place.

7. (6 pts) b. 0.229 moles
To get a relationship between grams and moles, we get the mass of the molecule:

$$23.0\ \text{amu} + 79.9\ \text{amu} + 3 \times 16.0\ \text{amu} = 150.9\ \text{amu}$$

This means 1 mole = 150.9 grams. Now we can use this in a conversion:

$$\frac{34.5\ \cancel{g}}{1} \times \frac{1\ \text{mole}}{150.9\ \cancel{g}} = \underline{0.229\ \text{moles}}$$

8. (4 pts) b. Multiply by the mass of 1 mole of that substance.

9. (8 pts) e. None of the above
We first need a balanced formation reaction. Remember nitrogen, hydrogen, and oxygen are homonuclear diatomics.

$$3N_2(g) + 12H_2(g) + 2P(s) + 4O_2\ (g) \rightarrow 2(NH_4)_3PO_4$$

For every 2 $(NH_4)_3PO_4$ we need 12 H_2. To get 5.0 moles of $(NH_4)_3PO_4$

$$5.0\ \text{mol}\ \cancel{(NH_4)_3PO_4} \times \frac{12\ \text{mol}\ H_2}{2\ \text{mol}\ \cancel{(NH_4)_3PO_4}} = \underline{3.0 \times 10^1\ \text{mol}\ H_2\ \text{needed}}$$

10. (8 pts) b. Li
To count atoms, we need to know how many moles. Thus, we need to convert both of these masses to moles:

$$\frac{150.0\ \cancel{g\ Au}}{1} \times \frac{1\ \text{mole Au}}{197.0\ \cancel{g\ Au}} = 0.7614\ \text{moles Au}$$

$$\frac{10\ \cancel{g\ Li}}{1} \times \frac{1\ \text{mole Li}}{6.94\ \cancel{g\ Li}} = 1.44\ \text{moles Li}$$

Thus, 10.0 g of lithium has more atoms than 150.0 g of Au because it has more moles.

11. (4 pts) False
The coefficients in a balanced chemical equation *do not* tell how many moles and grams of each molecule are needed for the reaction. The coefficients are an indication of either the number of molecules or moles of a molecule.

12. (6 pts: 2 pts for writing an equation that has all of the right reactants and products, and 4 pts for balancing the equation) $\underline{2P + 2H_2 + Br_2 \rightarrow 2PH_2Br}$
Remember, hydrogen and bromine are both homonuclear diatomics so their formulas are H_2 and Br_2.

13. (6 pts: 2 pts for writing an equation that has all of the right reactants and products, and 4 pts for balancing the equation) $Na_2CrO_4 \rightarrow 2Na + Cr + 2O_2$
Remember, oxygen is a homonuclear diatomic.

14. (8 pts: 4 pts for writing an equation that has all of the right reactants and products, and 4 pts for balancing the equation) $2C_{10}H_{22}\ (l) + 31O_2\ (g) \rightarrow 20CO_2\ (g) + 22H_2O\ (g)$

15. (8 pts: 4 pts for getting the mass, and 4 pts for the answer) 984 g
To get a relationship between grams and moles, we get the mass in amu:

$$2 \times 14.0 \text{ amu} + 4 \times 1.01 \text{ amu} + 3 \times 16.0 \text{ amu} = 80.0 \text{ amu}$$

This means 1 mole = 80.0 g. Now we can convert from moles to grams:

$$\frac{12.3 \text{ }\cancel{\text{moles}}}{1} \times \frac{80 \text{ g}}{1 \text{ }\cancel{\text{mole}}} = 984 \text{ g}$$

16. (8 pts: 4 pts for the equation, 4 pts for the answer) 0.68 moles O_2
To determine this, we need to figure out the decomposition reaction:

$$2K_2CO_3 \rightarrow 4K + 2C + 3O_2$$

Thus, 2 moles of K_2CO_3 = 3 moles of O_2.

$$\frac{0.45 \text{ }\cancel{\text{moles } K_2CO_3}}{1} \times \frac{3 \text{ moles } O_2}{2 \text{ }\cancel{\text{moles } K_2CO_3}} = 0.68 \text{ moles } O_2$$

17. (4 pts) You should be concerned about incomplete combustion producing carbon monoxide.

18. (6 pts) X = Ca
Since we have 1 mole, the mass of the sample in grams is also the mass of the molecule in amu. Thus, we know that this molecule's mass is 111.1 amu. Since it has 2 chlorine atoms, the chlorine alone takes up 71.0 amu of that mass. Thus, 40.1 amu are left over for X. The periodic table shows that the only atom with a mass of 40.1 amu is Ca.

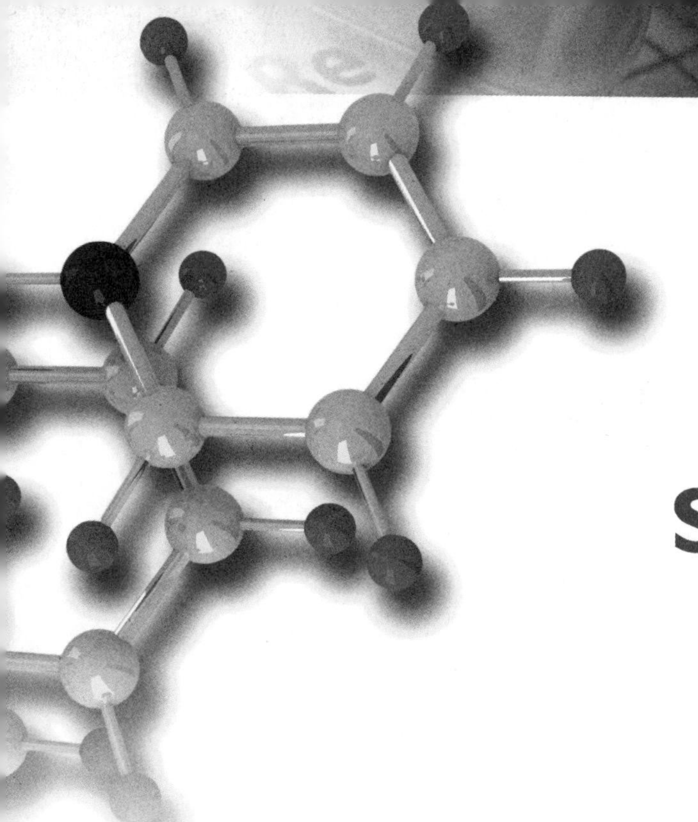

STOICHIOMETRY

SOLUTIONS TO THE MODULE 8 REVIEW QUESTIONS

1. Stoichiometry is the method used to relate the quantities of substances in chemical equations. It is useful because with the quantity of just one substance in the equation, we can learn something about the quantities of all other substances in that equation.

2. A limiting reactant is the reactant in a chemical equation that runs out first. It is important because its quantity determines the amount of products produced.

3. The limiting reactant is $K_2Cr_2O_7$ because 14 moles of HCl react with 1 mole of $K_2Cr_2O_7$. Since 15 moles of HCl are added, the 1 mole of $K_2Cr_2O_7$ will run out and there will still be 1 extra mole of HCl.

4. Gay-Lussac's law says that the stoichiometric coefficients in a chemical equation relate the volumes of gases in the equation as well as the number of moles of substances in the equation. It can be used to relate the quantities of gaseous substances in a chemical equation if those quantities are given in volume units.

5. The chemist can use Gay-Lussac's law only to relate the volumes of HCl and CO_2, since those are the only gases in the equation.

6. Since stoichiometry can be done only in moles (or volume in the case of gases), the first thing we must do is convert to moles. This conversion is done because in a balanced chemical reaction the coefficients in front of chemical compounds provides a ratio in moles. The coefficients do not relate the grams of one substance to another!

7. Molecular formulas provide the exact number of each type of atom in the molecule. Empirical formulas provide only a simple, whole-number ratio of atoms in the molecule.

8. The formulas given in (b) and (c) are empirical formulas because the subscripts have no common factor. The formula given in (a) is not an empirical formula because the subscripts have a common factor of 2.

9. The common factor between the subscripts is 7; thus we must divide each subscript by 7 to get C_2H_3O.

10. The molecular formula is also the empirical formula, since the subscripts have no common factor. The empirical formula is also H_3PO_4.

SOLUTIONS TO THE PRACTICE PROBLEMS FOR MODULE 8

1. To solve this problem, we must first come up with the chemical equation. This can be done because our definition of complete combustion gives us the unbalanced equation:

   $$C_3H_8 + O_2 \rightarrow CO_2 + H_2O$$

   Balancing:

   $$C_3H_8 + 5O_2 \rightarrow 3CO_2 + 4H_2O$$

   Now we can do stoichiometry. Since C_3H_8 is the limiting reactant, it determines the amount of product formed:

   $$1 \text{ mole } C_3H_8 = 3 \text{ moles } CO_2$$

   $$\frac{21.3 \cancel{\text{moles } C_3H_8}}{1} \times \frac{3 \text{ moles } CO_2}{1 \cancel{\text{mole } C_3H_8}} = \underline{63.9 \text{ moles } CO_2}$$

   <u>63.9 moles</u> of carbon dioxide will be formed.

2. This problem asks us to relate the quantity of the product back to the limiting reactant. According to the equation:

   $$2 \text{ moles } H_2S = 2 \text{ moles } Ag_2S$$

   Thus:

   $$\frac{0.0030 \cancel{\text{moles } Ag_2S}}{1} \times \frac{2 \text{ moles } H_2S}{2 \cancel{\text{moles } Ag_2S}} = \underline{0.0030 \text{ moles } H_2S}$$

   This means the silver was exposed to <u>0.0030 moles of H_2S.</u>

3. This problem also relates the quantity of a product back to the amount of reactant.

   $$3 \text{ moles } CCl_2F_2 = 2 \text{ moles } SbF_3$$

$$\frac{3.0 \times 10^6 \text{ moles } CCl_2F_2}{1} \times \frac{2 \text{ moles } SbF_3}{3 \text{ moles } CCl_2F_2} = 2.0 \times 10^6 \text{ moles } SbF_3$$

The chemist needs 2.0 × 10^6 moles of antimony trifluoride.

4. Since we are using liters and the 2 substances in the problem are gases, we can use Gay-Lussac's law and relate the liters of each substance:

$$3 \text{ liters } CCl_2F_2 = 3 \text{ liters } CCl_4$$

$$\frac{120.0 \text{ L } CCl_2F_2}{1} \times \frac{3 \text{ L } CCl_4}{3 \text{ L } CCl_2F_2} = 120.0 \text{ L } CCl_4$$

The chemist needs 120.0 liters of carbon tetrachloride.

5. This problem asks us to relate the quantity of limiting reactant to the quantity of product, but the quantities are both in grams. So first we must convert to moles:

$$\frac{9.80 \times 10^3 \text{ g } H_2SO_4}{1} \times \frac{1 \text{ mole } H_2SO_4}{98.1 \text{ g } H_2SO_4} = 99.9 \text{ moles } H_2SO_4$$

Now we can use stoichiometry to relate the 2 substances:

$$\frac{99.9 \text{ moles } H_2SO_4}{1} \times \frac{1 \text{ mole } CaH_4P_2O_8}{2 \text{ moles } H_2SO_4} = 50.0 \text{ moles } CaH_4P_2O_8$$

Now that we know how much fertilizer was made, we just need to get it in grams:

$$\frac{50.0 \text{ moles } CaH_4P_2O_8}{1} \times \frac{234.1 \text{ g } CaH_4P_2O_8}{1 \text{ mole } CaH_4P_2O_8} = 1.17 \times 10^4 \text{ g } CaH_4P_2O_8$$

Thus, 1.17 × 10^4 g of fertilizer will be made.

6. We assume that 5.00 g of HCl is deadly. If we relate that back to Phosgene through the chemical equation, we can determine how many grams of Phosgene are deadly. To do that, we must first convert to moles because stoichiometry can be done only in moles:

$$\frac{5.00 \text{ g HCl}}{1} \times \frac{1 \text{ mole HCl}}{36.5 \text{ g HCl}} = 0.137 \text{ moles moles HCl}$$

Now we can convert from HCl to Phosgene:

$$\frac{0.137 \text{ }\cancel{\text{moles HCl}}}{1} \times \frac{1 \text{ mole } COCl_2}{2 \text{ }\cancel{\text{moles HCl}}} = 0.0685 \text{ moles } COCl_2$$

Now we know how much Phosgene. All we need to do now is convert to grams:

$$\frac{0.0685 \text{ }\cancel{\text{moles } COCl_2}}{1} \times \frac{99.0 \text{ g } COCl_2}{1 \text{ }\cancel{\text{moles } COCl_2}} = \underline{6.78 \text{ g } COCl_2}$$

This means that only 6.78 g $COCl_2$ gas is deadly.

7. This problem asks us to relate the amount of one reactant to the amount of another. This is easy, as long as we start with moles, not grams:

$$\frac{2.8 \times 10^5 \text{ }\cancel{\text{g Mg}}}{1} \times \frac{1 \text{ mole Mg}}{24.3 \text{ }\cancel{\text{g Mg}}} = 1.2 \times 10^4 \text{ moles Mg}$$

Now we can convert from Mg to water:

$$\frac{1.2 \times 10^4 \text{ }\cancel{\text{moles Mg}}}{1} \times \frac{2 \text{ moles } H_2O}{1 \text{ }\cancel{\text{mole Mg}}} = 2.4 \times 10^4 \text{ moles } H_2O$$

Now we know how much water is needed. All we need to do now is convert to grams:

$$\frac{2.4 \times 10^4 \text{ }\cancel{\text{moles } H_2O}}{1} \times \frac{18.0 \text{ g } H_2O}{1 \text{ }\cancel{\text{mole } H_2O}} = \underline{4.3 \times 10^5 \text{ g } H_2O}$$

Thus, 4.3 × 10^5 g of water must be used.

8. The mass of the empirical formula is:

$$\text{Mass } CHBr_2 = 1 \times 12.0 \text{ amu} + 1 \times 1.01 \text{ amu} + 2 \times 79.9 \text{ amu} = 172.8 \text{ amu}$$

In order to get that equal to the molecular mass, we must multiply it by 2. Thus, the empirical formula must be multiplied by 2 as well:

$$C_{1x2}H_{1x2}Br_{2x2} = \underline{C_2H_2Br_4}$$

9. The unbalanced equation for the decomposition reaction is below. Recall that both hydrogen and oxygen are homonuclear diatomics.

$$C_xH_yO_z \rightarrow C + H_2 + O_2$$

To get the stoichiometric coefficients on the products side, we use the experimental data:

$$\frac{316\ \cancel{g\ C}}{1} \times \frac{1\text{ mole C}}{12.0\ \cancel{g\ C}} = 26.3\text{ moles C}$$

$$\frac{26.3\ \cancel{g\ H_2}}{1} \times \frac{1\text{ mole }H_2}{2.02\ \cancel{g\ H_2}} = 13.0\text{ moles }H_2$$

$$\frac{208\ \cancel{g\ O_2}}{1} \times \frac{1\text{ mole }O_2}{32.0\ \cancel{g\ O_2}} = 6.50\text{ moles }O_2$$

So the equation becomes:

$$C_xH_yO_z \rightarrow 26.3\ C + 13.0\ H_2 + 6.50\ O_2$$

We now must divide by the smallest number to make them integers:

$$C_xH_yO_z \rightarrow \frac{26.3}{6.50}\ C + \frac{13.0}{6.50}\ H_2 + \frac{6.50}{6.50}\ O_2$$

$$C_xH_yO_z \rightarrow 4C + 2H_2 + O_2$$

To balance the equation, then, x = 4, y = 4, z = 2. This makes a formula of $C_4H_4O_2$, but that is not an empirical formula because the subscripts have a common factor of 2. Thus, the real empirical formula is $\underline{C_2H_2O}$.

10. This is actually 2 problems rolled into one. First, we must find the empirical formula, then we must use the molecular mass to find the molecular formula:

$$C_xCl_y \rightarrow C + Cl_2$$

$$\frac{145\ \cancel{g\ C}}{1} \times \frac{1\text{ mole C}}{12.0\ \cancel{g\ C}} = 12.1\text{ moles C}$$

$$\frac{855\ \cancel{g\ Cl_2}}{1} \times \frac{1\text{ mole }Cl_2}{71.0\ \cancel{g\ Cl_2}} = 12.0\text{ moles }Cl_2$$

$C_xCl_y \rightarrow 12.1\ C + 12.0\ Cl_2$

Dividing both numbers by the smallest yields:

$C_xCl_y \rightarrow C + Cl_2$

For the equation to balance, the formula is:

CCl_2

To determine the molecular formula:

Mass of CCl_2 = 1 × 12.0 amu + 2 × 35.5 amu = 83.0 amu

To get that to equal the molar mass, we must multiply by 2. Therefore, we also must multiply the empirical formula by 2:

$\underline{C_2Cl_4}$

SOLUTIONS TO THE EXTRA PRACTICE PROBLEMS FOR MODULE 8

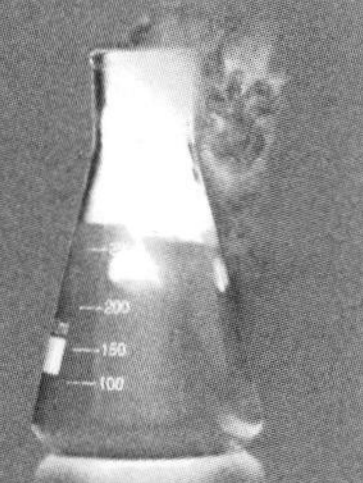

1. This question asks us to determine the mass of one substance in the equation given the mass of another substance. Thus, we must use stoichiometry. The first thing that we must do, then, is convert to moles:

Mass of HNO_3 = 1 × 1.01 amu + 1 × 14.0 amu + 3 × 16.0 amu = 63.0 amu

1 mole of HNO_3 = 63.0 g HNO_3

$$\frac{2.945 \times 10^6 \ \cancel{\text{g HNO}_3}}{1} \times \frac{1 \text{ mole HNO}_3}{63.0 \ \cancel{\text{g HNO}_3}} = 4.67 \times 10^4 \text{ moles HNO}_3$$

The chemical equation tells us:

3 moles NO_2 = 2 moles HNO_3

Thus, we can use it as a conversion relationship to convert moles of HNO_3 into moles of NO_2:

$$\frac{4.67 \times 10^4 \ \cancel{\text{moles HNO}_3}}{1} \times \frac{3 \text{ moles NO}_2}{2 \ \cancel{\text{moles HNO}_3}} = 7.01 \times 10^4 \text{ moles NO}_2$$

Now we can convert to grams of NO_2:

Mass of NO_2 = 1 × 14.0 amu + 2 × 16.0 amu = 46.0 amu

1 mole NO_2 = 46.0 g NO_2

$$\frac{7.01 \times 10^4 \ \cancel{\text{moles NO}_2}}{1} \times \frac{46.0 \text{ g NO}_2}{1 \ \cancel{\text{moles NO}_2}} = \underline{3.22 \times 10^6 \text{ g NO}_2}$$

2. The first thing that we must do is convert to moles:

Mass of H_2 = 2 × 1.01 amu = 2.02 amu

1 mole of H_2 = 2.02 g H_2

$$\frac{2.0 \times 10^{6}\ \cancel{g\ H_2}}{1} \times \frac{1\ mole\ H_2}{2.02\ \cancel{g\ H_2}} = 9.9 \times 10^{5}\ moles\ H_2$$

The chemical equation tells us:

$$3\ moles\ H_2 = 1\ mole\ W$$

Thus, we can use it as a conversion relationship to convert moles of H_2 into moles of W:

$$\frac{9.9 \times 10^{5}\ \cancel{moles\ H_2}}{1} \times \frac{1\ mole\ W}{3\ \cancel{moles\ H_2}} = 3.3 \times 10^{5}\ moles\ W$$

Now we can convert to grams W:

$$\frac{3.3 \times 10^{5}\ \cancel{moles\ W}}{1} \times \frac{183.9\ g\ W}{1\ \cancel{mole\ W}} = \underline{6.1 \times 10^{7}\ g\ W}$$

3. We already have moles of H_2, so we can use that to convert to moles of WO_3 using the chemical equation:

$$3\ moles\ H_2 = 1\ mole\ WO_3$$

$$\frac{9.9 \times 10^{5}\ \cancel{moles\ H_2}}{1} \times \frac{1\ mole\ WO_3}{3\ \cancel{moles\ H_2}} = 3.3 \times 10^{5}\ moles\ WO_3$$

Now we can convert to grams WO_3:

$$\text{Mass of } WO_3 = 1 \times 183.9\ amu + 3 \times 16.0\ amu = 231.9\ amu$$

$$1\ mole\ WO_3 = 231.9\ g\ WO_3$$

$$\frac{3.3 \times 10^{5}\ \cancel{moles\ WO_3}}{1} \times \frac{231.9\ g\ WO_3}{1\ \cancel{mole\ WO_3}} = \underline{7.7 \times 10^{7}\ g\ WO_3}$$

4. The first thing that we must do is convert to moles:

$$\frac{8.0 \times 10^{3}\ \cancel{g\ CCl_4}}{1} \times \frac{1\ mole\ CCl_4}{154\ \cancel{g\ CCl_4}} = 52\ moles\ CCl_4$$

The chemical equation tells us:

$$1 \text{ mole } CS_2 = 1 \text{ mole } CCl_4$$

Thus, we can use it as a conversion relationship to convert moles of CCl_4 into moles of CS_2:

$$\frac{52 \cancel{\text{ moles } CCl_4}}{1} \times \frac{1 \text{ mole } CS_2}{1 \cancel{\text{ mole } CCl_4}} = 52 \text{ moles } CS_2$$

Now we can convert to grams of CS_2:

$$\frac{52 \cancel{\text{ moles } CS_2}}{1} \times \frac{76.2 \text{ g } CS_2}{1 \cancel{\text{ mole } CS_2}} = \underline{4.0 \times 10^3 \text{ g } CS_2}$$

5. The first thing that we must do is convert to moles:

$$\frac{5.000 \times 10^3 \cancel{\text{ g } Ca_3P_2O_8}}{1} \times \frac{1 \text{ mole } Ca_3P_2O_8}{310.3 \cancel{\text{ g } Ca_3P_2O_8}} = 16.11 \text{ moles } Ca_3P_2O_8$$

The chemical equation tells us:

$$1 \text{ mole } Ca_3P_2O_8 = 1 \text{ mole } CaH_4P_2O_8$$

Thus, we can use it as a conversion relationship to convert moles of $Ca_3P_2O_8$ into moles of $CaH_4P_2O_8$:

$$\frac{16.11 \cancel{\text{ moles } Ca_3P_2O_8}}{1} \times \frac{1 \text{ mole } CaH_4P_2O_8}{1 \cancel{\text{ mole } Ca_3P_2O_8}} = 16.11 \text{ moles } CaH_4P_2O_8$$

Now we can convert to grams of $CaH_4P_2O_8$:

$$\frac{16.11 \cancel{\text{ moles } CaH_4P_2O_8}}{1} \times \frac{234.1 \text{ g } CaH_4P_2O_8}{1 \cancel{\text{ mole } CaH_4P_2O_8}} = \underline{3{,}771 \text{ g } CaH_4P_2O_8}$$

6. The first thing that we must do is convert to moles:

$$\frac{2.8 \times 10^4 \cancel{\text{ g } Mg(OH)_2}}{1} \times \frac{1 \text{ mole } Mg(OH)_2}{58.3 \cancel{\text{ g } Mg(OH)_2}} = \underline{480 \text{ moles } Mg(OH)_2}$$

The chemical equation tells us:

1 mole $Mg(OH)_2$ = 1 mole Mg

Thus, we can use it as a conversion relationship to convert moles of $Mg(OH)_2$ into moles of Mg:

$$\frac{480 \cancel{\text{moles } Mg(OH)_2}}{1} \times \frac{1 \text{ mole Mg}}{1 \cancel{\text{mole } Mg(OH)_2}} = 480 \text{ moles Mg}$$

Now we can convert to grams Mg:

$$\frac{480 \cancel{\text{moles Mg}}}{1} \times \frac{24.3 \text{ g Mg}}{1 \cancel{\text{mole Mg}}} = \underline{12{,}000 \text{ g Mg}}$$

7. Empirical formulas have no common factors in the subscripts. Thus, $\underline{SO_3}$ and $\underline{K_2S_2O_3}$ are empirical formulas.

8. We can determine the amount of oxygen from the law of mass conservation. Since we started with 100.0 g of matter, we must end with 100.0 g of matter. Thus, there were 200.0 g – 79.4 g – 55.8 g = 64.8 g of oxygen. Since potassium, manganese, and oxygen are in the sample, the decomposition reaction is:

$$K_xMn_yO_z \rightarrow K + Mn + O_2$$

To get the stoichiometric coefficients, we determine the number of moles produced in the decomposition reaction.

$$\frac{79.4 \cancel{\text{g K}}}{1} \times \frac{1 \text{ mole K}}{39.1 \cancel{\text{g K}}} = 2.03 \text{ moles K}$$

$$\frac{55.8 \cancel{\text{g Mn}}}{1} \times \frac{1 \text{ mole Mn}}{54.9 \cancel{\text{g Mn}}} = 1.02 \text{ moles Mn}$$

$$\frac{64.8 \cancel{\text{g } O_2}}{1} \times \frac{1 \text{ mole } O_2}{32.0 \cancel{\text{g } O_2}} = 2.03 \text{ moles } O_2$$

So the equation looks like this:

$$K_xMn_yO_z \rightarrow 2.03K + 1.02Mn + 2.03O_2$$

The problem with this equation is that the coefficients are not integers. We need to turn them into integers to be able to determine the empirical formula of the reactant. How do we do that? We divide by the smallest number:

$$K_xMn_yO_z \rightarrow \frac{2.03}{1.02}K + \frac{1.02}{1.02}Mn + \frac{2.03}{1.02}O_2$$

$$K_xMn_yO_z \rightarrow 1.99K + 1.00Mn + 1.99O_2$$

Since 1.99 is very, very close to 2, we can probably assume that they should both really be 2. Thus, the formula that balances the equation is $\underline{K_2MnO_4}$. This is already an empirical formula.

9. Since the mass of the molecule is the same as the mass of the empirical formula, the empirical formula is also the molecular formula: $\underline{K_2MnO_4}$.

10. The mass of CH_2O is 30.0 amu. To reach the mass of the molecule, we will need to multiply each element by 2. Thus, the molecular formula is $\underline{C_2H_4O_2}$.

TEST FOR MODULE 8

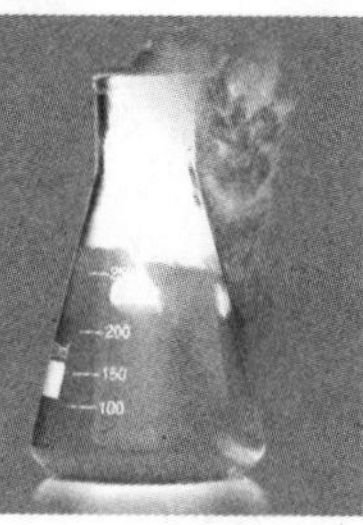

1. (4 pts) What is a stoichiometric coefficient?

2. (4 pts) Relating the quantities of different substances in a chemical equation is called:
   a. Molar mass
   b. Balancing equations
   c. Stoichiometry
   d. Limiting reactant
   e. None of the above

3. (4 pts) The chemical that is responsible for stopping reaction is called the:
   a. Excess reactant
   b. Product
   c. Stoichiometric coefficient
   d. Limiting reactant

4. (4 pts) True or False: The limiting reactant is responsible for determining how much product is produced.

5. (4 pts) Fill in the blanks using the equation:

   $2HF + CaO_2H_2 \rightarrow 2H_2O + CaF_2$

   2 moles of HF react with ___ mole(s) of CaO_2H_2 to make ____ moles(s) of H_2O and ____ mole(s) of CaF_2.

6. (4 pts) Which formula indicates a simple, whole-number ratio for the atoms in a molecule?
   a. Molecular formula
   b. Empirical formula
   c. Chemical formula
   d. Mathematical formula
   e. None of the above

7. (4 pts) What is needed to convert an empirical formula into a molecular formula?
   a. The nature of the atoms involved
   b. The identity of the atoms involved
   c. The mass of the molecule involved
   d. The density of the molecule involved
   e. None of the above

8. (4 pts) Which of the following is not an empirical formula?
   a. CH_3O
   b. H_2O
   c. NaCl
   d. $C_6H_9O_3$
   e. None of the above

9. (4 pts) According to this equation, how many moles of Ag_2S will be produced from 6.2 moles of Ag? H_2S and O_2 are in excess

$$4Ag + 2H_2S + O_2 \rightarrow 2Ag_2S + 2H_2O$$

   a. 3.1 moles
   b. 12 moles
   c. 6.2 moles
   d. 770 moles
   e. None of the above

10. (4 pts) State Gay-Lussac's law and its limitations.

For the following problems, please provide the correct answer and show the needed work to obtain the answer.

11. (12 pts) An unknown compound is decomposed into 6.9 g of Na, 3.1 g of P and 6.4 g of O. What is its empirical formula?

12. (4 pts) One type of stomach antacid, $Al(OH)_3$, can be made in the following way:

$$Al_2\,(SO_4)_3 + 6NaOH \rightarrow 2Al(OH)_3 + 3Na_2SO_4$$

    How many moles of $Al(OH)_3$ can be made with 2.3 moles of NaOH and excess $Al_2(SO_4)_3$?

13. (12 pts) AgBr, a chemical used in photography, can be made with this reaction:

$$2AgNO_3 + CaBr_2 \rightarrow 2AgBr + CaN_2O_6$$

    $AgNO_3$ is very expensive, so in making AgBr, you want to be sure this reactant is all used up. If a chemist starts with 15.0 g of $AgNO_3$, how many grams of $CaBr_2$ must be added to use up all of the $AgNO_3$?

14. (12 pts) A chemist performs the following reaction:

$$6ClO_2\,(g) + 3H_2O\,(l) \rightarrow 5HClO_3\,(l) + HCl\,(g)$$

    If the chemist wants to make 50.0 g of $HClO_3$, what is the minimum number of grams of ClO_2 that she must use?

15. (4 pts) If the reaction in problem 14 was run with excess water, how many liters of HCl would be produced from 10.0 liters of ClO_2?

16. (4 pts) A compound has an empirical formula of CH_2 and a molecular mass of 70.1 amu. What is its molecular formula?

17. (4 pts) What is wrong with the following statement? In the reaction $N_2 + 3H_2 \rightarrow 2NH_3$, 1 gram of N_2 reacts with 3 grams of H_2 to make 2 grams of NH_3.

18. (4 pts) Consider the following reaction:

$$Fe_2O_3\ (s) + 3CO\ (g) \rightarrow 2Fe\ (s) + 3CO_2\ (g)$$

If 2 moles of Fe_2O_3 are reacted with 3 moles CO, what is the limiting reactant?

19. (4 pts) With the reaction and quantities given in problem 18, how many moles of Fe would be formed?

SOLUTIONS TO THE TEST FOR MODULE 8

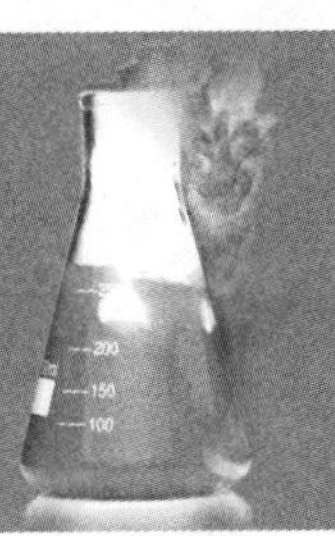

1. (4 pts) A stoichiometric coefficient is the number to the left of a substance in a chemical equation. Stoichiometry coefficients describe the ratio of one substance to another in moles.

2. (4 pts) c. Stoichiometry

3. (4 pts) d. Limiting reactant

4. (4 pts) True
   The limiting reactant is responsible for determining how much product is produced.

5. (4 pts) 2 moles of HF react with 1 mole(s) of CaO_2H_2 to make 2 moles(s) of H_2O and 1 mole(s) of CaF_2.

6. (4 pts) b. Empirical formula

7. (4 pts) c. The mass of the molecule involved

8. (4 pts) d. $C_6H_9O_3$
   This can be reduced to an empirical formula of C_2H_3O.

9. (4 pts) a. 3.1 moles
   The mole ratio from the balanced equation is 4 moles of Ag to 2 moles of Ag_2S.

$$6.2 \cancel{\text{mol Ag}} \times \frac{2 \text{ mol } Ag_2S}{4 \cancel{\text{mol Ag}}} = \underline{3.1 \text{ moles}}$$

10. (4 pts) Gay-Lussac's law states that the stoichiometric coefficients can be used to relate the volumes of gases in a chemical equation. The limitation is that it only works for gases.

11. (12 pts: 4 pts for writing a decomposition equation, 4 pts for converting to moles, and 4 pts for the answer) $\underline{Na_3PO_4}$

The unbalanced equation for this decomposition reaction is:

$$Na_xP_yO_z \rightarrow Na + P + O_2$$

We can now determine how many moles of each product were made:

$$\frac{6.9\ \cancel{g\ Na}}{1} \times \frac{1\ \text{mole Na}}{23.0\ \cancel{g\ Na}} = 0.30\ \text{moles Na}$$

$$\frac{3.1\ \cancel{g\ P}}{1} \times \frac{1\ \text{mole P}}{31.0\ \cancel{g\ P}} = 0.10\ \text{moles P}$$

$$\frac{6.4\ \cancel{g\ O_2}}{1} \times \frac{1\ \text{mole}\ O_2}{32.0\ \cancel{g\ O_2}} = 0.20\ \text{moles}\ O_2$$

Thus:

$$Na_xP_yO_z \rightarrow 0.30\ Na + 0.10\ P + 0.20\ O_2$$

Dividing by the smallest to make integers:

$$Na_xP_yO_z \rightarrow 3Na + P + 2O_2$$

To get the equation to balance, x = 3, y = 1, and z = 4. The empirical formula, then, is $\underline{Na_3PO_4}$.

12. (4 pts) $\underline{0.77\ \text{moles Al(OH)}_3}$
The chemical equation relates moles of one substance to moles of another.

$$\frac{2.3\ \cancel{\text{moles NaOH}}}{1} \times \frac{2\ \text{moles Al(OH)}_3}{6\ \cancel{\text{moles NaOH}}} = \underline{0.77\ \text{moles Al(OH)}_3}$$

13. (12 pts: 4 pts for each of the equations below)

$$\frac{15.0\ \cancel{g\ AgNO_3}}{1} \times \frac{1\ \text{mole}\ AgNO_3}{169.9\ \cancel{g\ AgNO_3}} = 8.83 \times 10^{-2}\ \text{moles}\ AgNO_3$$

$$\frac{8.83 \times 10^{-2} \cancel{\text{moles AgNO}_3}}{1} \times \frac{1 \text{ mole CaBr}_2}{2 \cancel{\text{moles AgNO}_3}} = 4.42 \times 10^{-2} \text{ moles 1 CaBr}_2$$

$$\frac{4.42 \times 10^{-2} \cancel{\text{moles CaBr}_2}}{1} \times \frac{199.9 \text{ g CaBr}_2}{1 \cancel{\text{mole CaBr}_2}} = 8.84 \text{ g CaBr}_2$$

14. (12 pts: 4 pts for each of the equations below) 47.9 g ClO_2

$$\frac{50.0 \cancel{\text{g HClO}_3}}{1} \times \frac{1 \text{ mole HClO}_3}{84.5 \cancel{\text{g HClO}_3}} = 0.592 \text{ moles HClO}_3$$

$$\frac{0.592 \cancel{\text{moles HClO}_3}}{1} \times \frac{6 \text{ moles ClO}_2}{5 \cancel{\text{moles HClO}_3}} = 0.710 \text{ moles ClO}_2$$

$$\frac{0.710 \cancel{\text{moles ClO}_2}}{1} \times \frac{67.5 \text{ g ClO}_2}{1 \cancel{\text{mole ClO}_2}} = \underline{47.9 \text{ g ClO}_2}$$

15. (4 pts) 1.67 L HCl
Since everything that we are interested in is now a gas, we can use Gay-Lussac's law:

$$\frac{10.0 \cancel{\text{L ClO}_2}}{1} \times \frac{1 \text{ L HCl}}{6 \cancel{\text{L ClO}_2}} = \underline{1.67 \text{ L HCl}}$$

16. (4 pts) C_5H_{10}
The empirical formula tells us that for every 1 C atom there must also be 2 atoms. To keep this relationship but still get the same mass we must compare the mass of CH_2 with the molecular mass. The molecular mass of 70.1 amu is 5x larger than that of CH_2, which means we must multiple the number of atoms in the empirical formula by 5 to obtain the molecular formula of C_5H_{10}.

17. (4 pts) The word *gram* should be replaced by *mole* (or *molecule*) each time it appears. Stoichiometric coefficients only relate moles (or molecules), not grams.

18. (4 pts) CO is the limiting reactant.
According to the equation, 3 moles of CO react with 1 mole of Fe_2O_3. Thus, when the 3 moles of CO are exhausted, there will still be an extra mole of Fe_2O_3.

19. (4 pts) 2 moles of Fe
Since CO is the limiting reactant, we use it in our calculation. According to the equation, 3 moles of CO make 2 moles of Fe.

$$\frac{3 \text{ moles CO}}{1} \times \frac{2 \text{ moles Fe}}{3 \text{ mole CO}} = \underline{2 \text{ moles of Fe}}$$

QUARTER 2 TEST FOR MOD. 5-8

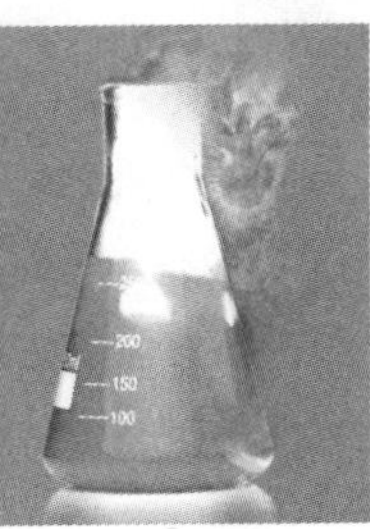

(1.00 amu = 1.66×10^{-24} g)

1. (4 pts) Give the chemical formulas for the following compounds:
   a. potassium carbonate
   b. aluminum sulfate

2. (4 pts) Name the following compounds
   a. $Ca_3(PO_4)_2$
   b. $Ca(NO_3)_2$

3. (6 pts) Determine the shape of a CCl_4 molecule. Give its bond angle and draw a picture of it.

4. (6 pts) Determine the shape of a NF_3 molecule. Give its bond angle and draw a picture of it.

5. (4 pts) Gold has a density of 19.3 grams per mL. If a gold nugget has a volume of 5.60 L, what is its mass?

6. (3 pts) If a liquid goes through a phase change and all you know is that the molecules slowed down and moved closer together, what phase did the liquid turn into?
   a. Solid
   b. Liquid
   c. Gas
   d. Unable to determine from the information given

7. (2 pts) Classify the following as a physical or chemical change: A priceless vase is shattered.
   a. Physical change
   b. Chemical change

8. (2 pts) Classify the following as a physical or chemical change: Coal burns in a furnace.
   a. Physical change
   b. Chemical change

9. (3 pts) To balance the following equation, what will be the coefficient in front of magnesium? HNO_3 (aq) + Mg (s) → MgN_2O_6 (aq) + H_2 (g)
   a. 1
   b. 2
   c. 3
   d. 4
   e. None of the above

10. (3 pts) To balance the following equation, what will be the coefficient in front of the carbon dioxide? CO_2 (g) + H_2O (l) → $C_6H_{12}O_6$ (s) + O_2 (g)
    a. 2
    b. 3
    c. 4
    d. 5
    e. None of the above

11. (3 pts) Classify the following reaction: 2KCl (s) + $MgBr_2$ (aq) → $MgCl_2$ (s) + 2KBr (aq)
    a. Decomposition
    b. Formation
    c. Complete combustion
    d. None of these

12. (3 pts) Classify the following reaction: $2H_3PO_4$ (s) → $3H_2$ (g) + 2P (s) + $4O_2$ (g)
    a. Decomposition
    b. Formation
    c. Complete combustion
    d. None of these

13. (3 pts) What is the difference between complete combustion and incomplete combustion?

14. (4 pts) Write a balanced chemical equation for the formation of $NaHSO_4$.

15. (4 pts) What is the mass of a $MgCO_3$ molecule in kg? (1.00 amu = 1.66×10^{-24} g)
    a. 1.39×10^{-25} kg
    b. 1.40×10^{-22} kg
    c. 1.40×10^{-25} kg
    d. 8.68×10^{-24} kg
    e. None of the above

16. (4 pts) How many moles of K_2CO_3 are in a 150.0 g sample of the compound?
    a. 0.922 moles K_2CO_3
    b. 1.085 moles K_2CO_3
    c. 1.514 moles K_2CO_3
    d. 277.3 moles K_2CO_3
    e. None of the above

17. (4 pts) What is the mass of a $MgBr_2$ sample if it contains 0.342 moles of the compound?
    a. 35.6 g $MgBr_2$
    b. 126 g $MgBr_2$
    c. 538 g $MgBr_2$
    d. 63.0 g $MgBr_2$
    e. None of the above

18. (3 pts) What is the limiting reactant when 2 moles of KCl are reacted with 2 moles of $MgBr_2$ in the following reaction: $2KCl\ (s) + MgBr_2\ (aq) \rightarrow MgCl_2\ (s) + 2KBr\ (aq)$
    a. KCl
    b. $MgBr_2$
    c. $MgCl_2$
    d. KBr
    e. None of the above

19. (3 pts) A chemist wants to perform the following reaction:

$$MgCO_3\ (s) + 2HCl\ (g) \rightarrow MgCl_2\ (aq) + CO_2\ (g) + H_2O\ (l)$$

    Which substances can she use Gay-Lussac's law to relate to one another?
    a. $MgCO_3$ and HCl
    b. HCl, $MgCl_2$ and CO_2
    c. HCl, $MgCl_2$ CO_2 and H_2O
    d. HCl and CO_2
    e. None of the above

20. (4 pts) Which of the following are empirical formulas?
    a. $C_{18}H_{36}O_{18}$ b. $Na_2S_2O_3$

21. (4 pts) Freon, a very useful refrigerant, is produced in the following reaction:

$$3CCl_4\ (g) + 2SbF_3\ (s) \rightarrow \underset{\text{(Freon)}}{3CCl_2F_2\ (g)} + 2SbCl_3\ (s)$$

    Suppose a chemist wanted to make 115.0 liters of Freon using excess antimony trifluoride. How many liters of carbon tetrachloride would the chemist need?

22. (9 pts) To make a phosphorus fertilizer, agricultural companies use the following reaction: $Ca_3P_2O_8 + 2H_2SO_4 + 4H_2O \rightarrow \underset{\text{(fertilizer)}}{CaH_4P_2O_8} + 2CaH_4SO_6$

    If 150.0 grams of $Ca_3P_2O_8$ are reacted with excess H_2SO_4 and H_2O, how many grams of fertilizer can be made?

QT 2

23. (9 pts) If you have 4.1×10^3 grams of Mg, how many grams of water must be used to have all of the Mg react to form $Mg(OH)_2$ in the following reaction?
$Mg (s) + 2H_2O (l) \rightarrow Mg(OH)_2 (s) + H_2 (g)$

24. (6 pts) An unknown compound was decomposed into 63.2 g carbon, 5.26 g hydrogen, and 41.6 g oxygen. What is its empirical formula?

SOLUTIONS TO THE QUARTER 2 TEST FOR MOD. 5-8

1. (4 pts: 2 pts each)
   a. K_2CO_3 The name indicates a potassium ion and a carbonate ion. Potassium is abbreviated with K, and since it is in group 1A, it has a charge of 1+. We are supposed to have memorized that the carbonate ion is CO_3^{2-}. Ignoring the signs and switching the numbers gives us:

   K_2CO_3

   b. $Al_2(SO_4)_3$ The name indicates an aluminum ion and a sulfate ion. Aluminum is abbreviated with Al, and since it is in group 3A, it has a charge of 3+. We are supposed to have memorized that the sulfate ion is SO_4^{2-}. Ignoring the signs and switching the numbers gives us:

   $Al_2(SO_4)_3$

2. (4 pts: 2 pts each)
   a. calcium phosphate Since we see that PO_4 is in parentheses, it is a polyatomic ion. We are supposed to have memorized that PO_4^{3-} is the phosphate ion, and the only other ion is the single-atom calcium ion. Thus, the name is calcium phosphate.

   b. calcium nitrate In looking at this molecule, we should notice the NO_3. It tells us the nitrate polyatomic ion is present. The only thing left after that is the calcium ion. Thus, the name is calcium nitrate.

3. (6 pts: 3 pts for the shape and bond angle, and 3 pts for the picture) To determine shapes, we must first draw the Lewis structure:

```
      ..
     :Cl:
  ..  |  ..
 :Cl—C—Cl:
  ..  |  ..
     :Cl:
      ..
```

We see that the central atom has 4 groups of electrons around it. Since there are 4 groups, the basic shape is that of a tetrahedron. None of the legs is missing because the molecule contains no nonbonding pairs of electrons. As a result, the molecule's shape is tetrahedral with a bond angle of 109°:

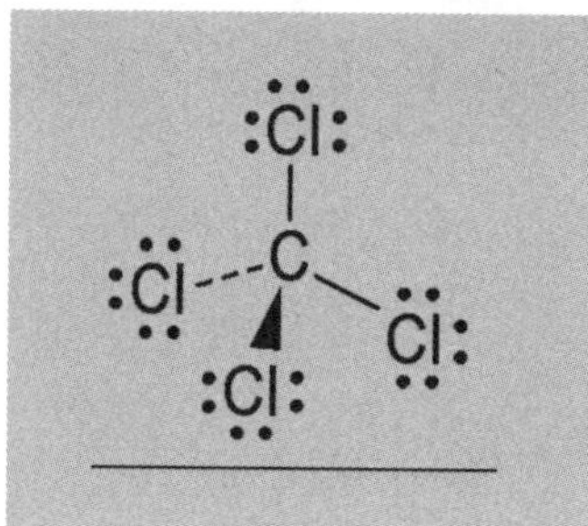

4. (6 pts: 3 pts for the shape and bond angle, and 3 pts for the picture) To determine shapes, we must first draw the Lewis structure:

We see that the central atom has 4 groups of electrons around it. Three of them are bonds, and 1 is a nonbonding pair. Since there are 4 groups, the basic shape is that of a tetrahedron. However, 1 of the legs is missing because it contains a nonbonding pair of electrons. As a result, the molecule's shape is pyramidal with a bond angle of 107°:

5. (4 pts: 2 pts for the conversion to L, and 2 pts for using density equation) We will use the density equation, but we have to convert kg to g and rearrange the equation to solve for mass:

$$\frac{5.60\ \cancel{\text{L}}}{1} \times \frac{1\ \text{mL}}{0.001\ \cancel{\text{L}}} = 5.60 \times 10^3\ \text{mL}$$

$$m = \rho \times V$$

$$= 19.3\ \text{g}/\cancel{\text{mL}} \times 5.60 \times 10^3\ \cancel{\text{mL}} = \underline{1.08 \times 10^5\ \text{g}}$$

6. (3 pts) a. Solid Since molecules move slower and are closer together in the solid phase compared to the liquid phase, the liquid must have turned into a solid.

7. (2 pts) a. Physical change

8. (2 pts) b. Chemical change

9. (3 pts) a. 1

10. (3 pts) e. None of the above The following is the balanced equation: $6CO_2$ (g) + $6H_2O$ (l) → $C_6H_{12}O_6$ (s) + $6O_2$ (g).

11. (3 pts) d. None of these

12. (3 pts) a. Decomposition

13. (3 pts) Complete combustion produces carbon dioxide and water. Incomplete combustion produces either carbon monoxide and water or carbon and water.

14. (4 pts: 2 pts for getting the equation and 2 pts for balancing it)
$2Na + H_2 + 2S + 4O_2 \rightarrow 2NaHSO_4$
The compound is made up of Na, H, S, and O. H and O are homonuclear diatomics, thus:

$$Na + H_2 + S + O_2 \rightarrow NaHSO_4$$

The Na atoms and S atoms are already balanced. To balance the H atoms without disturbing the others, we will use a fraction. The O atoms are easy to balance:

$$Na + \tfrac{1}{2}H_2 + S + 2O_2 \rightarrow NaHSO_4$$

Eliminating the fraction:

$$2 \times [Na + \tfrac{1}{2}H_2 + S + 2O_2] \rightarrow 2 \times [NaHSO_4]$$

$$2Na + H_2 + 2S + 4O_2 \rightarrow 2NaHSO_4$$

QT 2

15. (4 pts) c. 1.40×10^{-25} kg

$MgCO_3$ molecule has 1 Mg atom (24.3 amu each), 1 C atom (12.0 amu), and 3 O atoms (16.0 amu each), thus:

$$\text{Mass of } MgCO_3 = 1 \times 24.3 \text{ amu} + 12.0 \text{ amu} + 3 \times 16.0 \text{ amu} = 84.3 \text{ amu}$$

Since we can relate amu only to g, we need to do a 2-step conversion:

$$\frac{84.3 \cancel{\text{amu}}}{1} \times \frac{1.66 \times 10^{-24} \cancel{\text{g}}}{1.00 \cancel{\text{amu}}} \times \frac{1 \text{ kg}}{1000 \cancel{\text{g}}} = \underline{1.40 \times 10^{-25} \text{ kg}}$$

16. (4 pts) b. 1.085 moles K_2CO_3
The molecular mass of K_2CO_3 is 2 × 39.1 amu + 1 × 12.0 amu + 3 × 16.0 amu = 138.2 amu. This means:

$$138.2 \text{ g } K_2CO_3 = 1 \text{ mole } K_2CO_3$$

Now we convert the grams to moles:

$$\frac{150.0 \text{ g } \cancel{K_2CO_3}}{1} \times \frac{1 \text{ mole } K_2CO_3}{138.2 \text{ g } \cancel{K_2CO_3}} = \underline{1.085 \text{ moles } K_2CO_3}$$

17. (4 pts) d. 63.0 g $MgBr_2$
This is just another conversion problem, but this time we are converting moles into grams. We need to determine the molecular mass of $MgBr_2$ first, however:

$$\text{Mass of } MgBr_2 = 1 \times 24.3 \text{ amu} + 2 \times 79.9 \text{ amu} = 184.1 \text{ amu}$$

This means:

$$184.1 \text{ grams } MgBr_2 = 1 \text{ mole } MgBr_2$$

Now we can do our conversion:

$$\frac{0.342 \cancel{\text{mole } MgBr_2}}{1} \times \frac{184.1 \text{ g } MgBr_2}{1 \cancel{\text{mole } MgBr_2}} = \underline{63.0 \text{ g } MgBr_2}$$

18. (3 pts) a. <u>KCl</u>
The limiting reactant is KCl because 2 moles of KCl react with 1 mole of $MgBr_2$. Since 2 moles of $MgBr_2$ are added, the 2 moles of KCl will run out and there will still be 1 extra mole of $MgBr_2$ left over.

19. (3 pts) d. <u>HCl and CO_2</u>
The chemist can use Gay-Lussac's law only to relate the volumes of HCl and CO2, since those are the only gases in the equation.

20. (4 pts) b. <u>$Na_2S_2O_3$</u>
The formula in b. is an empirical formula because the subscripts have no common factor. $C_{18}H_{36}O_{18}$ is not an empirical formula because the subscripts have a common factor of 9.

21. (4 pts: 2 pts for the relationship, 2 pts for the final answer) <u>115.0 L CCl_4</u>
Since we are using liters and the 2 substances in the problem are gases, we can use Gay-Lussac's law and relate the liters of each substance:

$$3\text{ L }CCl_2F_2 = 3\text{ L }CCl_4$$

$$\frac{115.0\ \cancel{\text{L }CCl_2F_2}}{1} \times \frac{3\text{ L }CCl_4}{3\ \cancel{\text{L }CCl_2F_2}} = \underline{115.0\text{ L }CCl_4}$$

22. (9 pts: 3 pts for converting to moles of $Ca_3P_2O_8$, 3 pts for converting to moles of fertilizer, and 3 pts for converting to grams of fertilizer) <u>113.2 g $CaH_4P_2O_8$</u>
This problem asks us to relate the quantity of limiting reactant to the quantity of product, but the quantities are both in grams. So first we must convert to moles:

$$\frac{150.0\ \cancel{\text{g }Ca_3P_2O_8}}{1} \times \frac{1\text{ mole }Ca_3P_2O_8}{310.3\ \cancel{\text{g }Ca_3P_2O_8}} = 0.4834\text{ moles }Ca_3P_2O_8$$

Now we can use stoichiometry to relate the 2 substances:

$$\frac{0.4834\ \cancel{\text{moles }Ca_3P_2O_8}}{1} \times \frac{1\text{ mole }CaH_4P_2O_8}{1\ \cancel{\text{mole }Ca_3P_2O_8}} = 0.4834\text{ moles }CaH_4P_2O_8$$

Now that we know how much fertilizer was made, we just need to get it in grams:

$$\frac{0.4834\ \cancel{\text{moles }CaH_4P_2O_8}}{1} \times \frac{234.1\text{ g }CaH_4P_2O_8}{1\ \cancel{\text{mole }CaH_4P_2O_8}} = \underline{113.2\text{ g }CaH_4P_2O_8}$$

23. (9 pts: 3 pts for converting to moles of Mg, 3 pts for converting to moles of water, and 3 pts for converting to grams of water) $\underline{6.1 \times 10^3 \text{ g } H_2O}$
This problem asks us to relate the amount of one reactant to the amount of another. This is easy, as long as we start with moles, not grams:

$$\frac{4.1 \times 10^3 \cancel{\text{g Mg}}}{1} \times \frac{1 \text{ mole Mg}}{24.3 \cancel{\text{g Mg}}} = 1.7 \times 10^2 \text{ moles Mg}$$

Now we can convert from moles of Mg to moles of water:

$$\frac{1.7 \times 10^2 \cancel{\text{moles Mg}}}{1} \times \frac{2 \text{ moles } H_2O}{1 \cancel{\text{mole Mg}}} = 3.4 \times 10^2 \text{ moles } H_2O$$

Now we know how much water is needed. All we need to do now is convert to grams:

$$\frac{3.4 \times 10^2 \cancel{\text{moles } H_2O}}{1} \times \frac{18.0 \text{ g } H_2O}{1 \cancel{\text{mole } H_2O}} = \underline{6.1 \times 10^3 \text{ g } H_2O}$$

24. (6 pts: 3 pts for getting moles of each product, and 3 pts for getting the empirical formula) $\underline{C_2H_2O}$
The unbalanced equation for the decomposition is:

$$C_xH_yO_z \rightarrow C + H_2 + O_2$$

To get the stoichiometric coefficients on the products side, we use the experimental data:

$$\frac{63.2 \cancel{\text{g C}}}{1} \times \frac{1 \text{ mole C}}{12.0 \cancel{\text{g C}}} = 5.27 \text{ moles C}$$

$$\frac{5.26 \cancel{\text{g } H_2}}{1} \times \frac{1 \text{ mole } H_2}{2.02 \cancel{\text{g } H_2}} = 2.60 \text{ moles } H_2$$

$$\frac{41.6 \cancel{\text{g } O_2}}{1} \times \frac{1 \text{ mole } O_2}{32.0 \cancel{\text{g } O_2}} = 1.30 \text{ moles } O_2$$

So the equation becomes:

$$C_xH_yO_z \rightarrow 5.27 \text{ C} + 2.60 \text{ } H_2 + 1.30 \text{ } O_2$$

We now must divide by the smallest number to make them integers:

$$C_xH_yO_z \rightarrow \frac{5.27}{1.30}\,C + \frac{2.60}{1.30}\,H_2 + \frac{1.30}{1.30}\,O_2$$

$$C_xH_yO_z \rightarrow 4\,C + 2\,H_2 + O_2$$

To balance the equation, then, x = 4, y = 4, z = 2. This makes a formula of $C_4H_4O_2$, but that is not an empirical formula because the subscripts have a common factor of 2. Thus, the real empirical formula is $\underline{C_2H_2O}$.

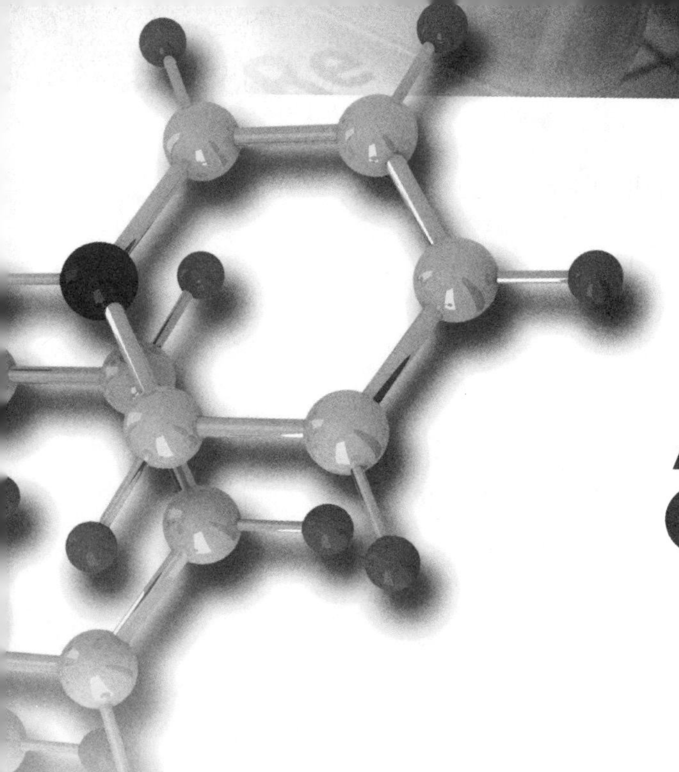

ACID-BASE CHEMISTRY

SOLUTIONS TO THE MODULE 9 REVIEW QUESTIONS

1. a. Bases usually taste bitter, so this is probably a base.
   b. Bases usually feel slippery, so this is probably a base.
   c. Acids turn blue litmus red, so this is an acid.

2. CH_4O
   An acid is an H^+ donor. In this equation, the CH_4O turned into CH_3O^-, indicating that it lost an H^+ ion. This means CH_4O is the acid.

3. We defined a base as an H^+ acceptor; but as discussed in the module, an H^+ ion is simply a proton. Therefore, the definitions are the same.

4. b. and d.
   Polyprotic acids have more than one H+ to donate. Thus, (b) and (d) are polyprotic acids. Although (c) has more than one H in its formula, it is a base, not an acid.

5. b. and d.
   Concentration refers to the amount of a substance (grams, moles) divided by volume (m^3, liters, etc.). Only (b) and (d) have units that involve an amount unit divided by a volume unit.

6. 6.0 M
   To make a new HCl solution from an old one, the chemist must perform a dilution. The only thing we can do in a dilution is *lower* the concentration from the original. Thus, the chemist must use the 6.0 M solution because only this one has a higher concentration than the one that the chemist wants to make.

7. 2 Al^{3+} ions and 3 CO_3^{2-} ions

You should recognize the carbonate ion in this compound. The metal forms the positive ion. Thus, this compound splits up into 2 Al^{3+} ions and 3 CO_3^{2-} ions.

8. HCO_3^-
   An amphiprotic substance can act like both an acid and a base. In these 2 equations, HCO_3^- is doing this.

9. An indicator can determine whether a substance is an acid or base. It can also help us find the endpoint of a titration.

10. The endpoint of a titration tells us that we have added just enough acid in our titration to eat up all of the base in our unknown solution. Alternatively, it can tell us that we have added just enough base to our titration to eat up all of the acid in our unknown solution, depending on whether our unknown is an acid or a base.

SOLUTIONS TO THE PRACTICE PROBLEMS FOR MODULE 9

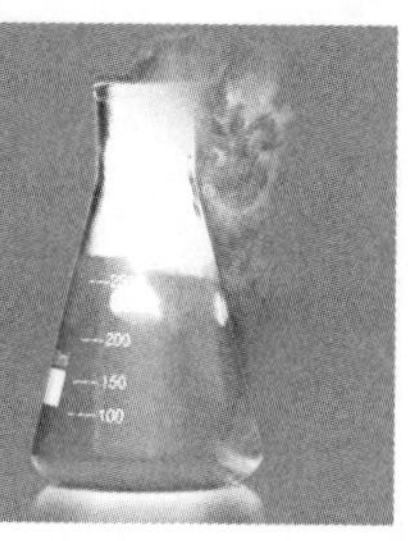

1. $3H_2SO_4 + 2Al(OH)_3 \rightarrow 6H_2O + Al_2(SO_4)_3$
We should have table 9.1 memorized. Thus, we should know that the hydroxide ion is OH^-. Since Al is in group 3A, it takes on a 3+ charge in ionic compounds. Switching the charges and dropping the signs tells us that aluminum hydroxide is $Al(OH)_3$. Acids and bases usually react to produce a salt and water. The salt is made up of the positive ion from the base (Al^{3+}) and the negative ion left over when the acid gets rid of its H^+ ions. In this case, that will be SO_4^{2-}. Switching the charges and dropping the signs gives us $Al_2(SO_4)_3$ as the chemical formula. The unbalanced equation, then, is:

$$H_2SO_4 + Al(OH)_3 \rightarrow H_2O + Al_2(SO_4)_3$$

Now all we have to do is balance it:

$$3H_2SO_4 + 2Al(OH)_3 \rightarrow 6H_2O + Al_2(SO_4)_3$$

2. $2HNO_3 + Ca(OH)_2 \rightarrow 2H_2O + Ca(NO_3)_2$
Once again, the hydroxide ion is OH^-. Calcium is in group 2A of the chart and thus takes on a 2^+ charge in ionic compounds. This tells us that calcium hydroxide is $Ca(OH)_2$. Acids and bases usually react to produce a salt and water. The salt is made up of the positive ion from the base (Ca^{2+}) and the negative ion left over when the acid gets rid of its H^+ ions. In this case, that will be NO_3^-. Switching the charges and dropping the signs tells us that these 2 ions form $Ca(NO_3)_2$. The unbalanced equation, then, is:

$$HNO_3 + Ca(OH)_2 \rightarrow H_2O + Ca(NO_3)_2$$

Now all we have to do is balance it:

$$2HNO_3 + Ca(OH)_2 \rightarrow 2H_2O + Ca(NO_3)_2$$

3. $H_2CO_3 + 2NH_3 \rightarrow 2NH_4^+ + CO_3^{2-}$
In this case, the base does not contain a hydroxide ion. In fact, it is not even ionic. Thus, a salt and water are not formed in this problem. Here, we just rely on the definition of acids and bases. Ammonia will want to gain an H^+ ion to become NH_4^+, and the carbonic acid will want to give up both of its H^+ ions. Since the acid

has 2 H^+ ions to give but the base can accept only 1, 2 ammonias will have to do the accepting. This will make 2 NH_4^+ ions:

$$\underline{H_2CO_3 + 2NH_3 \rightarrow 2NH_4^+ + CO_3^{2-}}$$

4. $\underline{HBr + H_2O \rightarrow H_3O^+ + Br^-}$
Water is an amphiprotic substance, so it can act as either an acid or a base. In this problem, it is being mixed with an acid, so it will want to act like a base and accept the H^+ ion that the acid gives away:

$$\underline{HBr + H_2O \rightarrow H_3O^+ + Br^-}$$

5. a. 2.9 M Molarity is given by number of moles divided by number of liters. We have both of those units, so we just divide them:

$$\text{Concentration} = \frac{\text{\# moles}}{\text{\# liters}} = \frac{3.51 \text{ moles } HNO_3}{1.2 \text{ L}} = 2.9 \text{ M}$$

b. 12.1 M In order to get concentration, we must have moles and liters. The problem gives us grams and mL, so we must make 2 conversions:

$$\text{Molecular Mass of KOH} = (1 \times 39.1 \text{ amu}) + (1 \times 16.0 \text{ amu}) + (1 \times 1.01 \text{ amu}) = 56.1 \text{ amu}$$

Therefore, 1 mole KOH = 56.1 grams KOH

$$\frac{234.1 \cancel{\text{g KOH}}}{1} \times \frac{1 \text{ mole KOH}}{56.1 \cancel{\text{g KOH}}} = \underline{4.17 \text{ moles KOH}}$$

$$\frac{345 \cancel{\text{mL}}}{1} \times \frac{0.001 \text{ L}}{1 \cancel{\text{mL}}} = 0.345 \text{ L}$$

Now we can calculate molarity:

$$\text{Concentration} = \frac{\text{\# moles}}{\text{\# liters}} = \frac{4.17 \text{ moles KOH}}{0.345 \text{ L}} = \frac{12.1 \text{ moles KOH}}{\text{L}} = \underline{12.1 \text{ M}}$$

c. 0.93 M In order to get concentration, we must have moles and liters. The problem gives us grams and mL, so we must make 2 conversions:

$$\text{Molecular Mass of } H_3PO_4 = (3 \times 1.01 \text{ amu}) + (1 \times 31.0 \text{ amu}) + (4 \times 16.0 \text{ amu}) = 98.0 \text{ amu}$$

MOD 9

Therefore, 1 mole H_3PO_4 = 98.0 grams H_3PO_4

$$\frac{4.1 \cancel{g\ H_3PO_4}}{1} \times \frac{1 \text{ mole } H_3PO_4}{98.0 \cancel{g\ H_3PO_4}} = 0.042 \text{ moles } H_3PO_4$$

$$\frac{45 \cancel{mL}}{1} \times \frac{0.001 \text{ L}}{1 \cancel{mL}} = 0.045 \text{ L}$$

Now we can calculate molarity:

$$\text{Concentration} = \frac{\#\text{ moles}}{\#\text{ liters}} = \frac{0.042 \text{ moles } H_3PO_4}{0.045 \text{ L}} = 0.93 \frac{\text{moles } H_3PO_4}{\text{L}} = \underline{0.93 \text{ M}}$$

6. <u>The chemist must take 1.5 × 10² mL of the original solution and dilute it with enough water to make 500.0 mL of solution.</u> This is a dilution problem, so we use the dilution equation. M_1 is 12.0 M. We need to determine V_1. M_2 is 3.5 M, and V_2 = 500.0 mL.

$$M_1V_1 = M_2V_2$$

$$(12.0 \text{ M})\ V_1 = (3.5 \text{ M})\ (500 \text{ mL})$$

$$V_1 = \frac{(3.5 \cancel{M})(500 \text{ mL})}{12.0 \cancel{M}} = 1.5 \times 10^2 \text{ ml}$$

7. <u>The chemist needs to take 0.84 mL of the stock solution and mix it with enough water to make 100.0 mL of solution.</u> The last part of this problem is a dilution problem, but in order to get the original concentration, we must deal with the first part of the problem, which is a concentration problem.

Molecular mass of NaOH = (1 × 23.0 amu) + (1 × 16.0 amu) + (1 × 1.01 amu) = 40.0 amu

Therefore, 1 mole NaOH = 40.0 grams NaOH

$$\frac{950.0 \cancel{g\ NaOH}}{1} \times \frac{1 \text{ mole NaOH}}{40.0 \cancel{g\ NaOH}} = 23.8 \text{ moles NaOH}$$

$$\text{Concentration} = \frac{\#\text{ moles}}{\#\text{ liters}} = \frac{23.8 \text{ moles NaOH}}{2.00 \text{ L}} = 11.9 \frac{\text{moles NaOH}}{\text{L}} = 11.9 \text{ M}$$

Now that we know the concentration of the stock solution, this is just a dilution problem:

$$M_1V_1 = M_2V_2$$

$$(11.9\text{ M})\ V_1 = (0.10\text{ M})\ (100.0\text{ mL})$$

$$V_1 = \frac{(0.10\ \cancel{\text{M}})(100.0\text{ mL})}{11.9\ \cancel{\text{M}}} = \underline{0.84\text{ mL}}$$

8. <u>32 g of potassium carbonate are produced.</u> In order to solve any stoichiometry problem, we must first figure out the balanced chemical equation. According to the problem, our reactants are H_2CO_3 and KOH. When they react, a salt and water will be produced. The salt will be composed of the positive ion from the base (K^+) and the negative ion left over when the acid gets rid of all of its H^+ ions. In this case, that will be the CO_3^{2-} ion. Thus, the reaction is:

$$H_2CO_3 + KOH \rightarrow K_2CO_3 + H_2O$$

Of course, this equation is not balanced, so that is the first thing to do:

$$H_2CO_3 + 2KOH \rightarrow K_2CO_3 + 2H_2O$$

Now that we have a balanced equation, we can start the stoichiometry. We were told that there is excess KOH, so we know that H_2CO_3 is the limiting reactant. Therefore, we need to know the moles of carbonic acid in order to be able to predict how much potassium carbonate it produces. To do this, we will multiply concentration by volume:

$$\frac{4.5\text{ moles }H_2CO_3}{1\ \cancel{\text{L }H_2CO_3}} \times \frac{0.0500\ \cancel{\text{L }H_2CO_3}}{1} = 0.23\text{ moles }H_2CO_3$$

We can now use this information to calculate the number of moles of potassium carbonate produced:

$$\frac{0.23\ \cancel{\text{moles }H_2CO_3}}{1} \times \frac{1\text{ mole }K_2CO_3}{1\ \cancel{\text{mole }H_2CO_3}} = 0.23\text{ moles }K_2CO_3$$

Now that we have the number of moles of potassium carbonate, we can convert back to grams:

$$\frac{0.23\ \cancel{\text{moles }K_2CO_3}}{1} \times \frac{138.2\text{ g }K_2CO_3}{1\ \cancel{\text{mole }K_2CO_3}} = \underline{32\text{ g }K_2CO_3}$$

9. 2.4 M Remember, titrations are just stoichiometry problems, so first we have to come up with a balanced chemical equation:

$$HCl + NaOH \rightarrow NaCl + H_2O$$

Since the endpoint was reached, we know that exactly enough acid was added to eat up all of the base. First, then, we calculate how many moles of acid were added:

$$\frac{3.5 \text{ moles HCl}}{1\cancel{L}} \times \frac{0.0343\ \cancel{L}}{1} = 0.12 \text{ moles HCl}$$

We can now use the chemical equation to determine how many moles of base were present:

$$\frac{0.12\ \cancel{\text{moles HCl}}}{1} \times \frac{1 \text{ moles NaOH}}{1\ \cancel{\text{mole HCl}}} = 0.12 \text{ moles NaOH}$$

Now that we have the number of moles of base present, we simply divide by the volume of base to get concentration:

$$\text{Concentration} = \frac{\#\text{ moles}}{\#\text{ liters}} = \frac{0.12 \text{ moles NaOH}}{0.0500 \text{ L}} = \underline{2.4 \text{ M}}$$

The NaOH solution has a concentration of 2.4 M.

10. 0.42 M Remember, titrations are just stoichiometry problems, so first we have to come up with a balanced chemical equation:

$$H_2SO_4 + 2KOH \rightarrow K_2SO_4 + 2H_2O$$

Since the endpoint was reached, we know that exactly enough base was added to eat up all of the acid. First, then, we calculate how many moles of base were added:

$$\frac{1.2 \text{ moles KOH}}{1\cancel{L}} \times \frac{0.3451\ \cancel{L}}{1} = 0.41 \text{ moles KOH}$$

We can now use the chemical equation to determine how many moles of acid were present:

$$\frac{0.41\ \cancel{\text{moles KOH}}}{1} \times \frac{1 \text{ moles } H_2SO_4}{2\ \cancel{\text{moles KOH}}} = 0.21 \text{ moles } H_2SO_4$$

Now that we have the number of moles of acid present, we simply divide by the volume of acid to get concentration:

$$\text{Concentration} = \frac{\#\text{ moles}}{\#\text{ liters}} = \frac{0.21 \text{ moles } H_2SO_4}{0.5000 \text{ L}} = \underline{0.42 \text{ M}}$$

The H_2SO_4 has a concentration of 0.42 M.

SAMPLE CALCULATIONS FOR EXPERIMENT 9.2

Mass of Graduated Cylinder: 254 g

Mass of Vinegar + Cylinder: 303 g

Mass of Vinegar: 303 g – 254 g = 49 g

Density of Vinegar: $\frac{49 \text{ g}}{50.0 \text{ mL}} = 0.98 \frac{\text{g}}{\text{mL}}$

Volume of Vinegar Added in Rough Titration: 22.4 mL

Volume of Vinegar Added in Careful Titration: 20.8 mL

We start with the grams of vinegar added:

$$20.8 \cancel{\text{mL}} \times 0.98 \frac{\text{g}}{\cancel{\text{mL}}} = 2.0 \times 10^1 \text{ g}$$

Note that the only way to properly report the significant figures is to use scientific notation. Now we have to determine the mass of acid in that mass of vinegar:

$$\text{Mass of acid used} = (\text{Mass of vinegar})\ (0.0500) = (2.0 \times 10^1 \text{ g})\ (0.0500) = 1.0 \text{ g}$$

The chemical formula of the acid ($C_2H_4O_2$) tells us that a single molecule has a mass of 60.0 amu. That also tells us that 60.0 g $C_2H_4O_2$ = 1 mole $C_2H_4O_2$.

$$\frac{1.0\ \cancel{g\ C_2H_4O_2}}{1} \times \frac{1\text{ mole NaOH}}{60.0\ \cancel{g\ C_2H_4O_2}} = 0.017\text{ moles } C_2H_4O_2$$

Now we can determine the amount of base:

$$\frac{0.017\ \cancel{\text{moles } C_2H_4O_2}}{1} \times \frac{1\text{ mole } NH_3}{1\ \cancel{\text{mole } C_2H_4O_2}} = 0.017\text{ moles } NH_3$$

We used 10.0 mL of ammonia, so the concentration of the ammonia is:

$$\text{Concentration} = \frac{\#\text{ moles}}{\#\text{ liters}} = \frac{0.017\text{ moles } NH_3}{0.010\text{ L}} = \underline{1.7\text{ M}}$$

PLEASE NOTE: Your answer may be quite different from ours, as the ammonia solution you used might have been stronger or more dilute than the one we used.

SOLUTIONS TO THE EXTRA PRACTICE PROBLEMS FOR MODULE 9

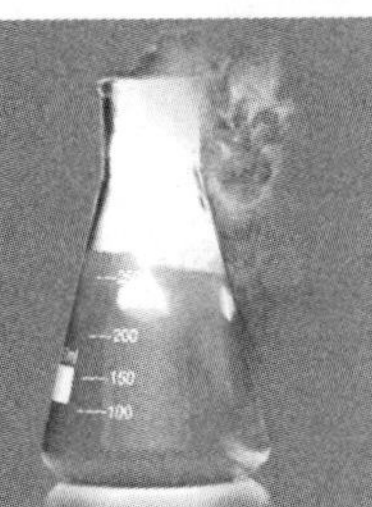

1. H_2CO_3 is the acid because it lost a H^+ ion to become HCO_3^-. That makes water the base because it accepted an H^+ ion to become H_3O^+.

2. KOH is the base because when its ions split apart, the hydroxide ion (OH^-) accepted an H^+ ion to become water. This make C_2H_6O the acid, since it lost an H^+ ion to become $C_2H_5O^-$, which became a part of the salt.

3. $Mg(OH)_2$ is the base because when its ions split apart, the hydroxide ion (OH^-) accepted an H^+ ion to become water. This make HCl the acid, since it lost an H^+ ion to become Cl^-, which became a part of the salt.

4. This is an acid and an ionic base, so it will follow the acid + base → salt + water formula. The salt comes from the metal ion of the base (Al^{3+}) and the negative ion left over when the acid donates its H^+ ions (I^-). To determine the formula, we switch the charges and drop the signs to make AlI_3. Thus, the unbalanced equation is:

   $$HI + Al(OH)_3 \rightarrow AlI_3 + H_2O$$

   Balancing gives us:

   $$3HI + Al(OH)_3 \rightarrow AlI_3 + 3H_2O$$

5. This is an acid and an ionic base, so it will follow the acid + base → salt + water formula. The salt comes from the metal ion of the base (Na^+), and the negative ion left over when the acid donates its H^+ ions. This acid need to donate 3 H^+ ions, and when that is done, PO_4^{3-} is left behind. To determine the formula, we switch the charges and drop the signs to make Na_3PO_4. Thus, the unbalanced equation is:

   $$H_3PO_4 + NaOH \rightarrow Na_3PO_4 + H_2O$$

   Balancing gives us:

   $$H_3PO_4 + 3NaOH \rightarrow Na_3PO_4 + 3H_2O$$

6. Since this involves a covalent base, we cannot use the acid + base → salt + water formula. Instead, we just have to rely on the definitions of acids and bases. Acids donate H^+ ions, and bases accept H^+ ions. H_3PO_4 wants to donate 3 H^+ ions, but the base can accept only 1, so it takes 3 bases to get the job done:

$$\underline{H_3PO_4 + 3CH_5N \rightarrow PO_4^{3-} + 3CH_6N^+}$$

7. a. Molarity is given by number of moles divided by number of liters. We have both those units, so we just divide them:

$$\text{Concentration} = \frac{\#\text{ moles}}{\#\text{ liters}} = \frac{2.22\text{ moles HCl}}{1.5\text{ L}} = \underline{1.5\text{ M}}$$

b. In order to get concentration, we must have moles and liters. The question gives us grams and mL, so we must make 2 conversions:

$$\frac{23.1\ \cancel{\text{g NaOH}}}{1} \times \frac{1\text{ mole NaOH}}{40.0\ \cancel{\text{g NaOH}}} = 0.578\text{ moles NaOH}$$

$$\frac{1000.0\ \cancel{\text{mL}}}{1} \times \frac{0.001\text{ L}}{1\ \cancel{\text{mL}}} = 1.000\text{ L}$$

Now we can calculate molarity:

$$\text{Concentration} = \frac{\#\text{ moles}}{\#\text{ liters}} = \frac{0.578\text{ moles NaOH}}{1.000\text{ L}} = 0.578\,\frac{\text{moles NaOH}}{\text{L}} = \underline{0.578\text{ M}}$$

c. In order to get concentration, we must have moles and liters. The question gives us grams and mL, so we must make 2 conversions:

$$\frac{29.0\ \cancel{\text{g H}_2\text{CO}_3}}{1} \times \frac{1\text{ mole H}_2\text{CO}_3}{62.0\ \cancel{\text{g H}_2\text{CO}_3}} = 0.468\text{ moles H}_2\text{CO}_3$$

$$\frac{400.0\ \cancel{\text{mL}}}{1} \times \frac{0.001\text{ L}}{1\ \cancel{\text{mL}}} = 0.4000\text{ L}$$

Now we can calculate molarity:

$$\text{Concentration} = \frac{\#\text{ moles}}{\#\text{ liters}} = \frac{0.468\text{ moles H}_2\text{CO}_3}{0.4000\text{ L}} = 1.17\,\frac{\text{moles H}_2\text{CO}_3}{\text{L}} = \underline{1.17\text{ M}}$$

8. This is a dilution question, so we use the dilution equation. M_1 is 20.34 M, we need to determine V_1. M_2 is 3.45 M and V_2 = 1500.0 mL.

$$M_1V_1 = M_2V_2$$

$$(20.34 \text{ M}) \times V_1 = (3.45 \text{ M}) \times (1500.0 \text{ mL})$$

$$V_1 = \frac{(3.45 \cancel{\text{M}}) \times (1500.0 \text{ mL})}{20.34 \cancel{\text{M}}} = \underline{254 \text{ mL}}$$

<u>The chemist must take 254 mL of the original solution and dilute it with enough water to make 1500.0 mL of solution.</u>

9. This is a dilution question, so we use the dilution equation. M_1 is 10.22 M, we need to determine V_1. M_2 is 9.0 M and V_2 = 100.0 mL.

$$M_1V_1 = M_2V_2$$

$$(10.22 \text{ M}) \times V_1 = (9.0 \text{ M}) \times (100.0 \text{ mL})$$

$$V_1 = \frac{(9.0 \cancel{\text{M}}) \times (100.0 \text{ mL})}{10.22 \cancel{\text{M}}} = \underline{88 \text{ mL}}$$

<u>You must take 88 mL of the original solution and dilute it with enough water to make 100.0 mL of solution.</u>

MOD 9

10. Remember, titrations are just stoichiometry questions, so first we have to come up with a balanced chemical equation:

$$HBr + NaOH \rightarrow NaBr + H_2O$$

Since the endpoint was reached, we know that exactly enough base was added to eat up all of the acid. First, then, we calculate how many moles of base were added:

$$\frac{1.14 \text{ moles NaOH}}{1 \cancel{\text{L}}} \times \frac{0.1350 \cancel{\text{L}}}{1} = 0.154 \text{ moles NaOH}$$

We can now use the chemical equation to determine how many moles of acid were present:

$$\frac{0.154 \cancel{\text{moles NaOH}}}{1} \times \frac{1 \text{ mole HBr}}{1 \cancel{\text{mole NaOH}}} = 0.154 \text{ moles HBr}$$

Now that we have the number of moles of acid present, we simply divide by the volume of acid to get concentration:

$$\text{Concentration} = \frac{\text{\# moles}}{\text{\# liters}} = \frac{0.154 \text{ moles HBr}}{0.0750 \text{ L}} = \underline{2.05 \text{ M}}$$

11. First we have to come up with a balanced chemical equation:

$$2HCl + Mg(OH)_2 \rightarrow MgCl_2 + 2H_2O$$

Since the endpoint was reached, we know that exactly enough acid was added to eat up all of the base. First, then, we calculate how many moles of acid were added:

$$\frac{1.00 \text{ mole HCl}}{1 \cancel{\text{L}}} \times \frac{0.00176 \cancel{\text{L}}}{1} = 0.00176 \text{ moles HCl}$$

We can now use the chemical equation to determine how many moles of base were present:

$$\frac{0.00176 \cancel{\text{moles HCl}}}{1} \times \frac{1 \text{ mole } Mg(OH)_2}{2 \cancel{\text{moles HCl}}} = 0.00088 \text{ moles } Mg(OH)_2$$

Now that we have the number of moles of base present, we simply divide by the volume of base to get concentration:

$$\text{Concentration} = \frac{\text{\# moles}}{\text{\# liters}} = \frac{0.000880 \text{ moles } Mg(OH)_2}{0.0250 \text{ L}} = \underline{0.0352 \text{ M}}$$

TEST FOR MODULE 9

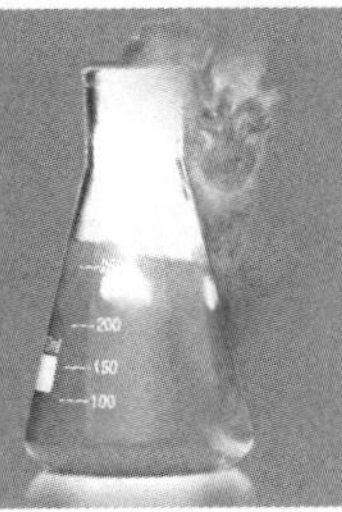

1. (4 pts) Which of the following is *not* a property of an acid?
   a. Acids taste sour.
   b. Acids are covalent compounds that conduct electricity when dissolved in water.
   c. Acids turn red litmus paper blue.
   d. None of the above are properties of acids.
   e. All of the above are properties of acids.

2. (4 pts) Identify the acid in this equation: $NH_3 + H_2O \rightarrow NH_4^+ + OH^-$
   a. NH_3
   b. H_2O
   c. NH_4^+
   d. OH^-
   e. None of the above

3. (4 pts) Which of the following is the same thing as a proton?
   a. Acid
   b. Base
   c. OH^{-1}
   d. H^+
   e. None of the above

4. (4 pts) Which of the following acids is/are diprotic?
   a. HNO_3 b. H_2CO_3 c. H_3PO_4 d. HSO_4^-

5. (4 pts) True or False: In order to be classified as an indicator, a chemical must change color when placed in an acid.

6. (4 pts) Which of the following is a property of a base?
   a. Bases taste bitter.
   b. When dissolved in water, bases have a slippery feel.
   c. Bases turn red litmus paper blue.
   d. All of the above
   e. None of the above

7. (4 pts) When $Mg(OH)_2$ dissolves in water, what ions form and how many of each ion are present?
   a. 1 Mg^{+} ion, and OH^{-} ion
   b. 2 Mg ions, and 1 OH ion
   c. 2 Mg^{+2} ions and 1 OH^{-} ions
   d. 1 Mg^{+} ions and 2 OH^{-2} ions
   e. None of the above

8. (4 pts) What is an amphiprotic substance? Give an example of one.

9. (4 pts) The general equation for the reaction between an acid and a ionic base is: Base + Acid $\rightarrow$
   a. Water
   b. Ionic compound
   c. Water + an ionic compound
   d. Covalent compound
   e. None of the above

10. (4 pts) Which of the following units would most likely be used as a concentration unit?
    a. mL/g
    b. moles/g
    c. %/moles
    d. moles/mL
    e. None of the above

11. (4 pts) Molarity is the moles of solute divided by the:
    a. Liters of solute
    b. Liters of solvent
    c. Liters of solution
    d. Milliliters of solvent
    e. None of the above

12. (8 pts) What would be the molarity of 25.6 g of H_2SO_4 dissolved in enough water to make 250.0 mL of solution?
    a. 1.04 M
    b. 15.3 M
    c. 0.958 M
    d. 1.04×10^{-3} M
    e. None of the above

For the following problems please provide the correct answer and show all the work needed to solve the problem.

13. (4 pts) Give a balanced chemical equation for the reaction between phosphoric acid (H_3PO_4) and CsOH.

14. (4 pts) What is the balanced chemical equation that represents the reaction of HCl with $Be(OH)_2$?

15. (4 pts) Write the balanced chemical equation for the reaction of HF with water.

16. (8 pts) What is the concentration (in M) of an ammonia (NH_3) solution if 12.23 grams of ammonia are dissolved in enough water to make 560.0 mL of solution?

17. (4 pts) If a chemist has a stock solution of HBr that is 10.0 M and would like to make 450.0 mL of 3.0 M HBr, how would he do it?

18. (12 pts) A chemist reacts 30.0 mL of 5.6 M HCl with an excess of $Mg(OH)_2$. How many grams of magnesium chloride will be produced?

19. (12 pts) If a chemist titrates 300.0 mL of H_2SO_4 with a 3.0 M solution of NaOH and requires only 3.4 mL of the base to reach the endpoint, what is the concentration of the sulfuric acid?

SOLUTIONS TO THE TEST FOR MODULE 9

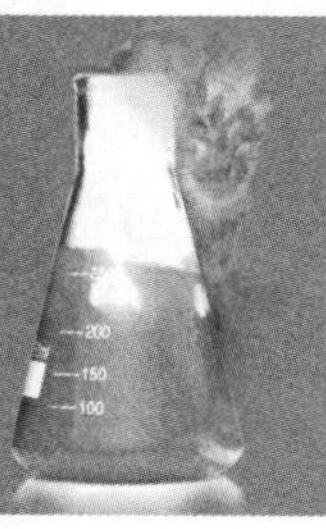

1. (4 pts) c. Acids turn red litmus paper blue.

2. (4 pts) b. H_2O

3. (4 pts) d. H^+

4. (4 pts) b. H_2CO_3 only

5. (4 pts) False An indicator changes color as it goes from an acid to a base.

6. (4 pts) d. All of the above

7. (4 pts) e. None of the above 1 Mg^+ ion and 2 OH^- ions are present.

8. (4 pts) Amphiprotic substances can act as either acids or bases. Water is a common example.

9. (4 pts) c. Water + an ionic compound

10. (4 pts) d. moles/mL

11. (4 pts) c. Liters of solution

12. (8 pts) a. 1.04 M

$$25.6 \text{ g } H_2SO_4 \times \frac{1 \text{ mol } H_2SO_4}{98.1 \text{ g}} = 0.261 \text{ moles } H_2SO_4$$

Convert volume to liters = 250.0 mL × 1 L/1000 mL = 0.2500 L water

Concentration = # mol / # L = $\frac{\text{0.261 mol } H_2SO_4}{\text{0.2500 L water}}$ = 1.04 M

13. (4 pts: 2 pts for the correct substances, 2 pts for the equation being balanced)

$H_3PO_4 + 3CsOH \rightarrow Cs_3PO_4 + 3H_2O$

14. (4 pts: 2 pts for the correct substances, 2 pts for the equation being balanced)

$2HCl + Be(OH)_2 \rightarrow BeCl_2 + 2H_2O$

15. (4 pts: 2 pts for the correct substances, 2 pts for the equation being balanced)

$HF + H_2O \rightarrow H_3O^+ + F^-$

16. (8 pts: 4 pts for both conversions, and 4 pts for the answer) 12.8 M
Concentration is number of moles divided by number of liters. Thus, first convert from grams to moles:

$$\frac{12.23 \text{ g } NH_3}{1} \times \frac{1 \text{ mole } NH_3}{17.0 \text{ g } NH_3} = 0.719 \text{ moles } NH_3$$

Now divide by the volume, making sure to convert 560.0 mL into 0.5600 L first:

$$\text{Concentration} = \frac{\text{\# moles}}{\text{\# liters}} = \frac{0.719 \text{ moles}}{0.5600 \text{ L}} = \underline{1.28 \text{ M}}$$

17. (4 pts) The chemist should take 1.4 × 10² mL of the stock solution and dilute it to 450.0 mL. This is a dilution problem, so we use the dilution equation:

$M_1V_1 = M_2V_2$

$(10.0 \text{ M}) \times V_1 = (3.0 \text{ M}) \times (450.0 \text{ mL})$

$$V_1 = \frac{(3.0 \text{ M}) \times (450.0 \text{ mL})}{10.0 \text{ M}} = \underline{1.4 \times 10^2 \text{ mL}}$$

18. (12 pts: 4 pts for the balanced equation, 8 points for conversion to moles, mole to mole conversion, and conversion to grams) 8.1 g $MgCl_2$
To solve this stoichiometry problem, we first must get the chemical equation:

$$2HCl + Mg(OH)_2 \rightarrow 2H_2O + MgCl_2$$

Now we can do stoichiometry:

$$\text{moles HCl} = 5.6\,\frac{\text{moles}}{\cancel{\text{L}}} \times 0.0300\,\cancel{\text{L}} = 0.17 \text{ moles HCl}$$

$$\frac{0.17\,\cancel{\text{moles HCl}}}{1} \times \frac{1 \text{ mole } MgCl_2}{2\,\cancel{\text{moles HCl}}} = 0.085 \text{ moles } MgCl_2$$

$$\frac{0.085\,\cancel{\text{moles } MgCl_2}}{1} \times \frac{95.3 \text{ g } MgCl_2}{1\,\cancel{\text{mole } MgCl_2}} = 8.1 \text{ g } MgCl_2$$

19. (12 pts: 4 pts for the balanced equation, and 8 pts for the stoichiometry) 0.017 M
To do any titration problem, we must first get the chemical equation:

$$H_2SO_4 + 2NaOH \rightarrow 2H_2O + Na_2SO_4$$

The endpoint means that just enough base has been added to completely react with the acid.

$$\text{moles NaOH} = 3.0\,\frac{\text{moles}}{\cancel{\text{L}}} \times 0.0034\,\cancel{\text{L}} = 0.010 \text{ moles NaOH}$$

$$\frac{0.010\,\cancel{\text{moles NaOH}}}{1} \times \frac{1 \text{ mole } H_2SO_4}{2\,\cancel{\text{moles NaOH}}} = 0.0050 \text{ moles } H_2SO_4$$

$$\text{Concentration} = \frac{\#\text{ moles}}{\#\text{ liters}} = \frac{0.0050 \text{ moles}}{0.3000 \text{ L}} = 0.017 \text{ M}$$

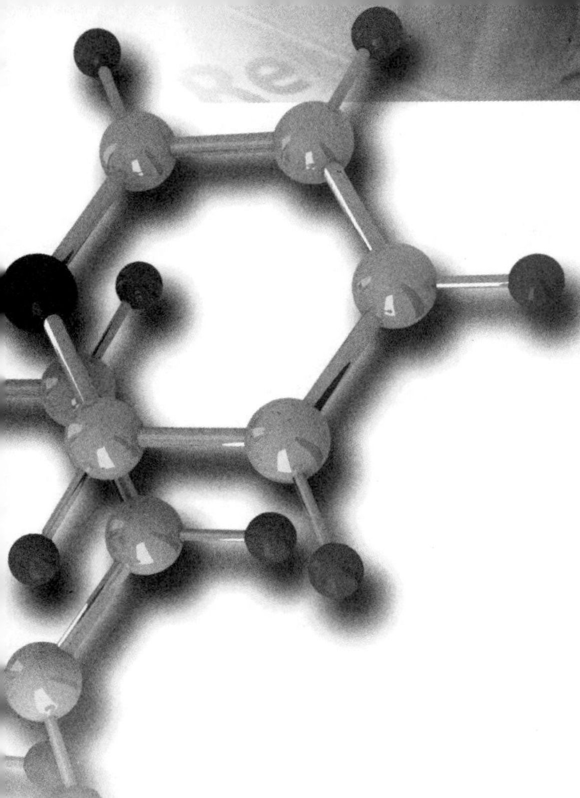

THE CHEMISTRY OF SOLUTIONS

SOLUTIONS TO THE MODULE 10 REVIEW QUESTIONS

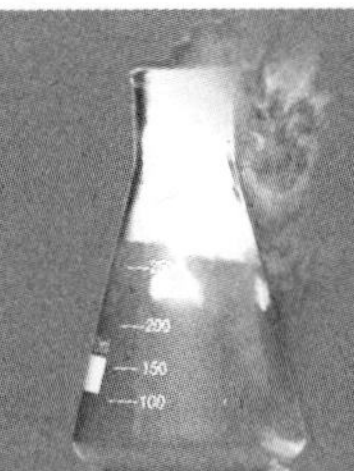

1. The solute is what we are dissolving, and the solvent is what we are dissolving the solute into. Therefore, sodium fluoride is the solute, and water is the solvent.

2. Ionic compounds split up into their ions when they dissolve. Thus, an ionic compound will split up into 2 or more ions in solution. On the other hand, polar covalent compounds dissolve 1 molecule at a time.

3. It does matter what the solvent is. The same solute will dissolve differently in different solvents.

4. A saturated solution contains as much dissolved solute as is possible for the given temperature and pressure.

5. Precipitation is the process by which a solid solute leaves a solution and turns back into its solid phase.

6. Solids dissolve best at high temperature.

7. Under high-pressure conditions, gases dissolve best.

8. Liquid solutes are not affected strongly by the conditions under which the solution is made.

9. To increase the solubility of a solid, we can increase the temperature of the solvent.

10. Increasing pressure and/or decreasing temperature will increase the solubility of a gas solute in water.

11. You should expect the beaker to get cold. When something dissolves endothermically, it cools the solution.

12. Molality takes number of moles of solute and divides by the *kilograms* of *solvent.* Molarity takes the number of moles of solute and divides by the *liters* of the *solution.*

13. $Al(NO_3)_3$
The only solute characteristic that affects the freezing point depression of a solvent is the number of molecules (or ions) it splits up into when it dissolves. The more molecules (or ions) the solute splits into, the larger the value of i. The larger the value of i, the larger the freezing point depression. $Al(NO_3)_3$ splits into 4 ions, so it does the best job of protecting water from freezing.

SOLUTIONS TO THE PRACTICE PROBLEMS FOR MODULE 10

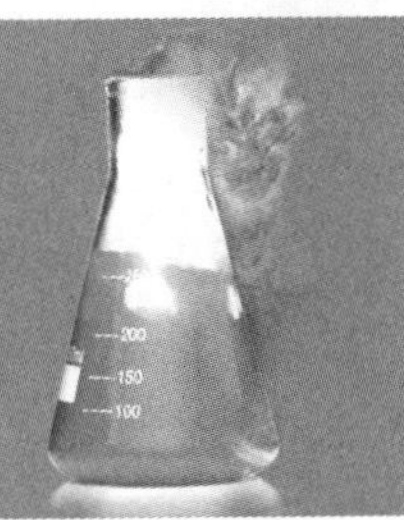

1. If the hot tub cools down, the solubility of the solutes will decrease. If it gets cold enough, the solubilities might get so low that some of the solute must exit the solution, forming a precipitate.

2. A soda pop gets flat because the CO_2 dissolved in it escapes. Since the solubility of gases increase with decreasing temperature, a colder soda pop will hold onto more CO_2 than a warm soda pop.

3. 296 g of aluminum sulfate will be produced. This is just a stoichiometry problem. We can tell this by the fact that we are being asked to determine the amount of one substance when we are given the amount of another substance. The only way to do that is by stoichiometry. In order to do stoichiometry, we must first get our amount in moles. The amount is given in concentration and volume, so we must turn that into moles. To do that, though, we must convert mL into liters, so that our volumes units are consistent with our concentration unit (remember, M means moles/liter).

$$\frac{690.0\ \cancel{\text{mL}}}{1} \times \frac{0.001\ \text{L}}{1\ \cancel{\text{mL}}} = 0.6900\ \text{L}$$

Now we can convert from volume and concentration into moles:

$$\frac{2.50\ \text{moles Al(NO}_3)_3}{1\ \cancel{\text{L}}} \times 0.6900\ \cancel{\text{L}} = 1.73\ \text{moles Al(NO}_3)_3$$

Now that we have moles, we can do stoichiometry:

$$\frac{1.73\ \cancel{\text{moles Al(NO}_3)_3}}{1} \times \frac{1\ \text{mole Al}_2(\text{SO}_4)_3}{2\ \cancel{\text{moles Al(NO}_3)_3}} = 0.865\ \text{moles Al}_2(\text{SO}_4)_3$$

Now, of course, this is not quite the answer we need. We were asked to figure out how many grams of aluminum sulfate were produced, so we have to convert from moles back to grams:

$$\frac{0.865\ \cancel{\text{moles Al}_2(\text{SO}_4)_3}}{1} \times \frac{342.3\ \text{g Al}_2(\text{SO}_4)_3}{1\ \cancel{\text{moles Al}_2(\text{SO}_4)_3}} = 296\ \text{g Al}_2(\text{SO}_4)_3$$

This means that 296 g of aluminum sulfate will be produced.

4. 0.23 liters of silver nitrate Once again, we can tell that this is a stoichiometry problem because we are asked to convert from amount of one substance to amount of another. In order to do stoichiometry, however, we must convert to moles. Since we have the number of grams of silver bromide, we will use that as our starting point:

$$\frac{150.0\ \cancel{\text{g AgBr}}}{1} \times \frac{1\ \text{mole AgBr}}{187.8\ \cancel{\text{g AgBr}}} = 0.7987\ \text{moles AgBr}$$

Now that we have moles, we can use stoichiometry to determine how much $AgNO_3$ is needed:

$$\frac{0.7987\ \cancel{\text{moles AgBr}}}{1} \times \frac{1\ \text{mole AgNO}_3}{1\ \cancel{\text{mole AgBr}}} = 0.7987\ \text{moles AgNO}_3$$

This tells us how much $AgNO_3$, but it doesn't answer the problem. The problem asks how many liters of a 3.5 M solution is needed. To determine this, we must remember that M means moles per liter. The molarity of a solution is a conversion relationship that allows us to relate the number of moles to the number of liters. We can therefore do the following conversion:

$$\frac{0.7987\ \cancel{\text{moles AgNO}_3}}{1} \times \frac{1\ \text{L AgNO}_3}{3.5\ \cancel{\text{moles AgNO}_3}} = 0.23\ \text{L of solution}$$

Thus, 0.23 liters of silver nitrate must be added.

5. 0.056 M In this problem, we can use the number of grams of $PbCl_2$ to determine the amount of Pb^{2+} that was there. First, however, we need to get to the number of moles of lead chloride:

$$\frac{50.0\ \cancel{\text{g PbCl}_2}}{1} \times \frac{1\ \text{mole PbCl}_2}{278.2\ \cancel{\text{g PbCl}_2}} = 0.180\ \text{moles PbCl}_2$$

Now we can use stoichiometry to determine the number of moles of Pb^{2+} that were in the water sample:

$$\frac{0.180\ \cancel{\text{moles PbCl}_2}}{1} \times \frac{1\ \text{mole Pb}^{2+}}{1\ \cancel{\text{mole PbCl}_2}} = 0.180\ \text{moles Pb}^{2+}$$

Now that we have the number of moles of Pb^{2+}, we can divide by the volume of the solution to get molarity:

$$\text{Molarity} = \frac{\#\ \text{moles}}{\#\ \text{liters}} = \frac{0.180\ \text{moles}}{3.2\ \text{L}} = \underline{0.056\ \text{M}}$$

The concentration of Pb^{2+} in the water is 0.056 M.

6. This problem is a direct application of the molality equation.

$$\text{molality} = \frac{\text{\# moles solute}}{\text{\# kg solvent}} = \frac{75.0 \text{ moles KOH}}{4.50 \text{ kg water}} = 16.7 \text{ m}$$

The molality is 16.7 m.

7. 0.266 m Molality is number of moles of solute divided by kg of solvent. So we have to get our units into moles and kg:

$$\frac{70.0 \cancel{\text{g CaBr}_2}}{1} \times \frac{1 \text{ mole CaBr}_2}{199.9 \cancel{\text{g CaBr}_2}} = 0.350 \text{ moles CaBr}_2$$

$$\frac{1314 \cancel{\text{g}}}{1} \times \frac{1 \text{ kg}}{1{,}000 \cancel{\text{g}}} = 1.314 \text{ kg}$$

$$\text{molality} = \frac{\text{\# moles solute}}{\text{\# kg solvent}} = \frac{0.350 \text{ moles CaBr}_2}{1.314 \text{ kg water}} = \underline{0.266 \text{ m}}$$

The molality is 0.266 m.

8. 4.8 m Freezing point depression is determined by equation 10.2. We are already given 2 of the 4 variables in the equation (K_f,ΔT) and we can calculate a third (i). Molality is the only unknown, so we can solve for it. Since NaCl is ionic, it will split up into ions (1 sodium ion and 1 chloride ion), so i = 2:

$$\Delta T = -i \times K_f \times m$$

$$-18°\text{C} = -2 \times 1.86 \frac{°\text{C}}{\text{molal}} \times m$$

$$m = \frac{-18 \cancel{°\text{C}}}{-2 \times 1.86 \frac{\cancel{°\text{C}}}{\text{molal}}} = 4.8 \text{ molal}$$

The molality is 4.8 m.

9. −10.9 °C In a freezing point depression problem, we must use equation 10.2. However, in order to use that equation, we must know K_f, i, and m. Right now, we

MOD 10

only know K_f. However, we have been given enough information to calculate both i and m. To calculate m:

$$\frac{42.0\ \cancel{g\ NH_3}}{1} \times \frac{1\ \text{mole}\ NH_3}{17.0\ \cancel{g\ NH_3}} = 2.47\ \text{moles}\ NH_3$$

$$\frac{420.0\ \cancel{g}}{1} \times \frac{1\ kg}{1{,}000\ \cancel{g}} = 0.4200\ kg$$

$$m = \frac{2.47\ \text{moles}\ NH_3}{0.4200\ \text{kg water}} = 5.88\ m$$

To figure out i, we just have to think about how NH_3 dissolves. In a polar covalent compound, each molecule dissolves individually, so i = 1.

Now that we have all of the components of equation 10.2, we can use it:

$$\Delta T = -i \times K_f \times m = -1 \times 1.86\ \frac{°C}{\cancel{m}} \times 5.88\ \cancel{m} = -10.9°C$$

Our answer indicates that the freezing point of this solution is 10.9 °C lower than that of water. The answer to our problem is that the freezing point of the solution is <u>–10.9 °C</u>.

10. <u>102.3 °C</u> To calculate boiling points, we must use equation 10.3. To do that, however, we must know i and m. To calculate m:

$$\frac{75.0\ \cancel{g\ ZnCl_2}}{1} \times \frac{1\ \text{mole}\ ZnCl_2}{136.4\ \cancel{g\ ZnCl_2}} = 0.550\ \text{moles}\ ZnCl_2$$

$$\frac{375.0\ \cancel{g}}{1} \times \frac{1\ kg}{1{,}000\ \cancel{g}} = 0.3750\ kg$$

$$m = \frac{0.550\ \text{moles}\ ZnCl_2}{0.3750\ \text{kg water}} = 1.47\ m$$

Since zinc(II) chloride is an ionic compound, it dissolves by splitting up into its 1 zinc ion and its 2 chloride ions. Thus, i = 3.

$$\Delta T = i \times K_b \times m = 3 \times 0.512\ \frac{°C}{\cancel{m}} \times 1.47\ \cancel{m} = 2.26°C$$

This means that the boiling point of the solution is 2.26 °C *higher* than that of pure water. The boiling point of pure water is 100.0 °C, so the boiling point of this solution is <u>102.3 °C</u>.

SOLUTIONS TO THE EXTRA PRACTICE PROBLEMS FOR MODULE 10

1. The solubility of gases increases with decreasing temperature. Thus, you should <u>cool the liquid</u>.

2. This is just a stoichiometry question. We can tell this by the fact that we are being asked to determine the amount of one substance when we are given the amount of another substance. The only way to do that is by stoichiometry, so we must first get our amount in moles:

$$\frac{1.25 \text{ moles } Al(NO_3)_3}{1 \cancel{L}} \times 0.382 \cancel{L} = 0.478 \text{ moles } Al(NO_3)_3$$

Now that we have moles, we can do stoichiometry:

$$\frac{0.478 \cancel{\text{moles } Al(NO_3)_3}}{1} \times \frac{1 \text{ mole } Al_2(CO_3)_3}{2 \cancel{\text{moles } Al(NO_3)_3}} = 0.239 \text{ moles } Al_2(CO_3)_3$$

Of course, this is not quite the answer we need. We were asked to figure out how many grams of aluminum carbonate were produced, so we have to convert from moles back to grams:

$$\frac{0.239 \cancel{\text{moles } Al_2(CO_3)_3}}{1} \times \frac{234.0 \text{ g } Al_2(CO_3)_3}{1 \cancel{\text{mole } Al_2(CO_3)_3}} = \underline{55.9 \text{ g } Al_2(CO_3)_3}$$

3. We must first get our amount in moles.

$$\frac{25.0 \cancel{\text{g KCN}}}{1} \times \frac{1 \text{ mole KCN}}{65.1 \cancel{\text{g KCN}}} = 0.384 \text{ moles KCN}$$

Now that we have moles, we can do stoichiometry:

$$\frac{0.384 \cancel{\text{moles KCN}}}{1} \times \frac{1 \text{ mole HCN}}{1 \cancel{\text{mole KCN}}} = \underline{0.384 \text{ moles HCN}}$$

Of course, this is not quite the answer we need. We were asked to figure out how many mL of the HCN solution is needed:

$$\frac{0.384 \text{ \sout{moles HCN}}}{1} \times \frac{1 \text{ L}}{1.51 \text{ \sout{moles HCN}}} = 0.254 \text{ L} = \underline{254 \text{ mL}}$$

4. We must first get our amount in moles.

$$\frac{500.0 \text{ \sout{g Cu}}}{1} \times \frac{1 \text{ mole Cu}}{63.5 \text{ \sout{g Cu}}} = 7.87 \text{ moles Cu}$$

Now that we have moles, we can do stoichiometry:

$$\frac{7.87 \text{ \sout{moles Cu}}}{1} \times \frac{8 \text{ moles } HNO_3}{3 \text{ \sout{moles Cu}}} = 21.0 \text{ moles } HNO_3$$

Of course, this is not quite the answer we need. We were asked to figure out how many mL of the HNO_3 solution is needed:

$$\frac{21.0 \text{ \sout{moles HNO}}_3}{1} \times \frac{1 \text{ L}}{3.50 \text{ \sout{moles HNO}}_3} = 6.00 \text{ L} = \underline{6.00 \times 10^3 \text{ mL}}$$

5. To calculate molality, we must have moles of solute and kg of solvent.

$$\frac{100.0 \text{ \sout{g Mg(NO}}_3)_2}{1} \times \frac{1 \text{ mole } Mg(NO_3)_2}{148.3 \text{ \sout{g Mg(NO}}_3)_2} = 0.6742 \text{ moles } Mg(NO_3)_2$$

$$\frac{500.0 \text{ \sout{g}}}{1} \times \frac{1 \text{ kg}}{1{,}000 \text{ \sout{g}}} = 0.5000 \text{ kg}$$

Now that we have moles of solute and kg of solvent, we can use equation 10.1:

$$\text{molality} = \frac{\text{\# moles solute}}{\text{\# kg solvent}} = \frac{0.6742 \text{ moles } Mg(NO_3)_2}{0.5000 \text{ kg water}} = \underline{1.348 \text{ m}}$$

6. First, we need to see how many moles of $CaCl_2$ to add:

$$\text{molality} = \frac{\text{\# moles solute}}{\text{\# kg solvent}}$$

$$\frac{\text{moles } CaCl_2}{1.25 \text{ kg water}} = 2.0 \text{ m}$$

$$\text{moles } CaCl_2 = 2.5 \text{ moles}$$

Thus, we have to add 2.5 moles of $CaCl_2$ to 1.25 kg of water to make a 2.0 m solution. Now we just need to see how many grams that is:

$$\frac{2.5\ \cancel{\text{moles CaCl}_2}}{1} \times \frac{111.1\text{ g CaCl}_2}{1\ \cancel{\text{mole CaCl}_2}} = \underline{2.8 \times 10^2\text{g CaCl}_2}$$

7. You want the solute that splits up into the most ions. $\underline{Ca_3(PO_4)_2}$ splits into 5 ions (3 calcium ions and 2 phosphate ions.) That is more than the other 2, so it would give the lowest freezing point to water.

8. In a freezing-point depression question, you must use equation 10.2. However, in order to use that equation, we must know K_f, i, and m. Right now, we know only K_f. However, we have been given enough information to calculate both i and m. First let's calculate m:

$$\frac{20.0\ \cancel{\text{g KF}}}{1} \times \frac{1\text{ mole KF}}{58.1\ \cancel{\text{g KF}}} = 0.344\text{ moles KF}$$

$$m = \frac{0.344\text{ moles KF}}{0.1000\text{ kg water}} = 3.44\text{ m}$$

To figure out i, we just have to realize that according to its formula, KF splits up into 1 potassium ion and 1 fluoride ion. Thus, i = 2. Now that we have all of the components of equation 10.2, we can use it:

$$\Delta T = -i \times K_f \times m = -2 \times 1.86\ \frac{°C}{\cancel{m}} \times 3.44\ \cancel{m} = -12.8°C$$

So the freezing point is 12.8 °C lower than that of normal water, or $\underline{-12.8\ °C}$.

9. We can use equation 10.2 to solve this. Since $CaCl_2$ is made up of 1 calcium ion and 2 chloride ions, i = 3.

$$\Delta T = -i \times K_f \times m$$

$$m = \frac{\Delta T}{-i \times K_f} = \frac{-10.00\ \cancel{°C}}{-3 \times 1.86\ \frac{\cancel{°C}}{\text{molal}}} = \underline{1.79\text{ molal}}$$

10. To calculate boiling points, we must use equation 10.3. To do that, however, we must know i and m. To calculate m:

$$\frac{50.0\ \cancel{g\ (NH_4)_2S}}{1} \times \frac{1\ \text{mole}\ (NH_4)_2S}{68.2\ \cancel{g\ (NH_4)_2S}} = 0.733\ \text{moles}\ (NH_4)_2S$$

$$m = \frac{0.733\ \text{moles}\ (NH_4)_2S}{0.3750\ \text{kg water}} = 1.95\ m$$

Since ammonium sulfide is an ionic compound, it dissolves by splitting up into its 2 ammonium ions and its 1 sulfide ion. Thus, i = 3.

$$\Delta T = i \times K_b \times m = 3 \times 0.512\ \frac{°C}{\cancel{m}} \times 1.95\ \cancel{m} = 3.00\ °C$$

This means that the boiling point of the solution is 3.00 °C *higher* than that of pure water. The boiling point of pure water is 100.0 °C, so the boiling point of this solution is <u>103.0 °C</u>.

TEST FOR MODULE 10

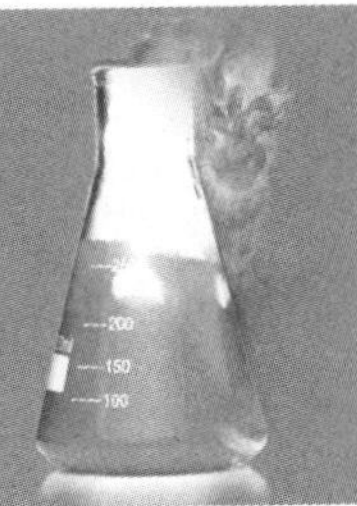

1. (4 pts) The maximum amount of solute that can dissolve in a given amount of solvent is:
   a. Supersaturated
   b. Solution
   c. Dissolving
   d. Saturated
   e. None of the above

2. (4 pts) If a solute's solubility in a liquid solvent is not affected by temperature or pressure, is the solute most likely a:
   a. Solid
   b. Liquid
   c. Gas
   d. All of the above
   e. None of the above

3. (4 pts) If a solute's solubility in a liquid solvent decreases when the temperature increases, is the solute most likely a:
   a. Solid
   b. Liquid
   c. Gas
   d. All of the above
   e. None of the above

4. (4 pts) A chemist is trying to dissolve a solid in water. If the chemist feels the beaker get hot while trying to make the solution, does the solute dissolve exothermically or endothermically?
   a. Exothermically
   b. Endothermically

5. (4 pts) What kind of solute usually increases in solubility with increasing temperature?
   a. Solid
   b. Liquid
   c. Gas
   d. All of the above
   e. None of the above

6. (4 pts) Pick the solute that will raise a liquid's boiling point the most, assuming that the concentration of each solute is the same:
   a. NH_3
   b. Na_3PO_4
   c. K_2CO_3
   d. NaCl
   e. All of the above

7. (4 pts) What is responsible for an ionic solid dissolving in water?
   a. The molecule fits in between the water molecules.
   b. The ions in the water are attracted to the ions in the solid.
   c. The ions in the solid are repulsed by the other ions and the water helps the solid break up.
   d. The polar nature of water attracts the opposite ions in the solid and separates them.
   e. None of the above

8. (4 pts) True or False: For a gas solute dissolving in a liquid solvent, the solvent molecules must be attracted to the solute molecules enough to pull the solute molecules closer to one another.

9. (4 pts) If a solute dissolves in water endothermically, what can you do to decrease its solubility?
   a. Decrease the temperature
   b. Increase the temperature
   c. Add heat
   d. Add more solute
   e. None of the above

10. (4 pts) A student makes a solution by measuring 100 grams of solute and dissolving it in lots of water. The student then measures the mass of the resulting solution. He converts the mass of the solute into moles and divides that by the mass (in kg) of the solution. He reports the result as the molality of the solution. Why is the student wrong?

For the following problems, please provide the correct answer and show the work that is needed to answer the problem.

11. (12 pts) When NaI is added to a solution of $Cu(NO_3)_2$, the following reaction occurs: $2NaI\ (aq) + Cu(NO_3)_2\ (aq) \rightarrow CuI_2\ (s) + 2NaNO_3\ (aq)$

    If a chemist needs to make 350.0 g of CuI_2, how many mL of a 3.3 M solution of NaI must be used? Assume that there is excess copper (II) nitrate.

12. (12 pts) Hydrogen peroxide is used to clean small wounds. It has a limited shelf-life, however, because the following decomposition reaction occurs:
$2H_2O_2\ (aq) \rightarrow 2H_2O\ (l) + O_2\ (g)$

    This is why you often hear a gas release when you open a bottle of old hydrogen peroxide. If 35 mL of a 1.20 M solution of hydrogen peroxide completely decomposes, how many grams of oxygen are produced?

13. (4 pts) What is the molality of a solution made from 5.61 moles of KCl and 2.11 kg of water?

14. (4 pts) If you have 670.0 grams of water and wish to make a 2.13 m solution of KBr, how many grams of the solute would you have to add to the water that you have?

15. (8 pts) When a certain amount of MgF_2 is added to water, the freezing point lowers by 3.5 °C. What was the molality of the magnesium fluoride? (K_f for water = 1.86 °C/m)

16. (12 pts) Benzene (a popular nonpolar covalent solvent) has a freezing point of 5.5 °C and a K_f of 5.12 °C/m. If 30.0 g of CCl_4 are dissolved in 350.0 g of benzene, what will the freezing point of the solution be?

17. (8 pts) Acetic acid has a boiling point of 118.5 °C and a K_b of 3.08 °C/m. What is the boiling point of a 3.20 m solution of $Ca(NO_3)_2$ in acetic acid?

SOLUTIONS TO THE TEST FOR MODULE 10

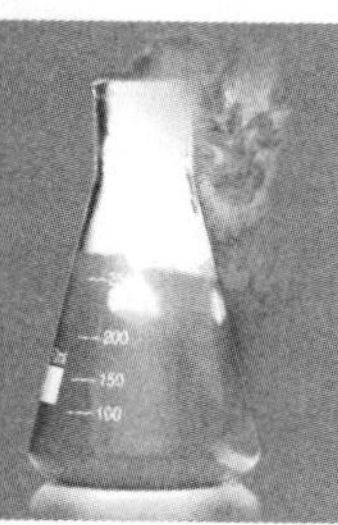

1. (4 pts) d. Saturated

2. (4 pts) b. Liquid

3. (4 pts) c. Gas

4. (4 pts) a. Exothermically
   Remember, exothermic processes *release* heat, making their surroundings hotter.

5. (4 pts) a. Solid

6. (4 pts) b. Na_3PO_4
   The solute that will raise the boiling point the most is the one that splits into the most ions when dissolved. This would be Na_3PO_4, which splits into 4 ions.

7. (4 pts) d. The polar nature of water attracts the opposite ions in the solid and separates them.

8. (4 pts) True
   For a gas solute dissolving in a liquid solvent, the solvent molecules must be attracted to the solute molecules enough to pull the solute molecules closer to one another.

9. (4 pts) a. Decrease the temperature

10. (4 pts) He has divided by the mass of the *solution*. Molality is calculated by dividing by the mass of the *solvent*.

11. (12 pts: 4 pts for each step) 670 mL
This is just a stoichiometry problem:

$$\frac{350.0 \cancel{\text{ g CuI}_2}}{1} \times \frac{1 \text{ mole CuI}_2}{317.3 \cancel{\text{ g CuI}_2}} = 1.103 \text{ moles CuI}_2$$

$$\frac{1.103 \cancel{\text{ moles CuI}_2}}{1} \times \frac{2 \text{ moles NaI}}{1 \cancel{\text{ mole CuI}_2}} = 2.206 \text{ moles NaI}$$

$$\frac{2.206 \cancel{\text{ moles NaI}}}{1} \times \frac{1 \text{ L NaI}}{3.3 \cancel{\text{ mole NaI}}} = 0.67 \text{ L} = \underline{670 \text{ mL}}$$

12. (12 pts: 4 pts for each step) $\underline{0.67 \text{ g } O_2}$
This is just a stoichiometry problem:

$$\frac{0.035 \cancel{\text{ L H}_2\text{O}_2}}{1} \times \frac{1.20 \text{ mole H}_2\text{O}_2}{1 \cancel{\text{ L H}_2\text{O}_2}} = 0.042 \text{ moles H}_2\text{O}_2$$

$$\frac{0.042 \cancel{\text{ moles H}_2\text{O}_2}}{1} \times \frac{1 \text{ mole O}_2}{2 \cancel{\text{ moles H}_2\text{O}_2}} = 0.021 \text{ moles O}_2$$

$$\frac{0.021 \cancel{\text{ moles O}_2}}{1} \times \frac{32.0 \text{ g O}_2}{1 \cancel{\text{ mole O}_2}} = \underline{0.67 \text{ g O}_2}$$

13. (4 pts) 2.66 m

$$m = \frac{\#\text{ moles solute}}{\#\text{ kg solvent}} = \frac{5.61 \text{ moles}}{2.11 \text{ kg}} = 2.66 \frac{\text{moles}}{\text{kg}} = \underline{2.66 \text{ m}}$$

14. (4 pts: 2 pts for # moles, and 2 pts for grams) $\underline{1.43 \text{ moles}, 1.70 \times 10^2 \text{ g KBr}}$

$$m = \frac{\#\text{ moles solute}}{\#\text{ kg solvent}}$$

$$2.13 \text{ m} = \frac{\#\text{ moles}}{0.670 \text{ kg}}$$

$$\#\text{ moles} = 1.43$$

$$\frac{1.43 \cancel{\text{ moles KBr}}}{1} \times \frac{119.0 \text{ g KBr}}{1 \cancel{\text{ mole KBr}}} = \underline{1.70 \times 10^2 \text{ g KBr}}$$

15. (8 pts: 4 pts for getting i correct, 4 pts for the answer) 0.63 m
In order to solve a freezing point depression problem, we need to know the value for i. MgF_2 splits into 1 Mg^{2+} ion and 2 F^- ions. Thus, i = 3.

$$\Delta T = -i \times K_f \times m$$

$$-3.5\ ^\circ C = -3 \times \left(1.86 \frac{^\circ C}{\text{molal}}\right) \times m$$

$$m = \underline{0.63\ m}$$

16. (12 pts: 4 pts for i, 4 pts for the molality, and 4 pts for the answer) 2.7 °C
Since CCl_4 is covalent, it does not split into ions when dissolved. Thus, i = 1. To use the freezing point depression equation, however, we need to calculate the molality of the solution:

$$\frac{30.0\ \cancel{g\ CCl_4}}{1} \times \frac{1\text{ mole }CCl_4}{154.0\ \cancel{g\ CCl_4}} = 0.195\text{ moles }CCl_4$$

$$m = \frac{\#\text{ moles solute}}{\#\text{ kg solvent}} = \frac{0.195\text{ moles}}{0.3500\text{ kg}} = \underline{0.557\ m}$$

Now we can use the freezing point depression equation:

$$\Delta T = -i \times K_f \times m$$

$$\Delta T = -1 \times \left(5.12 \frac{^\circ C}{\cancel{m}}\right) \times 0.557\cancel{m}$$

$$\Delta T = \underline{-2.85\ ^\circ C}$$

This is not the answer. This tells us how much the freezing point lowered! Thus, the new freezing point is 5.5 °C – 2.85 °C = 2.7 °C.

17. (8 pts: 4 pts for i, and 4 pts for the answer) 148.1 °C
Since $Ca(NO_3)_2$ splits into 1 Ca^{2+} and 2 NO_3^- ions, i = 3.

$$\Delta T = i \times K_b \times m$$

$$\Delta T = 3 \times \left(3.08 \frac{^\circ C}{\cancel{m}}\right) \times 3.20\ \cancel{m}$$

$$\Delta T = 29.6\ ^\circ C$$

This is not the answer. This tells us how much the boiling point was raised! Thus, the new boiling point is 118.5 °C + 29.6 °C = 148.1 °C.

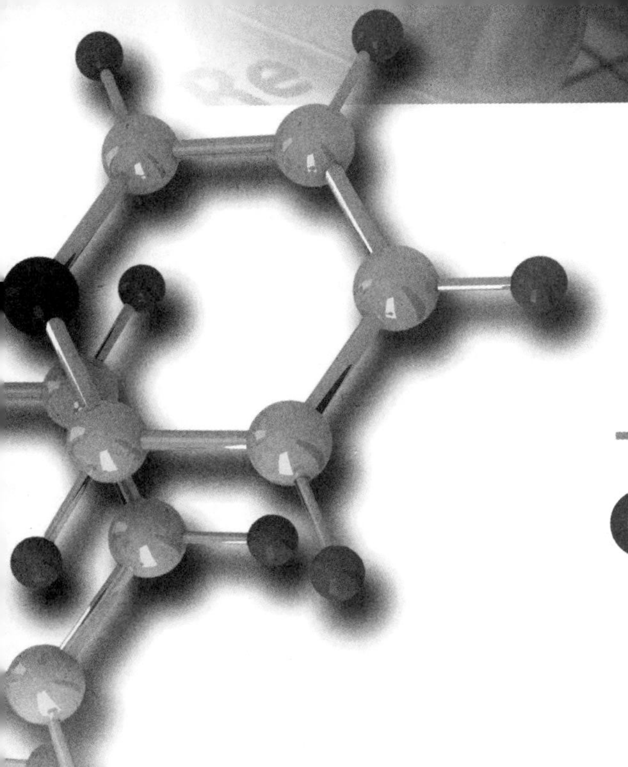

THE GAS PHASE

SOLUTIONS TO THE MODULE 11 REVIEW QUESTIONS

1. Pressure is defined as the force per unit area that a gas exerts on its surroundings. The units used to measure pressure are Pa, kPa, atm, torr, and mmHg. The student needs to name only 3 of these units.

2. Boyle's law states that under conditions of constant temperature, the product of a gas's pressure and volume is always constant.

3. The Kelvin temperature scale derives from Charles's law. It is the result of the fact that when we extrapolate the volume versus temperature data for all gases, zero volume occurs at –273.15 °C. This means that nothing can ever get colder than –273.15 °C, or 0.00 K.

4. A careful scientist can extrapolate data only when the amount of data is large compared to the extrapolation.

5. The molecules (or atoms) that make up an ideal gas must be small compared to the volume available to the gas. The gas molecules (or atoms) must be so far apart that they do not attract or repel each other. Also, all collisions that occur must be elastic.

6. Gases behave ideally when their pressure is near or lower than 1.00 atm and when their temperature is near or higher than 273K.

7. STP is defined as 1.00 atm and 273 K.

8. They both have exactly the same pressure. Dalton's law tells us that the pressure of an ideal gas is independent of its identity.

9. When the temperature of a liquid is lowered, its vapor pressure lowers. Thus, the vapor pressure decreased.

10. Mole fraction represents the fraction of molecules represented by the component of interest. Thus, a mole fraction of 0.78 tells us that for every 100 molecules, 78 will be nitrogen. Thus, for every 1,000 molecules, 780 will be nitrogen.

SOLUTIONS TO THE PRACTICE PROBLEMS FOR MODULE 11

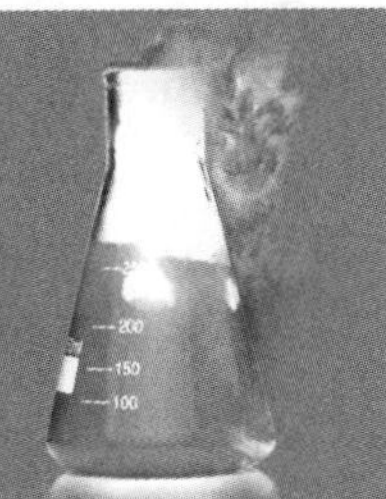

1. 1.62 liters This problem asks us to predict how a gas will change when we change some of the conditions under which it is stored. This means that we need to use the combined gas law.

$$\frac{P_1V_1}{T_1} = \frac{P_2V_2}{T_2}$$

According to this problem, P_1 = 812 mm Hg, V_1 = 1.25 L, and P_2 = 625 mm Hg. Also, the problem states that the temperature does not change, thus T_1 and T_2 cancel out:

$$\frac{P_1V_1}{\cancel{T_1}} = \frac{P_2V_2}{\cancel{T_2}}$$

We can now rearrange the equation to solve for the new volume:

$$\frac{P_1V_1}{P_2} = V_2$$

Now we can put in the numbers and determine the new volume:

$$\frac{812\ \cancel{\text{mm Hg}} \times 1.25\text{ L}}{625\ \cancel{\text{mm Hg}}} = \underline{1.62\text{ L}}$$

Thus, the balloon expands to 1.62 liters.

2. 22.2 mL This is obviously another combined gas law problem, with P_1 = 795 torr, V_1 = 23.0 mL, T_1 = 23.0 °C, P_2 = 1.00 atm (standard pressure), and T_2 = 273 K (standard temperature). The problem asks us to determine the new volume, so we have to rearrange to solve for V_2:

$$\frac{P_1V_1T_2}{T_1P_2} = V_2$$

Before we can plug in the numbers, however, we need to convert T_1 to Kelvin.

$$T_1 = 23.0 + 273.15 = 296.2\text{ K}$$

Additionally, we need to make the pressure units the same. We can do this by converting torr into atm or vice versa. We will choose to do the latter:

$$P_2 = \frac{1.00\ \cancel{\text{atm}}}{1} \times \frac{760\ \text{torr}}{1\ \cancel{\text{atm}}} = 7.60 \times 10^2\ \text{torr}$$

Now we can plug in the numbers:

$$\frac{795\ \cancel{\text{torr}} \times 23.0\ \text{mL} \times 273\ \cancel{\text{K}}}{296.2\ \cancel{\text{K}} \times 7.60 \times 10^2\ \cancel{\text{torr}}} = V_2$$

$$\underline{22.2\ \text{mL}} = V_2$$

So the volume increases to <u>22.2 mL</u>.

3. <u>106 atm</u> In this combined gas law problem, we are asked to calculate the pressure of a container of gas under conditions of constant volume. Thus, we need to rearrange the equation to solve for P_2, realizing that the volumes cancel because they are the same:

$$\frac{P_1V_1}{T_1} = \frac{P_2V_2}{T_2} \qquad \frac{P_1T_2}{T_1} = P_2$$

To be able to calculate the new volume, we first need to get the temperatures into Kelvin:

$$T_1 = 20.0 + 273.15 = 293.2\ \text{K}$$

$$T_2 = 55.0 + 273.15 = 328.2\ \text{K}$$

Now we can plug in our numbers:

$$\frac{95.0\ \text{atm} \times 328.2\ \cancel{\text{K}}}{293.2\ \cancel{\text{K}}} = \underline{106\ \text{atm}}$$

The pressure in the container after it warms up is <u>106 atm</u>.

4. <u>768 torr</u> This problem requires us to recognize that when a gas is collected over water, the gas is contaminated with water vapor. The 790 torr of gas is the total pressure of carbon dioxide *plus* water vapor. To determine the partial pressure of water vapor, we need only look at table 11.2. At 24 °C, the vapor pressure of water is 22.4 torr. Thus, Dalton's law becomes:

$$P_T = P_{carbon\ dioxide} + P_{water\ vapor}$$

$$790\ torr = P_{carbon\ dioxide} + 22.4\ torr$$

$$P_{carbon\ dioxide} = 790\ torr - 22.4\ torr = \underline{768\ torr}$$

Thus, only 768 torr of carbon dioxide was collected.

5. The mole fractions of SO_2, NO, and SO_3 are 0.448, 0.502, and 0.051, respectively. Mole fraction is defined as the number of *moles* of component divided by the total number of moles. Right now, the problem gives us *grams*, not moles. Thus, we must first convert from grams to moles:

$$\frac{25.0\ \cancel{g\ SO_2}}{1} \times \frac{1\ mole\ SO_2}{64.1\ \cancel{g\ SO_2}} = 0.390\ moles\ SO_2$$

$$\frac{13.1\ \cancel{g\ NO}}{1} \times \frac{1\ mole\ NO}{30.0\ \cancel{g\ NO}} = 0.437\ moles\ NO$$

$$\frac{3.5\ \cancel{g\ SO_3}}{1} \times \frac{1\ mole\ SO_3}{80.1\ \cancel{g\ SO_3}} = 0.044\ moles\ SO_3$$

Now that we have the number of moles of each component, we can calculate the total number of moles in the mixture:

$$\text{Total number of moles} = 0.390\ moles + 0.437\ moles + 0.044\ moles = 0.871\ moles$$

Plugging that into equation 11.10:

$$X_{SO_2} = \frac{0.390\ \cancel{moles}}{0.871\ \cancel{moles}} = 0.448$$

$$X_{NO} = \frac{0.437\ \cancel{moles}}{0.871\ \cancel{moles}} = 0.502$$

$$X_{SO_3} = \frac{0.044\ \cancel{moles}}{0.871\ \cancel{moles}} = 0.051$$

The mole fractions of SO_2, NO, and SO_3 are 0.448, 0.502, and 0.051, respectively.

6. The partial pressures of NO, SO_2, and SO_3 are 0.54 atm, 0.60 atm, and 0.061 atm, respectively. Using the mole fractions we just obtained, this problem is an easy application of equation 11.11:

$$P_1 = X_1 \times P_T$$

$$P_{SO_2} = 0.502 \times 1.2 \text{ atm} = 0.60 \text{ atm}$$

$$P_{NO} = 0.448 \times 1.2 \text{ atm} = 0.54 \text{ atm}$$

$$P_{SO_3} = 0.051 \times 1.2 \text{ atm} = 0.061 \text{ atm}$$

The partial pressures of SO_2, NO, and SO_3 are 0.60 atm, 0.54 atm, and 0.061 atm, respectively.

7. In this problem, we are given the partial pressure of each gas. By Dalton's law, the total pressure is just the sum of the individual pressures:

$$P_T = 10.00 \text{ atm} + 4.00 \text{ atm} + 1.00 \text{ atm} = 15.00 \text{ atm}$$

By equation 11.11, then, we can calculate the mole fractions:

$$P_1 = X_1 \times P_T \qquad X_1 = \frac{P_1}{P_T}$$

Plugging the numbers in for each gas:

$$X_{N_2} = \frac{10.00 \cancel{\text{atm}}}{15.00 \cancel{\text{atm}}} = 0.6667$$

$$X_{O_2} = \frac{4.00 \cancel{\text{atm}}}{15.00 \cancel{\text{atm}}} = 0.267$$

$$X_{Ar} = \frac{1.00 \cancel{\text{atm}}}{15.00 \cancel{\text{atm}}} = 0.0667$$

The mole fractions of N_2, O_2, and Ar are 0.667, 0.267, and 0.067, respectively.

8. 11.1 liters In this problem, we are given pressure and temperature and the number of moles. We are then asked to calculate V. We can do this by rearranging the ideal gas law:

$$PV = nRT \qquad V = \frac{nRT}{P}$$

We know that R = 0.0821 $\frac{L \times atm}{mole \times K}$, so for the equation to work, our temperature must be converted into 298.0 K. Also, we do not have n yet. We do, however, have mass, so we can convert it into moles:

$$\frac{32.2\ \cancel{g\ Cl_2}}{1} \times \frac{1\ mole\ Cl_2}{71.0\ \cancel{g\ Cl_2}} = 0.454\ moles\ Cl_2$$

Now that we have all of the correct units, we can plug the numbers into the equation.

$$V = \frac{0.454\ \cancel{moles} \times 0.0821 \frac{L \times \cancel{atm}}{\cancel{mole} \times \cancel{K}} \times 298\ \cancel{K}}{1.00\ \cancel{atm}} = \underline{11.1\ L}$$

The volume is 11.1 liters.

9. 0.634 g of silver In this problem, we are given the amount of limiting reactant and asked to determine how much of another reactant is used. The problem here is that the amount of limiting reactant is not given in grams or moles. Instead it is given in P, V, and T. Thus, we must use the ideal gas law to determine the number of moles of limiting reactant. Before we can do that, however, volume must be converted to liters to make it consistent with the volume unit in R.

$$\frac{62.1\ \cancel{mL}}{1} \times \frac{0.001 L}{1\ \cancel{mL}} = 0.0621\ L$$

We also must convert the temperature to 296.2 K. Now we can plug the numbers into the equation:

$$n = \frac{PV}{RT} = \frac{1.15\ \cancel{atm} \times 0.0621\ \cancel{L}}{0.0821 \frac{\cancel{L} \times \cancel{atm}}{mole \times \cancel{K}} \times 296.2\ \cancel{K}} = 0.00294\ moles$$

Now that we have the moles of limiting reactant, this becomes a stoichiometry problem:

$$\frac{0.00294\ \cancel{moles\ H_2S}}{1} \times \frac{4\ moles\ Ag}{2\ \cancel{moles\ H_2S}} = 0.0058\ moles\ Ag$$

$$\frac{0.00588\ \cancel{moles\ Ag}}{1} \times \frac{107.9\ g\ Ag}{1\ \cancel{mole\ Ag}} = \underline{0.634\ g\ Ag}$$

Therefore, 0.634 g of silver will tarnish.

10. $\underline{3.6 \times 10^3\ L}$ In this stoichiometry problem, we are given the amount of limiting reactant and asked to calculate how much product will be made. We start by converting the amount of limiting reactant to moles:

$$\frac{2.89\ \cancel{kg}}{1} \times \frac{1000\ \cancel{g\ H_2O_2}}{1\ \cancel{kg}} \times \frac{1\ \text{mole}\ H_2O_2}{34.0\ \cancel{g\ H_2O_2}} = 85.0\ \text{moles}\ H_2O_2$$

We can then use stoichiometry to determine the number of moles of H_2O produced:

$$\frac{85.0\ \cancel{\text{moles}\ H_2O_2}}{1} \times \frac{8\ \text{moles}\ H_2O}{7\ \cancel{\text{moles}\ H_2O_2}} = 97.1\ \text{moles}\ H_2O$$

Now we need to use the ideal gas law, realizing that we must convert the temperature to Kelvin:

$$PV = nRT$$

$$V = \frac{nRT}{P} = \frac{97.1\ \cancel{\text{moles}} \times 0.0821\ \frac{L \times \cancel{atm}}{\cancel{\text{mole}} \times \cancel{K}} \times 773.2\ \cancel{K}}{1.5\ \cancel{atm}} = \underline{4.1 \times 10^3\ L}$$

The volume produced is $\underline{4.1 \times 10^3\ L}$.

SAMPLE CALCULATIONS FOR EXPERIMENT 11.1

Atmospheric Pressure:

$$\frac{30.12\ \cancel{\text{in Hg}}}{1} \times \frac{2.54\ \cancel{cm}}{1.00\ \cancel{in}} \times \frac{10\ \cancel{mm}}{1\ \cancel{cm}} \times \frac{1.000\ \text{atm}}{760.0\ \cancel{\text{mm Hg}}} = 1.01\ \text{atm}$$

Initial Mass of Butane Lighter: 21.5 g

Water Temperature: 23.1 °C + 273.15 = 296.3 K

Volume of Butane: 200 mL = 0.200 L

Final Mass of Butane Lighter: 21.0 g

Solve for R from PV = nRT:

$$R = \frac{PV}{nT}$$

Calculate the mass of butane used:

Mass of butane = Initial mass of butane lighter – Final mass of butane lighter

Mass of butane = 21.5 g – 21.0 g = 0.5 g butane

Calculate molar mass of butane, C_4H_{10}:

4 C + 10 H = 4 (12.0 g) + 10 (1.01 g) = 48.0 g + 10.1 g = 58.1 g/mol

Calculate moles of butane in cylinder:

$$\frac{0.5 \text{ g } C_4H_{10}}{1} \times \frac{1 \text{ mole}}{58.1 \text{ g}} = 0.009 \text{ moles}$$

Calculate R:

$$R = \frac{PV}{nT} = \frac{(1.01 \text{ atm})(0.200 \text{ L})}{(0.009 \text{ moles})(296.3 \text{ K})} = 0.08 \frac{\text{L} \times \text{atm}}{\text{mole} \times \text{K}}$$

The accepted value of R is $0.0821 \frac{\text{L} \times \text{atm}}{\text{mole} \times \text{K}}$ so this result is slightly off. This should be expected for this lab as it is very hard to get the R value due to lack of precision.

SAMPLE CALCULATIONS FOR EXPERIMENT 11.2

Mass of Vinegar: 2.00×10^2 g
Since your mass scale is most likely marked off in units of 10 g, the most precision you have is to the ones place. Thus, scientific notation is the only way you can report this answer.

Circumference of the balloon: 6.158 dm

Radius of the balloon: $\frac{6.158 \text{ dm}}{2\pi} = \frac{6.158 \text{ dm}}{2 \times (3.1416)} = 0.9801 \text{ dm}$

Volume of the balloon: $\frac{4}{3}\pi r^3 = \frac{4}{3} \times (3.1416) \times (0.9801\text{ dm})^3 = 3.944\text{ dm}^3 = 3.944\text{ L}$

Atmospheric Pressure: 0.945 atm

Temperature: 23.8 °C = 297.0 K

Water Vapor Pressure: 22.4 torr = 0.0295 atm

Pressure of CO_2 Formed: 0.945 atm – 0.0295 atm = 0.916 atm

Now we can get the moles of CO_2 made in the reaction:

$$n = \frac{PV}{RT} = \frac{0.916\ \cancel{\text{atm}} \times 3.944\ \cancel{\text{L}}}{0.0821\ \frac{\cancel{\text{L}} \times \cancel{\text{atm}}}{\text{mole} \times \cancel{\text{K}}} \times 297.0\ \cancel{\text{K}}} = 0.148\text{ moles}$$

Now we can use stoichiometry to determine the number of moles of acetic acid:

$$\frac{0.148\ \cancel{\text{moles } CO_2}}{1} \times \frac{1\text{ mole } C_2H_4O_2}{1\ \cancel{\text{mole } CO_2}} = 0.148\text{ moles } C_2H_4O_2$$

The number of grams of acetic acid used in the experiment, then, is:

$$\frac{0.148\ \cancel{\text{moles } C_2H_4O_2}}{1} \times \frac{60\text{ g } C_2H_4O_2}{1\ \cancel{\text{mole } C_2H_4O_2}} = 8.88\text{ g } C_2H_4O_2$$

Since we used 200.0 g initially, this means that 4.44% of the vinegar was acid.

SOLUTIONS TO THE EXTRA PRACTICE PROBLEMS FOR MODULE 11

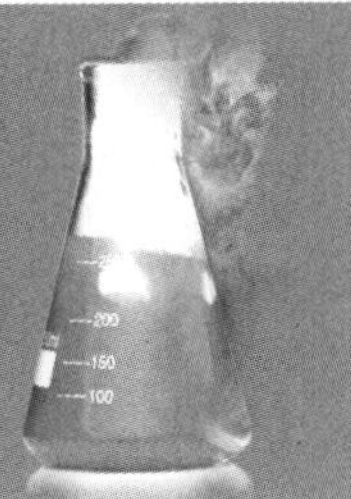

1. This question asks us to predict how a gas will change when we change some of the conditions under which it is stored. This means that we need to use the combined gas law (equation 11.7).

$$\frac{P_1V_1}{T_1} = \frac{P_2V_2}{T_2}$$

According to this question, T_1 = 298.2 K, V_1 = 11.2 L, and T_2 = 77.2 K. Also, the question states that the pressure does not change; thus, P_1 and P_2 cancel out:

$$\frac{\cancel{P_1}V_1}{T_1} = \frac{\cancel{P_2}V_2}{T_2}$$

We can now rearrange the equation to solve for the new volume:

$$\frac{V_1 \times T_2}{T_1} = V_2$$

Now we can put in the numbers and determine the new volume:

$$\frac{11.2\text{ L} \times 77.2\text{ }\cancel{\text{K}}}{298.2\text{ }\cancel{\text{K}}} = \underline{2.90\text{ L}}$$

MOD 11

2. This is obviously another combined gas law question, with P_1 = 755 mmHg, V_1 = 13.3 L, T_1 = 298.2 K, P_2 = 625 mm Hg, and T_2 = 288.2 K. The question asks us to determine the new volume, so we have to rearrange equation 11.7 to solve for V_2:

$$\frac{P_1V_1T_2}{T_1P_2} = V_2$$

Now we can plug in the numbers:

$$V_2 = \frac{755\text{ }\cancel{\text{mmHg}} \times 13.3\text{ L} \times 288.2\text{ }\cancel{\text{K}}}{298.2\text{ }\cancel{\text{K}} \times 625\text{ }\cancel{\text{mmHg}}} = \underline{15.5\text{ L}}$$

3. This is obviously another combined gas law question, with P_1 = 370 torr, V_1 = 56.7 mL, T_1 = 298 K, P_2 = 1.00 atm (standard pressure), and T_2 = 273 K (standard temperature). The question asks us to determine the new volume, so we have to rearrange equation 11.7 to solve for V_2:

$$\frac{P_1V_1T_2}{T_1P_2} = V_2$$

We need to make the pressure units the same. We can do this by converting torr into atm or vice versa. We will choose to do the latter:

$$P_2 = \frac{1.00\ \cancel{\text{atm}}}{1} \times \frac{760\ \text{torr}}{1\ \cancel{\text{atm}}} = 7.60 \times 10^2\ \text{torr}$$

Now we can plug in the numbers:

$$V_2 = \frac{370\ \cancel{\text{torr}} \times 56.7\ \text{mL} \times 273\ \cancel{\text{K}}}{298\ \cancel{\text{K}} \times 7.60 \times 10^2\ \cancel{\text{torr}}} = \underline{25\ \text{mL}}$$

4. The total pressure is just the sum of the partial pressures. Thus, if the total pressure is 2.0 atm, the partial pressure of oxygen is:

$$2.0\ \text{atm} - 1.4\ \text{atm} = \underline{0.6\ \text{atm}}$$

5. To determine partial pressure from total pressure, we need to know the mole fractions involved:

$$\frac{2.00\ \cancel{\text{g}\ H_2}}{1} \times \frac{1\ \text{mole}\ H_2}{2.02\ \cancel{\text{g}\ H_2}} = 0.990\ \text{moles}\ H_2$$

$$\frac{40.0\ \cancel{\text{g}\ CO_2}}{1} \times \frac{1\ \text{mole}\ CO_2}{44.0\ \cancel{\text{g}\ CO_2}} = 0.909\ \text{moles}\ CO_2$$

$$\frac{14.5\ \cancel{\text{g}\ N_2}}{1} \times \frac{1\ \text{mole}\ N_2}{28.0\ \cancel{\text{g}\ N_2}} = 0.518\ \text{moles}\ N_2$$

Now that we have the number of moles of each component, we can calculate the total number of moles in the mixture:

$$\text{Total number of moles} = 0.990\ \text{moles} + 0.909\ \text{moles} + 0.518\ \text{moles} = 2.417\ \text{moles}$$

Plugging that into equation 11.10:

$$X_{H_2} = \frac{0.990 \cancel{\text{moles}}}{2.417 \cancel{\text{moles}}} = 0.410$$

$$X_{CO_2} = \frac{0.909 \cancel{\text{moles}}}{2.417 \cancel{\text{moles}}} = 0.376$$

$$X_{N_2} = \frac{0.518 \cancel{\text{moles}}}{2.417 \cancel{\text{moles}}} = 0.214$$

Using the mole fractions we just obtained:

$$P_{H_2} = 0.410 \times 15.0 \text{ atm} = \underline{6.15 \text{ atm}}$$

$$P_{CO_2} = 0.376 \times 15.0 \text{ atm} = \underline{5.64 \text{ atm}}$$

$$P_{N_2} = 0.214 \times 15.0 \text{ atm} = \underline{3.21 \text{ atm}}$$

6. In this question, we are given pressure and temperature and the mass (from which we can get moles). We are then asked to calculate V. We can do this by rearranging the ideal gas law:

$$PV = nRT \qquad V = \frac{nRT}{P}$$

Now we just need to get n:

$$\frac{24.2 \cancel{\text{g } N_2}}{1} \times \frac{1 \text{ mole } N_2}{28.0 \cancel{\text{g } N_2}} = 0.864 \text{ moles } N_2$$

Now we can use the equation, remembering to convert temperature to K:

$$V = \frac{0.864 \cancel{\text{moles}} \times 0.0821 \frac{\text{L} \times \cancel{\text{atm}}}{\cancel{\text{mole}} \times \cancel{\text{K}}} \times 273 \cancel{\text{K}}}{1.00 \cancel{\text{atm}}} = \underline{19.4 \text{ L}}$$

7. In this question, we are given temperature and volume and the mass (from which we can get moles). We are then asked to calculate P. We can do this by rearranging the ideal gas law:

MOD 11

$$P = \frac{nRT}{V}$$ $$V = \frac{nRT}{P}$$

Now we just need to get n:

$$\frac{15.0\ \cancel{g\ N_2}}{1} \times \frac{1\ \text{mole}\ N_2}{28.0\ \cancel{g\ N_2}} = 0.536\ \text{moles}\ N_2$$

Now we can use the equation, remembering to convert temperature to K:

$$P = \frac{0.536\ \cancel{\text{moles}} \times 0.0821 \frac{\cancel{L} \times \text{atm}}{\cancel{\text{mole}} \times \cancel{K}} \times 294.2\ \cancel{K}}{1.00\ \cancel{L}} = \underline{12.9\ \text{atm}}$$

8. In this stoichiometry question, we are given the amount of limiting reactant and asked to calculate how much product will be made. We start by converting the amount of limiting reactant to moles:

$$\frac{11.0\ \cancel{g\ CS_2}}{1} \times \frac{1\ \text{mole}\ CS_2}{76.2\ \cancel{g\ CS_2}} = 0.144\ \text{moles}\ CS_2$$

We can then use stoichiometry to determine the number of moles of SO_2 produced:

$$\frac{0.144\ \cancel{\text{moles}\ CS_2}}{1} \times \frac{2\ \text{moles}\ SO_2}{1\ \cancel{\text{mole}\ CS_2}} = 0.288\ \text{moles}\ SO_2$$

Now we need to use the ideal gas law, realizing that we must convert the temperature to Kelvin:

$$PV = nRT$$

$$V = \frac{nRT}{P} = \frac{0.288\ \cancel{\text{moles}} \times 0.0821 \frac{L \times \cancel{\text{atm}}}{\cancel{\text{mole}} \times \cancel{K}} \times 614\ \cancel{K}}{2.1\ \cancel{\text{atm}}} = \underline{5.5\ L}$$

9. We start by converting the amount of limiting reactant to moles:

$$\frac{1000.0\ \cancel{g\ TiO_2}}{1} \times \frac{1\ \text{mole}\ TiO_2}{79.9\ \cancel{g\ TiO_2}} = 12.5\ \text{moles}\ TiO_2$$

We can then use stoichiometry to determine the number of moles of Cl_2 used:

$$\frac{12.5\ \cancel{\text{moles } TiO_2}}{1} \times \frac{6\ \text{moles } Cl_2}{3\ \cancel{\text{moles } TiO_2}} = 25.0\ \text{moles } Cl_2$$

Now we need to use the ideal gas law, realizing that we must convert the temperature to Kelvin:

$$PV = nRT$$

$$V = \frac{nRT}{P} = \frac{25.0\ \cancel{\text{moles}} \times 0.0821 \frac{L \times \cancel{atm}}{\cancel{mole} \times \cancel{K}} \times 273\ \cancel{K}}{1.00\ \cancel{atm}} = \underline{5.60 \times 10^2\ L}$$

10. We start by converting the amount of limiting reactant to moles:

$$\frac{25.0\ \cancel{g\ H_2SO_4}}{1} \times \frac{1\ \text{mole } H_2SO_4}{98.1\ \cancel{g\ H_2SO_4}} = 0.255\ \text{moles } H_2SO_4$$

We can then use stoichiometry to determine the number of moles of HCl produced:

$$\frac{0.255\ \cancel{\text{moles } H_2SO_4}}{1} \times \frac{1\ \text{mole HCl}}{1\ \cancel{\text{mole } H_2SO_4}} = 0.255\ \text{moles HCl}$$

Finishing:

$$PV = nRT$$

$$V = \frac{nRT}{P} = \frac{0.255\ \cancel{\text{moles}} \times 0.0821 \frac{L \times \cancel{atm}}{\cancel{mole} \times \cancel{K}} \times 623.2\ \cancel{K}}{1.00\ \cancel{atm}} = \underline{13.0\ L}$$

TEST FOR MODULE 11

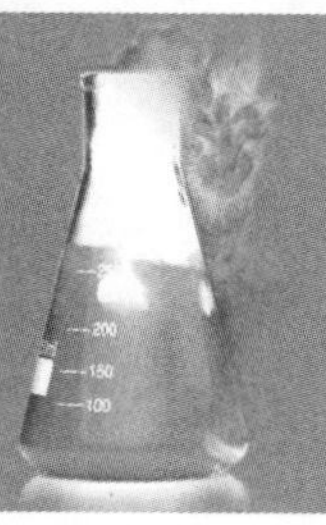

1. (4 pts) The force per unit of area is defined as
   a. Newton
   b. Volume
   c. Boyle's law
   d. Pressure
   e. None of the above

2. (4 pts) Which of the following relationships is true?
   a. 1 atm = 101.3 kPa
   b. 1 atm = 760 torr
   c. 1 atm = 760 mm Hg
   d. All of the above
   e. None of the above

3. (4 pts) Which of the following describes Boyle's law?
   a. $P \times V = \text{constant}$
   b. As long as temperature is constant, when pressure increases, volume decreases.
   c. As long as temperature is constant, when pressure decreases, volume increases.
   d. All of the above
   e. None of the above

4. (4 pts) Which of the following describes Charles's law?
   a. As long as pressure is constant, temperature and volume are linearly proportional to each other.
   b. As long as pressure is constant, when temperature increases, volume will decrease.
   c. All of the above
   d. None of the above

5. (4 pts) What does – 273.15 °C represent?
   a. 0 K
   b. Absolute zero
   c. The temperature at which a gas has zero volume
   d. The temperature at which all atoms stop moving
   e. All of the above

6. (4 pts) Following an established trend in the data even though no data are available for that region is called:
   a. Theorizing
   b. Extrapolation
   c. Estimating
   d. Hypothesizing
   e. None of the above

7. (4 pts) Which of the following are properties of an ideal gas?
   a. The molecules that make up the gas take up most of the volume.
   b. The molecules are fairly close to one another.
   c. The molecules are always losing energy with one another when they collide.
   d. All of the above
   e. None of the above

8. (4 pts) Which of the following conditions is the closest to STP?
   a. 273 K and 273 atm
   b. 1.00 K and 1.00 atm
   c. 1.00 K and 273 atm
   d. 273 K and 1.00 atm
   e. None of the above

9. (4 pts) Which of the following statements is true about vapor pressure?
   a. The vapor pressure for any liquid increases as the temperature increases.
   b. The vapor pressure of water is always constant.
   c. Vapor pressure is the pressure exerted by a gas on its container.
   d. Vapor pressure only occurs when the liquid is boiling.
   e. None of the above

10. (4 pts) What is the temperature at which the vapor pressure of a liquid is equal to normal atmospheric pressure?
    a. Standard temperature
    b. Standard pressure
    c. Melting point
    d. Boiling point
    e. None of the above

11. (4 pts) Which of the following is equal to the ideal gas constant?
    a. R = 0.0821 l atm/mole °C
    b. R = 0.0821 cm^3 atm/mole K
    c. R = 0.0821 l kPa /mole K
    d. R = 0.0821 l atm/mole K
    e. None of the above

For the following problems, please provide a correct answer and show the needed work to solve the problem.

12. (4 pts) A hot air balloon is filled with 1.89×10^2 liters of air at 21 °C. If atmospheric pressure does not change, how hot must the air become in order to increase the volume to 4.5×10^2 liters?

13. (4 pts) A weather balloon is filled with 34.6 liters of helium at 24 °C and 1.02 atm. As the weather balloon rises, the surrounding temperature decreases, as does the pressure. When the balloon reaches an altitude where the temperature is 11 °C and the pressure is 0.21 atm, what will the volume of the balloon be?

14. (4 pts) The vapor pressure of water is 30.0 torr at 29 °C. If a reaction at that temperature produces oxygen which is collected over water, what total pressure will have to be in the reaction vessel to ensure that the oxygen collected had a partial pressure of 567 torr?

15. (8 pts) The gas mixture for an acetylene torch should be about 12.0 grams of oxygen for every 100.0 grams of acetylene (C_2H_2). What is the mole fraction of each component in such a mixture?

16. (4 pts) What is the mole fraction of each component of a gas mixture that contains sulfur trioxide at a pressure of 1.45 atm and sulfur dioxide at a pressure of 0.32 atm?

17. (8 pts) If 345.1 grams of CO_2 are placed in a vessel whose volume is 32.1 liters at a temperature of 20.0 °C, what will the pressure be?

18. (12 pts) Iron rusts according to the following reaction:
    $4Fe\ (s) + 3O_2\ (g) + 4H_2O\ (l) \rightarrow 2Fe_2O_3(H_2O)_2$

    If 1.4 liters of oxygen were added to excess water and iron at a pressure of 0.97 atm and a temperature of 55 °C, how many grams of iron would rust?

19. (12 pts) The bright light that comes from a flash bulb is due to a quick combustion of magnesium, according to the following chemical equation:
    $2Mg\ (s) + O_2(g) \rightarrow 2MgO\ (s)$

    If a flashbulb contains 1.3 g of Mg, what is the minimum pressure of O_2 needed to burn up that magnesium? Assume the flashbulb has a volume of 10.0 mL and a temperature of 25 °C.

SOLUTIONS TO THE TEST FOR MODULE 11

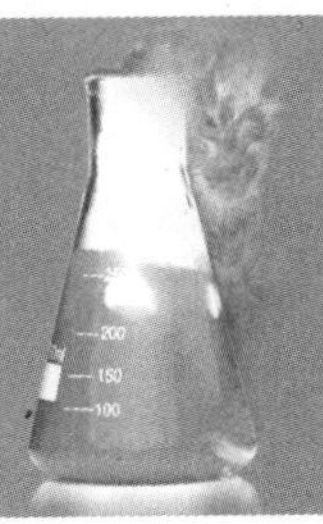

1. (4 pts) d. Pressure

2. (4 pts) d. All of the above

3. (4 pts) d. All of the above

4. (4 pts) a. As long as pressure is constant, temperature and volume are linearly proportional to each other.

5. (4 pts) e. All of the above

6. (4 pts) b. Extrapolation

7. (4 pts) e. None of the above

8. (4 pts) d. 273 K and 1.00 atm

9. (4 pts) a. The vapor pressure for any liquid increases as the temperature increases.

10. (4 pts) d. Boiling point

11. (4 pts) d. R = 0.0821 l atm/mole K

12. (4 pts) 7.0×10^2 K

$$\frac{P_1V_1}{T_1} = \frac{P_2V_2}{T_2}$$

$$\frac{(189\text{ L})}{294\text{ K}} = \frac{(4.5 \times 10^2\text{ L})}{T_2}$$

$$T_2 = \frac{(4.5 \times 10^2\text{ }\cancel{\text{L}}) \times 294\text{ K}}{189\text{ }\cancel{\text{L}}} = \underline{7.0 \times 10^2\text{ K}}\text{ or }430\text{ °C}$$

13. (4 pts) $\underline{1.6 \times 10^2\text{ L}}$

$$\frac{P_1V_1}{T_1} = \frac{P_2V_2}{T_2}$$

$$\frac{(1.02\text{ atm}) \times (34.6\text{ L})}{297\text{ K}} = \frac{(0.21\text{ atm}) \times V_2}{284\text{ K}}$$

$$V_2 = \frac{(1.02\text{ }\cancel{\text{atm}}) \times (34.6\text{ L}) \times 284\text{ }\cancel{\text{K}}}{(0.21\text{ }\cancel{\text{atm}}) \times 297\text{ }\cancel{\text{K}}} = \underline{1.6 \times 10^2\text{ L}}$$

14. (4 pts) $P_{total} = P_{oxygen} + P_{vapor} = 567\text{ torr} + 30.0\text{ torr} = \underline{597\text{ torr}}$

15. (8 pts: 4 pts for getting everthing into moles, and 4 pts for the answers) 0.0887, 0.910 To calculate mole fractions, we must get everything into moles:

$$\frac{12.0\text{ }\cancel{\text{g } O_2}}{1} \times \frac{1\text{ mole } O_2}{32.0\text{ }\cancel{\text{g } O_2}} = 0.375\text{ moles } O_2$$

$$\frac{100.0\text{ }\cancel{\text{g } C_2H_2}}{1} \times \frac{1\text{ mole } C_2H_2}{26.0\text{ }\cancel{\text{g } C_2H_2}} = 3.85\text{ moles } C_2H_2$$

Now we can use the definition of mole fraction.

$$X_{O_2} = \frac{0.375\text{ }\cancel{\text{moles}}}{4.23\text{ }\cancel{\text{moles}}} = \underline{0.0887}$$

$$X_{C_2H_2} = \frac{3.85\text{ }\cancel{\text{moles}}}{4.23\text{ }\cancel{\text{moles}}} = \underline{0.910}$$

16. (4 pts: 2 pts for each answer) 0.18, 0.819

Rather than use the definition of mole fraction here, it is best to use Dalton's law.

$$X_{SO_2} = \frac{0.32 \cancel{atm}}{1.77 \cancel{atm}} = \underline{0.18}$$

$$X_{SO_3} = \frac{1.45 \cancel{atm}}{1.77 \cancel{atm}} = \underline{0.819}$$

17. (8 pts: 4 pts for converting to moles, 4 pts for the answer) 5.88 atm
This uses the ideal gas law, but first we need to convert grams to moles:

$$\frac{345.1 \cancel{g\ CO_2}}{1} \times \frac{1 \text{ mole } CO_2}{44.0 \cancel{g\ CO_2}} = 7.84 \text{ moles } CO_2$$

Now we can use the ideal gas law:

$$PV = nRT$$

$$P = \frac{nRT}{V} = \frac{7.84 \cancel{moles} \times 0.0821 \frac{\cancel{L} \times atm}{\cancel{mole} \times \cancel{K}} \times 293.2 \cancel{K}}{32.1 \cancel{L}} = \underline{5.88 \text{ atm}}$$

18. (12 pts: 4 pts for each step) 3.7 g Fe
This is a stoichiometry problem, once we use the ideal gas law to calculate the moles of oxygen:

$$n = \frac{PV}{RT} = \frac{0.97 \cancel{atm} \times 1.4 \cancel{L}}{0.0821 \frac{\cancel{L} \times \cancel{atm}}{mole \times \cancel{K}} \times 328 \cancel{K}} = 0.050 \text{ moles}$$

Now that we have the moles of limiting reactant, this is a stoichiometry problem.

$$\frac{0.050 \cancel{moles\ O_2}}{1} \times \frac{4 \text{ moles Fe}}{3 \cancel{moles\ O_2}} = 0.067 \text{ moles Fe}$$

$$\frac{0.067 \cancel{moles\ Fe}}{1} \times \frac{55.8 \text{ g Fe}}{1 \cancel{mole\ Fe}} = \underline{3.7 \text{ g Fe}}$$

19. (12 pts: 4 pts for each step) 66 atm
This is like question 18, but we need to do it backwards. We start with stoichiometry

MOD 11

and end with the ideal gas law:

$$\frac{1.3\ \cancel{\text{g Mg}}}{1} \times \frac{1\ \text{mole Mg}}{24.3\ \cancel{\text{g Mg}}} = 0.053\ \text{moles Mg}$$

$$\frac{0.053\ \cancel{\text{moles Mg}}}{1} \times \frac{1\ \text{mole } O_2}{2\ \cancel{\text{moles Mg}}} = 0.027\ \text{moles } O_2$$

Now we use the ideal gas law to calculate pressure.

$$PV = nRT$$

$$P = \frac{nRT}{V} = \frac{0.027\ \cancel{\text{moles}} \times 0.0821 \frac{\cancel{\text{L}} \times \text{atm}}{\cancel{\text{mole}} \times \cancel{\text{K}}} \times 298\ \cancel{\text{K}}}{0.0100\ \cancel{\text{L}}} = \underline{66\ \text{atm}}$$

ENERGY, HEAT AND TEMPERATURE

SOLUTIONS TO THE MODULE 12 REVIEW QUESTIONS

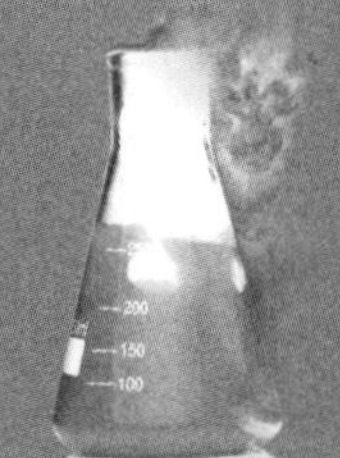

1. For the first 1.5 minutes, the man did no work. Motion is required in order to do work. Since the car did not move during that time, no work was done. For the last 0.5 minutes, however, the man did do work.

2. a. A gold bar has potential energy in it because all matter has stored energy.

   b. Sunlight has no matter. Therefore, it cannot have potential energy. However, light is in motion, so it has kinetic energy.

   c. An apple is matter and therefore it will have potential energy.

   d. A hurricane is a swirling mass of air. Since air is matter, it has potential energy, but because the air is moving, it also has kinetic energy. Therefore, it has both.

3. If a substance's temperature increases, we can conclude that it is gaining energy.

4. Since the object cannot interact with anything else, it will never be able to give away any of its energy or absorb energy from anything. Its temperature can never change.

5. Experimental scatter is made of data points that are a little above or below the accepted value.

6. Since it takes 4.184 Joules to make 1 calorie, the Joule is a smaller energy unit. The object that absorbs 50.0 cal is absorbing more energy and will therefore be the hottest.

7. Our bodies have an internal temperature of about 37 °C. Ice water has a temperature of 0.0 °C. Your body must therefore warm up the water. That takes energy, which our bodies get from the food that we eat. Thus, drinking ice-cold water is a way of burning off excess Calories.

8. 55 °C
In experiment 12.1, we learned that the heating curve for water has 2 flat regions. The first occurs when ice melts, and the second ocurs when water boils. Based on this fact, the unknown liquid must melt at 5 °C and boil at 55 °C. Your answer can be slightly different from this one because you are reading it from a graph.

9. 450 °C
Since the aluminum has a larger specific heat, it is harder to heat up. Thus, the iron will come out hottest. Since iron's specific heat is 2 times smaller than aluminum, we can conclude that it will come out 2 times hotter. Thus, if the iron increased in temperature by 900 °C, the aluminum would increase in temperature by only half or 450 °C.

10. A calorimeter should be made out of insulating material because energy should never be allowed to escape from it. If energy does escape from a calorimeter, the measurement for which we are using the calorimeter will be in error.

SOLUTIONS TO THE PRACTICE PROBLEMS FOR MODULE 12

1. $\underline{1.046 \times 10^7 \text{ Joules}}$ One food Calorie = 1,000 calories. We must use this fact first because the only relationship we know that contains Joules is the one that relates Joules to chemistry calories. So we first have to convert food calories to chemistry calories:

$$\frac{2{,}500.0 \cancel{\text{Cal}}}{1} \times \frac{1000 \text{ cal}}{1 \cancel{\text{Cal}}} = 2.5000 \times 10^6 \text{ cal}$$

Since the conversion relationship is exact, the answer must have the same number of significant figures as the original measurement. Thus, the answer must have 5 significant figures. Now we can convert calories to Joules with the relationship 1 cal = 4.184 J:

$$\frac{2.500.0 \times 10^6 \cancel{\text{cal}}}{1} \times \frac{4.184 \text{ J}}{1 \cancel{\text{cal}}} = 1.046 \times 10^7 \text{ J}$$

So the average person burns $\underline{1.046 \times 10^7 \text{ Joules}}$ of energy per day! Remember, this conversion relationship is not exact. The integers, of course, are still exact, but as we mentioned in the module, the 4.184 is not exact. Since it contains only 4 significant figures, the answer can have only 4 significant figures.

2. $\underline{3.8 \times 10^5 \text{ J}}$ According to table 12.1, glass has a specific heat of $0.8372 \ \frac{\text{J}}{\text{g°C}}$. Since we have specific heat, mass, initial temperature, and final temperature, we are obviously supposed to use equation 12.1. Before we can do that, though, we have to get our mass in grams so that its units agree with the specific heat units:

$$\frac{15.1 \cancel{\text{kg}}}{1} \times \frac{1{,}000 \text{ g}}{1 \cancel{\text{kg}}} = 1.51 \times 10^4 \text{ g}$$

Now we can use equation 12.1:

$$q = m \times c \times \Delta T$$

$$q = (1.51 \times 10^4 \text{ g}) \times \left(0.8372 \ \frac{\text{J}}{\text{g°C}}\right) \times (45 \text{ °C} - 15 \text{ °C})$$

$$q = (1.51 \times 10^4 \text{ g}) \times \left(0.8372 \ \frac{\text{J}}{\cancel{\text{g°C}}}\right) \times (3.0 \times 10^1 \cancel{\text{°C}}) = \underline{3.8 \times 10^5 \text{ J}}$$

MOD 12

Now look at the significant figures in this problem. First, we subtracted 15 from 45. For that, we had to use the rule of addition and subtraction. Since both 45 and 15 have their last significant figure in the ones place, the answer must have its last significant figure in the ones place. Thus, the only way we could report that answer to indicate that the resulting zero in the ones place is significant is to use scientific notation. That's why the change in temperature is reported at 3.0×10^1 °C. After that, the equation uses only multiplication, so at that point, we must count significant figures. The lowest number of significant figures in the equation is 2 (3.0×10^1 °C), so the answer can have only 2.

3. <u>$11.1 \frac{J}{g°C}$</u> In this problem, we are given ΔT, mass, and the heat absorbed, and we must calculate specific heat. So, first we rearrange equation 12.1 to solve for specific heat, and then we plug our numbers in:

$$c = \frac{q}{m \times \Delta T}$$

$$c = \frac{50.0 \text{ kJ}}{(124.1 \text{ g})(36.3 \text{ °C})} = 0.0111 \frac{\text{kJ}}{\text{g°C}}$$

You might wonder why we didn't convert kJ into J. In this problem, we were given no restrictions on units. We didn't need any units to cancel out, and the problem didn't specify what units to give specific heat in; thus, we didn't need to convert the energy unit. This unit is a perfectly acceptable unit for specific heat. If you did convert from kJ to J, your answer should be $11.1 \frac{J}{g°C}$.

4. <u>2.1×10^1 °C</u> In order to get the copper's new temperature, we need to solve for ΔT in equation 12.1. We can do this because we have the mass and heat given in the problem and the specific heat from table 12.1. Remember, though, since the copper lost heat, its q is negative! So first we rearrange the equation to solve for ΔT:

$$\Delta T = \frac{q}{m \times c}$$

$$\Delta T = \frac{-456.7 \cancel{\text{J}}}{(245 \text{ g}) \times \left(0.3851 \frac{\cancel{\text{J}}}{\text{g°C}}\right)} = -4.84 \text{ °C}$$

Now that we have ΔT, we can rearrange equation 12.2 to solve for final temperature:

$$T_{final} = \Delta T + T_{initial}$$

$$T_{final} = -4.84\ °C + 25\ °C = \underline{2.0 \times 10^1\ °C}$$

Note that the final temperature is lower than the initial temperature, which should make sense since the copper lost energy. Also, notice that according to the rule of addition and subtraction, we must report our answer to the ones place. That means the resulting zero in the ones place is significant. The only way we can report this answer properly, then, is with scientific notation.

5. 12.6 Calories You are supposed to have the specific heat of water memorized. Thus, you have all the information needed to calculate the heat required to raise water from 0.0 °C to 37.0 °C:

$$q = m \times c \times \Delta T$$

$$q = (3.40 \times 10^2\ g) \times \left(1.000\ \frac{cal}{g°C}\right) \times (37.0\ °C - 0.0\ °C)$$

$$q = (3.40 \times 10^2\ \cancel{g}) \times \left(1.000\ \frac{cal}{\cancel{g°C}}\right) \times (37.0\ \cancel{°C}) = 1.26 \times 10^4\ cal$$

After subtracting 0.0 from 37.0, we are left with a ΔT of 37.0 °C. Since both 37.0 and 3.40×10^2 each contain 3 significant figures, the answer can have only 3. That's a lot of calories, but the problem asks for the answer in Calories (with a capital "C"), which means food calories. It takes 1,000 cal to make 1 Cal:

$$\frac{1.26 \times 10^4\ \cancel{cal}}{1} \times \frac{1\ Cal}{1{,}000\ \cancel{cal}} = 12.6\ Cal$$

Drinking a 12–ounce glass of ice–cold water burns 12.6 Calories when you drink it.

6. 490 g Take a look at the information given in this problem. The only substance mentioned is silver, so all of the measurements given are for silver. Since the problem asks for the mass, we must find an equation with mass in it. We should use equation 12.1 for this, but we must first convert the kJ into J.

$$\frac{1.00\ \cancel{kJ}}{1} \times \frac{1{,}000\ J}{1\ \cancel{kJ}} = 1.00 \times 10^3\ J$$

The ΔT is the difference between 41.8 °C and 33.0 °C which is 8.8 °C. Solving for mass in equation 12.1 gives:

$$m = \frac{q}{c\,\Delta T}$$

$$m = \frac{1.00 \times 10^3 \text{ J}}{(0.233 \frac{\text{J}}{\text{g°C}})(8.8\ °\text{C})}$$

$$m = \underline{490 \text{ g}}$$

The mass of silver is 490 g.

7. $0.96 \frac{\text{J}}{\text{g°C}}$ To solve this, we must use the calorimetry equation. To use that equation, however, we need to calculate as many q's as we can. We know that $q_{calorimeter} = 0$ since the problem says that we can ignore the calorimeter. We also have enough information to calculate the heat absorbed by the water:

$$q_{water} = m \times c \times \Delta T$$

$$q_{water} = (150.0 \text{ g}) \times \left(4.184 \frac{\text{J}}{\text{g°C}}\right) \times (5.4\ °\text{C})$$

$$q_{water} = (3.4 \times 10^3 \text{ J})$$

Now that we know q_{water} and $q_{calorimeter}$, we can use the calorimetry equation to determine the heat lost by the metal:

$$-q_{object} = q_{water} + q_{calorimeter}$$

$$-q_{object} = 3.4 \times 10^3 \text{ J}$$

We can use this information in equation 12.1 to determine the specific heat of the metal. However, we have to determine the ΔT of the metal. The metal starts at 100.0 °C and ends at the same temperature as the water and calorimeter. Well, if the water started out at 24.1 °C, and its temperature raised 5.4 °C, that tells us that the final temperature of the water (which is the same as the final temperature of the metal) must be 29.5 °C.

$$c = \frac{q}{m \times \Delta T} = \frac{-3.4 \times 10^3 \text{ J}}{(50.0 \text{ g})(29.5\ °\text{C} - 100\ °\text{C})} = \underline{0.96 \frac{\text{J}}{\text{g°C}}}$$

8. $c_{object} = 0.96 \frac{\text{J}}{\text{g°C}}$ In problem 7, we set $q_{calorimeter}$ to 0. Now we need to find out how much energy the calorimeter absorbs:

$$q_{calorimeter} = m \times c \times \Delta T$$

$$q_{calorimeter} = (2.0\ \cancel{g}) \times \left(3.5\ \frac{J}{\cancel{g°C}}\right) \times (5.4\ \cancel{°C})$$

$$q_{calorimeter} = 38\ J$$

Now we will plug this 38 J into the calorimeter equation:

$$-q_{object} = q_{water} + q_{calorimeter}$$

$$-q_{object} = 3.4 \times 10^3\ J + 38\ J$$

$$q_{object} = 3.4 \times 10^3\ J$$

So the 38 J does not change the heat absorbed by the object because the heat absorbed by the water was measured to the hundreds place. Since q_{object} does not change then the final answer will not change. $c_{object} = \underline{0.96\ \frac{J}{g°C}}$

9. $\underline{7.6\ \frac{J}{g°C}}$ We are trying to discover the specific heat of the liquid. To find this, we will need the heat absorbed, the mass, and the change in temperature of the liquid. We need to figure out the q_{copper} and $q_{calorimeter}$ as the problem does not give the q_{liquid}. We have enough information to determine the q's of the copper and the calorimeter, so we should start there:

$$q_{copper} = m \times c \times \Delta T$$

$$q_{copper} = (150.0\ g) \times \left(0.3851\ \frac{J}{g°C}\right) \times (31.2\ °C - 200.0°C)$$

$$q_{copper} = (150.0\ \cancel{g}) \times \left(0.3851\ \frac{J}{\cancel{g°C}}\right) \times (-168.8\ \cancel{°C}) = -9{,}751\ J$$

$$q_{calorimeter} = m \times c \times \Delta T$$

$$q_{calorimeter} = (5.0\ g) \times \left(50.00\ \frac{J}{g°C}\right) \times (31.2\ °C - 25.0°C)$$

$$q_{calorimeter} = (5.0\ \cancel{g}) \times \left(50.00\ \frac{J}{\cancel{g°C}}\right) \times (6.2\ \cancel{°C}) = 1600\ J$$

We can now use the calorimetry equation:

$$-q_{object} = q_{liquid} + q_{calorimeter}$$

$$-(-9{,}751\text{ J}) = q_{liquid} + 1{,}600\text{ J}$$

$$q_{liquid} = 8{,}200\text{ J}$$

Look at the significant figures. To get the answer, we subtract 1,600 from 9,750. Since the least precise number (600) has its only significant figure in the hundreds place, the answer must be given to the hundreds place. We can now use the heat of the liquid in equation 12.1 to determine the specific heat of the liquid:

$$c = \frac{q}{m \times \Delta T} = \frac{8200\text{ J}}{(175.0\text{ g})(6.2\text{ °C})} = \underline{7.6\ \frac{\text{J}}{\text{g°C}}}$$

10. $\underline{2{,}000\ \frac{\text{J}}{\text{g°C}}}$ In this problem, we're trying to discover the specific heat of the calorimeter, not the specific heat of the metal, as is usually the case. Instead, the specific heat of the metal can be found in table 12.1 ($c = 0.3851\ \frac{\text{J}}{\text{g°C}}$). To find the calorimeter's specific heat, we will need to use the calorimetry equation. Thus, we need to figure out as many q's as we can. We have enough information to determine the q's of the metal and the water, so we should start there:

$$q_{metal} = m \times c \times \Delta T$$

$$q_{metal} = (345.1\text{ g}) \times \left(0.3851\ \frac{\text{J}}{\text{g°C}}\right) \times (25.1\text{ °C} - 100.0\text{°C})$$

$$q_{metal} = (345.1\text{ g}) \times \left(0.3851\ \frac{\text{J}}{\text{g°C}}\right) \times (-74.9\text{ °C}) = -9{,}950\text{ J}$$

$$q_{water} = m \times c \times \Delta T$$

$$q_{water} = (150.0\text{ g}) \times \left(4.184\ \frac{\text{J}}{\text{g°C}}\right) \times (25.1\text{ °C} - 24.2\text{ °C})$$

$$q_{water} = (150.0\text{ g}) \times \left(4.184\ \frac{\text{J}}{\text{g°C}}\right) \times (0.9\text{ °C}) = 600\text{ J}$$

Notice what happened with the significant figures when we calculated q_{water}. In determining ΔT, we can report our answer only to the tenths place since both temperature measurements have their last significant figure in the tenths place. This leaves us with only 1 significant figure for ΔT. Thus, when we multiply by ΔT, the answer can have only 1 significant figure and therefore must be rounded up to 600 J. We can now use the calorimetry equation:

$$-q_{object} = q_{water} + q_{calorimeter}$$

$$-(-9950 \text{ J}) = 600 \text{ J} + q_{calorimeter}$$

$$q_{calorimeter} = 9,400$$

Once again, look at the significant figures. To get the answer, we subtract 600 from 9950. Since the least precise number (600) has its only significant figure in the hundreds place, the answer must be given to the hundreds place. We can now use the heat of the calorimeter to determine the specific heat of the calorimeter:

$$c = \frac{q}{m \times \Delta T} = \frac{9400 \text{ J}}{(4.5 \text{ g})(0.9 \text{ °C})} = \underline{2,000 \frac{\text{J}}{\text{g°C}}}$$

Once again, consider the significant figures. As discussed above, the value for ΔT can be reported only to the tenths place. This leaves only 1 significant figure, so the answer must be rounded down to 2,000 J/g°C.

SAMPLE CALCULATIONS FOR EXPERIMENT 12.2

Mass of the metal: 53 g

Mass of the calorimeter: 5 g

Mass of the calorimeter + water: 79 g

Mass of the water: 79 g – 5 g = 74 g
We can report the mass to the ones place, since this is subtraction and both measurements used in the subtraction are reported to the ones place.

Initial temperature: 24.8 °C
Most likely, your thermometer is marked off in individual degrees (or in units of 2 degrees). You are supposed to estimate to the next decimal place, so you should report your temperatures to the tenths place.

Final temperature: 27.4 °C

$$\Delta T = 27.4\text{ °C} - 24.8\text{ °C} = 2.6\text{ °C}$$

Since both temperatures are reported to the tenths place, the difference must be reported to the tenths place.

$$q_{water} = m \times c \times \Delta T$$

$$q_{water} = (74\text{ g}) \times \left(4.184 \frac{\text{J}}{\text{g°C}}\right) \times (2.6\text{ °C}) = 810\text{ J}$$

Since 74 and 2.6 have only 2 significant figures, the result of this multiplication can have only 2 significant figures. Since we are ignoring the calorimeter, we can easily calculate the heat lost by the metal:

$$-q_{object} = q_{water} + q_{calorimeter}$$

$$q_{object} = -810\text{ J}$$

Now we can determine the specific heat:

$$c = \frac{q}{m \times \Delta T} = \frac{-810\text{ J}}{(53\text{ g})(27.4\text{ °C} - 100.0\text{ °C})} = \underline{-0.21 \frac{\text{J}}{\text{g°C}}}$$

There can be only 2 significant figures in the specific heat because the mass and heat have only 2.

SOLUTIONS TO THE EXTRA PRACTICE PROBLEMS FOR MODULE 12

1. Glass has a lower specific heat than water. This means that glass is easier to heat up because it takes less energy to raise its temperature by 1 °C.

2. Since both pieces are the same mass and on the same burner for the same amount of time, they are each getting the same amount of heat. Therefore, the piece made out of the substance which is more difficult to heat up will be the coolest one. Since aluminum has a larger specific heat, it is more difficult to heat up, so it will be cooler than the silver. That means the aluminum temperature will be lower than 50.0 °C.

3. To solve this question, we must rearrange equation 12.1. Remember, since energy is *removed*, the q of the liquid is *negative*:

$$\Delta T = \frac{q}{m \times c} = \frac{-3250 \text{ J}}{(150.0 \text{ g}) \times \left(2.40 \frac{\text{J}}{\text{g°C}}\right)} = -9.03 \text{ °C}$$

This is not the answer, however. The question wants the final temperature. We must rearrange equation 12.2:

$$T_{final} = T_{initial} + \Delta T = 25.0 \text{ °C} + -9.03 \text{ °C} = \underline{16.0 \text{ °C}}$$

4. To solve this question, we must rearrange equation 12.1. This time, q is positive because heat is added:

$$\Delta T = \frac{q}{m \times c} = \frac{506 \text{ J}}{(50.0 \text{ g}) \times \left(4.184 \frac{\text{J}}{\text{g°C}}\right)} = 2.42 \text{ °C}$$

This is not the answer, however. The question asks for the final temperature. Thus, we must rearrange equation 12.2:

$$T_{final} = T_{initial} + \Delta T = 45.0 \text{ °C} + 2.42 \text{ °C} = \underline{47.4 \text{ °C}}$$

5. This is a direct application of equation 12.1:

$$q = m \times c \times \Delta T$$

$$q = (15.0\ g) \times \left(1.91\ \frac{J}{g°C}\right) \times (35.0\ °C - 15.0\ °C)$$

$$q = (15.0\ \cancel{g}) \times \left(1.91\ \frac{J}{\cancel{g°C}}\right) \times (20.0\ \cancel{°C}) = \underline{573\ J}$$

6. We can ignore the calorimeter in this question, so that makes it a bit easier. We have all of the information that we need to calculate q_{water}, so we might as well start there:

$$q_{water} = m \times c \times \Delta T$$

$$q_{water} = (120.0\ g) \times \left(4.184\ \frac{J}{g°C}\right) \times (30.0\ °C - 25.0\ °C)$$

$$q_{water} = (120.0\ \cancel{g}) \times \left(4.184\ \frac{J}{\cancel{g°C}}\right) \times (5.0\ \cancel{°C}) = 2500\ J$$

Since we can assume $q_{calorimeter} = 0$, we can now determine q_{metal}:

$$-q_{metal} = q_{water} + q_{calorimeter} = 2500\ J + 0$$

$$q_{metal} = -2500\ J$$

The value for q_{metal} is negative because the metal *lost* energy. We can calculate the ΔT of the metal:

$$\Delta T_{metal} = T_{final} - T_{initial} = 30.0\ °C - 100.0\ °C = \underline{-70.0\ °C}$$

We now have all the information we need to calculate the specific heat of the metal:

$$c = \frac{q}{m \times \Delta T}$$

$$c = \frac{-2500\ J}{500.0\ g \times -70.0\ °C} = \underline{0.071\ \frac{J}{g°C}}$$

7. We are given the details of the calorimeter in this question and we are not told that we can ignore it. Thus, to solve this question, we will need to determine the heat gained by the water *and* the heat gained by the calorimeter. Let's start with the calorimeter:

$$q_{calorimeter} = m \times c \times \Delta T$$

$$q_{calorimeter} = (5.0\text{ g}) \times \left(1.40 \frac{\text{J}}{\text{g°C}}\right) \times (31.0\text{ °C} - 25.0\text{ °C})$$

$$q_{calorimeter} = (5.0\text{ }\cancel{\text{g}}) \times \left(1.40 \frac{\text{J}}{\cancel{\text{g°C}}}\right) \times (6.0\text{ }\cancel{\text{°C}}) = 42\text{ J}$$

Now we can move on to the water:

$$q_{water} = m \times c \times \Delta T$$

$$q_{water} = (150.0\text{ }\cancel{\text{g}}) \times \left(4.184 \frac{\text{J}}{\cancel{\text{g°C}}}\right) \times (6.0\text{ }\cancel{\text{°C}}) = 3800\text{ J}$$

Now that we have calculated the q's of the water and calorimeter, we can use equation 12.3 to determine the q of the metal:

$$-q_{metal} = q_{water} + q_{calorimeter} = 3{,}800\text{ J} + 42\text{ J} = 3{,}800\text{ J}$$

$$q_{metal} = -3{,}800\text{ J}$$

Now that we have q_{metal}, we can determine ΔT for the metal and then use equation 12.1 to determine the specific heat:

$$\Delta T_{metal} = T_{final} - T_{initial} = 31.0\text{ °C} - 112.4\text{ °C} = -81.4\text{ °C}$$

Notice that this ΔT is negative because the object cooled down.

$$c = \frac{q}{m \times \Delta T}$$

$$c = \frac{-3{,}800\text{ J}}{125.0\text{ g} \times (-81.4\text{ °C})} = \underline{0.37 \frac{\text{J}}{\text{g°C}}}$$

8. When we look at this question, we see that we're trying to discover the specific heat of the liquid in the calorimeter, not the specific heat of the metal, as is usually

the case. Instead, the specific heat of the metal is given. In order to find the liquid's specific heat, we need to find out q_{liquid}. How can we do that? We have enough information to calculate q_{metal} and $q_{calorimeter}$, so we can start there.

$$q_{metal} = m \times c \times \Delta T$$

$$q_{metal} = (50.0\ g) \times \left(0.506\ \frac{J}{g°C}\right) \times (25.0\ °C - 60.0\ °C)$$

$$q_{metal} = (50.0\ \cancel{g}) \times \left(0.506\ \frac{J}{\cancel{g°C}}\right) \times (-35.0\ \cancel{°C}) = -886\ J$$

Notice that the heat is negative. We should expect that because the metal lost energy. We can now determine the heat gained by the calorimeter:

$$q_{calorimeter} = m \times c \times \Delta T$$

$$q_{calorimeter} = (5.0\ \cancel{g}) \times \left(1.40\frac{J}{\cancel{g°C}}\right) \times (25.0\ \cancel{°C} - 15.0\ \cancel{°C}) = 7.0 \times 10^1\ J$$

Now we can use equation 12.3 to determine q_{liquid}. Since the unknown liquid is replacing water in the calorimeter, we can replace q_{water} with q_{liquid} in the equation:

$$-q_{metal} = q_{liquid} + q_{calorimeter}$$

$$q_{liquid} = -q_{metal} - q_{calorimeter} = -(-886\ J) - 7.0 \times 10^1\ J = 816\ J$$

When determining significant figures above we must round the answer to the 10ths place through the use of the addition-subtraction rule. Since the q of the calorimeter and the metal both have their last significant figure in the ones place, the answer must be reported to the ones place. We can now determine the specific heat of the liquid:

$$c = \frac{q}{m \times \Delta T}$$

$$c = \frac{816\ J}{(200.0\ g)(10.0\ °C)} = \underline{0.408\ \frac{J}{g°C}}$$

9. In this question, we're trying to discover the specific heat of the calorimeter. In order to find the calorimeter's specific heat, we need to find out $q_{calorimeter}$. How can we do that? We have enough information to calculate q_{metal} and q_{liquid}, so we can start there.

$$q_{metal} = m \times c \times \Delta T$$

$$q_{metal} = (150.0\text{ g}) \times \left(0.560 \frac{\text{J}}{\text{g°C}}\right) \times (27.0\text{ °C} - 100.0\text{ °C})$$

$$q_{metal} = (150.0\text{ g}) \times \left(0.560 \frac{\text{J}}{\text{g°C}}\right) \times (-73.0\text{ °C}) = -6{,}130\text{ J}$$

We can now determine the heat gained by the water:

$$q_{water} = m \times c \times \Delta T$$

$$q_{water} = (400.0\text{ g}) \times \left(4.184 \frac{\text{J}}{\text{g°C}}\right) \times (27.0\text{ °C} - 25.0\text{ °C}) = 3{,}300\text{ J}$$

Now we can use equation 12.3 to determine $q_{calorimeter}$.

$$-q_{metal} = q_{water} + q_{calorimeter}$$

$$q_{calorimeter} = -q_{metal} - q_{water} = -(-6{,}130\text{ J}) - 3{,}300\text{ J} = 2{,}800\text{ J}$$

Now we can get the specific heat of the calorimeter:

$$c = \frac{q}{m \times \Delta T}$$

$$c = \frac{2{,}800\text{ J}}{(5.0\text{ g})(2.0\text{ °C})} = 280 \frac{\text{J}}{\text{g°C}}$$

10. In this case, we are trying to determine the mass of water in the calorimeter. We will need to determine q_{water}. To do that, we need to get q_{metal} and $q_{calorimeter}$.

$$q_{metal} = m \times c \times \Delta T$$

$$q_{metal} = (75.0\text{ g}) \times \left(0.3851 \frac{\text{J}}{\text{g°C}}\right) \times (30.0\text{ °C} - 100.0\text{ °C})$$

$$q_{metal} = (75.0\text{ g}) \times \left(0.3851 \frac{\text{J}}{\text{g°C}}\right) \times (-70.0\text{ °C}) = -2{,}020\text{ J}$$

$$q_{calorimeter} = m \times c \times \Delta T$$

$$q_{calorimeter} = (5.0\ g) \times \left(1.40\ \frac{J}{g°C}\right) \times (30.0\ °C - 25.0\ °C) = 35\ J$$

Now we can use the calorimetry equation to get q_{water}:

$$-q_{metal} = q_{water} + q_{calorimeter}$$

$$q_{water} = -q_{metal} - q_{calorimeter} = -(-2{,}020\ J) - 35\ J = 1{,}990\ J$$

We can get the mass of water by rearranging equation 12.1:

$$m = \frac{q}{c \times \Delta T}$$

$$m = \frac{1{,}990\ J}{\left(4.184\ \frac{J}{g°C}\right) \times (5.0\ °C)} = \underline{95\ g}$$

The ΔT has 2 significant figures, therefore the final answer is 2 significant figures.

TEST FOR MODULE 12

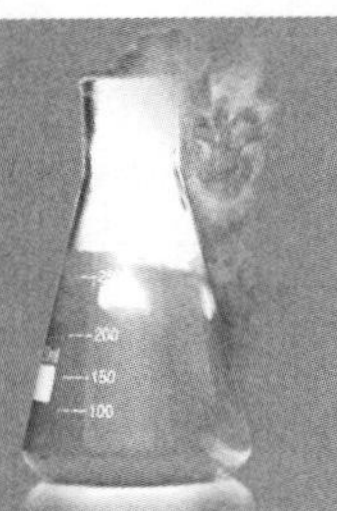

1. (8 pts) Write the first law of thermodynamics in your own words. Use it to explain where the flame of a burning candle gets its heat.

2. (4 pts) How are the terms *energy* and *work* related?
   a. Energy is the creation of motion in the presence of an opposing force.
   b. Work is the ability to produce energy.
   c. Energy is the ability to do work.
   d. Work is energy being transferred.
   e. None of the above

3. (4 pts) What 2 quantities are needed in order for work to be calculated?
   a. Force and energy
   b. Distance and energy
   c. Distance and force
   d. Heat and energy
   e. None of the above

4. (8 pts) Explain the difference between kinetic and potential energy. Give at least one example of each.

5. (4 pts) What kind of energy does an apple have?
   a. Kinetic
   b. Potential
   c. Both kinetic and potential
   d. Apples aren't energy; they're fruit, Silly!

6. (4 pts) If the temperature of an object starts to increase, the object is:
   a. Gaining energy
   b. Losing energy
   c. All of the above
   d. None of the above

7. (4 pts) The amount of energy needed to raise the temperature of 1 gram of water by 1 degree Celsius is:
   a. Heat
   b. A calorie
   c. A Calorie
   d. A Joule

8. (4 pts) The specific heat of plastic is 50 times larger than the specific heat of lead and 10 times larger than the specific heat of stone. Equal masses of lead, plastic, and stone have the same initial temperature. They are each given same amount of energy. Which ends up the hottest?
   a. Plastic
   b. Lead
   c. Stone
   d. They would all have the same temperature since they were heated for the same amount of time.
   e. None of the above

9. (4 pts) Which of the following statements about calorimetry is not true?
   a. Calorimetry involves an insulated container holding a liquid that is usually water.
   b. An object of known temperature is dropped into the calorimeter.
   c. The temperature change of the water and the object will be equal.
   d. The heat absorbed by the water is equal to the heat released by the object.

10. (4 pts) True or False: A heating curve, which is a graph of temperature vs. time, for water will contain 2 flat areas. One flat area will occur at 0 °C, called the freezing point, and the other will be at 100 °C, called the melting point.

11. (4 pts) True or False: Styrofoam is a good insulator because it has a low heat capacity.

12. (4 pts) Many recipes call for cooking food at a very constant temperature of 212 °F (100 °C). Why do these recipes recommend that you boil the food to achieve this constant temperature?

For the following problems, please remember to show all of your work.

13. (8 pts) A 10.0 kg copper skillet ($c = 0.3851 \frac{J}{g°C}$) must be heated from room temperature (25.0 °C) to a temperature of 175.0 °C. How many Joules of heat are required?

14. (8 pts) A 1.50 kg iron object ($c = 0.4521 \frac{J}{g°C}$) at 110.0 °C releases 5,505 Joules of heat. What is its new temperature?

15. (4 pts) If a 50.0 g object needs 1,145 Joules to increase its temperature by 10.0 °C, what is its specific heat capacity?

16. (12 pts) In a calorimetry experiment, a calorimeter is filled with 125 grams of water. The initial temperature of the water is 22.3 °C. A 50.0 g chunk of metal at 123.0 °C is dropped into the calorimeter, and the temperature increases to 24.5 °C. What is the specific heat of the metal? You can ignore the heat absorbed by the calorimeter.

17. (12 pts) In a calorimetry experiment, an unknown mass of glass (c = 0.8372 $\frac{J}{g°C}$) at 90.0 °C is dropped into a calorimeter (c = 1.23 $\frac{J}{g°C}$, m = 7.0 g) that contains 75.0 g of water. If the temperature increases from 24.3 °C at the beginning of the experiment to 26.6 °C by the end, what was the mass of the glass?

SOLUTIONS TO THE TEST FOR MODULE 12

1. (8 pts: 4 pts for the first law, 4 pts for the candle explanation) The first law of thermodynamics states that energy cannot be created or destroyed. It can only change forms. Thus, the heat in the flame of a burning candle was always there; it was simply stored in the candle and the surrounding oxygen. Only after the candle was lit could the energy be released.

2. (4 pts) c. Energy is the ability to do work.

3. (4 pts) c. Distance and force

4. (8 pts: 4 pts for the difference between the 2, 4 pts for the examples) Kinetic energy is energy in motion. Potential energy is energy that has been stored. Heat, lightning, and flames are all examples of kinetic energy. All matter has stored energy, so any substance would be an example of potential energy.

5. (4 pts) b. Potential

6. (4 pts) a. Gaining energy

7. (4 pts) b. A calorie

8. (4 pts) b. Lead
   The lead has the smallest specific heat, so it is easiest to heat. Therefore, the lead will be the hottest.

9. (4 pts) c. The temperature change of the water and the object will be equal.

10. (4 pts) False
    A heating curve, which is a graph of temperature vs. time, for water will contain 2 flat areas. One flat area will occur at 0 °C, called the freezing point, and the other will be at 100 °C, called the boiling point.

11. (4 pts) False
    Styrofoam is a good insulator because it is a poor conductor of heat.

12. (4 pts) Water boils at 100 °C. While it boils, its temperature stays constant.

13. (8 pts: 4 pts for converting to make the units consistent, 4 pts for the answer,

minus 1 pt for incorrect significant figures) $\underline{5.78 \times 10^5 \text{ J}}$
This is an application of equation 12.1. The only problem is that there is a unit discrepancy here. The mass is in kg, but the specific heat uses g. Thus, we need to convert one of those numbers. Converting the mass from kg to g:

$$\frac{10.0 \cancel{\text{kg}}}{1} \times \frac{1{,}000 \text{ g}}{1 \cancel{\text{kg}}} = 1.00 \times 10^4 \text{ g}$$

Now that the units agree, we can use equation 12.1:

$$q = m \times c \times \Delta T = (1.00 \times 10^4 \text{ g}) \times \left(0.3851 \frac{\text{J}}{\text{g°C}}\right) \times (175.0 \text{ °C} - 25.0 \text{ °C})$$

$$q = (1.00 \times 10^4 \cancel{\text{g}}) \times \left(0.3851 \frac{\text{J}}{\cancel{\text{g°C}}}\right) \times (150.0 \cancel{\text{°C}}) = \underline{5.78 \times 10^5 \text{ J}}$$

Notice that there are only 3 significant figures because the mass has only 3.

14. (8 pts: 4 pts for converting to make the units consistent, 4 pts for the answer, minus 1 pt for incorrect significant figures) $\underline{T_{final} = 101.9 \text{ °C}}$
This is another application of equation 12.1. The only problem is that there is a unit discrepancy here. The mass is in kg, but the specific heat uses g. Thus, we need to convert one of those numbers.

Converting the mass from kg to g:

$$\frac{1.50 \cancel{\text{kg}}}{1} \times \frac{1{,}000 \text{ g}}{1 \cancel{\text{kg}}} = 1.50 \times 10^3 \text{ g}$$

Now that the units agree, we can use equation 12.1. Remember, though, that when an object releases heat, the heat is negative. Thus, we will use –5,505 cal as q in the equation:

$$q = m \times c \times \Delta T$$

$$-5{,}505 \text{ J} = (1.50 \times 10^3 \text{ g}) \times \left(0.4521 \frac{\text{J}}{\text{g°C}}\right) \times (T_{final} - 110.0 \text{ °C})$$

$$(T_{final} - 110.0 \text{ °C}) = \frac{-5{,}505 \cancel{\text{J}}}{(1.50 \times 10^3 \cancel{\text{g}})\left(0.4521 \frac{\cancel{\text{J}}}{\cancel{\text{g}}\text{°C}}\right)} = -8.12 \text{ °C}$$

$$T_{final} = \underline{101.9 \text{ °C}}$$

MOD 12

Notice that the difference in temperature (–8.12 °C) has only 3 significant figures. However, to get T_{final}, we must *add* 110.0 °C to that number. At that point, we do not count significant figures. Instead, we look at decimal place. Since the least precise number (110.0) has its last significant figure in the tenths place, the answer must be reported to the tenths place.

15. (4 pts) $\underline{2.29 \frac{J}{g°C}}$
This is another application of equation 12.1. There are no unit conflicts here, so we can just use the equation:

$$q = m \times c \times \Delta T$$

$$1{,}145\ J = (50.0\ g) \times (c) \times (10.0\ °C)$$

$$c = \frac{1{,}145\ J}{(50.0\ g)(10.0\ °C)} = \underline{2.29 \frac{J}{g°C}}$$

16. (12 pts: 4 pts for q_{water}, 4 pts for q_{metal} and 4 pts for the answer) $\underline{0.24 \frac{J}{g°C}}$
We can ignore the calorimeter here, so all we need to do is determine q_{water}:

$$q_{water} = m \times c \times \Delta T = (125\ g) \times \left(4.184 \frac{J}{g°C}\right) \times (24.5\ °C - 22.3\ °C) = (125\ \cancel{g}) \times \left(4.184 \frac{J}{\cancel{g°C}}\right) \times (2.2\ \cancel{°C})$$

$$q_{water} = 1{,}200\ J$$

Now we can determine q_{metal}:

$$-q_{object} = q_{water} + q_{calorimeter}$$

$$q_{metal} = -1{,}200\ J$$

Now we can use equation 12.1 to determine the specific heat.

$$q = m \times c \times \Delta T$$

$$-1{,}200\ J = (50.0 g) \times (c) \times (24.5\ °C - 123.0\ °C)$$

$$c = \frac{-1{,}200\ J}{(50.0\ g)(-98.5\ °C)} = \underline{0.24 \frac{J}{g°C}}$$

17. (12 pts: 2 pts for q_{water}, 2 pts for $q_{calorimeter}$, 2 pts for q_{glass}, and 6 pts for the answer) 14 g

To figure out the mass of the glass, we need to figure out how much energy it released. We cannot ignore the calorimeter in this problem, so we must determine both q_{water} and $q_{calorimeter}$:

$$q_{water} = m \times c \times \Delta T = (75.0\text{ g}) \times \left(4.184 \frac{\text{J}}{\text{g°C}}\right) \times (26.6\text{ °C} - 24.3\text{ °C}) =$$

$$(75.0\text{ g}) \times \left(4.184 \frac{\text{J}}{\text{g°C}}\right) \times (2.3\text{ °C})$$

$$q_{water} = 720\text{ J}$$

$$q_{calorimeter} = m \times c \times \Delta T = (7.0\text{ g}) \times \left(1.23 \frac{\text{J}}{\text{g°C}}\right) \times (26.6\text{ °C} - 24.3\text{ °C}) =$$

$$(7.0\text{ g}) \times \left(1.23 \frac{\text{J}}{\text{g°C}}\right) \times (2.3\text{ °C})$$

$$q_{calorimeter} = 2.0 \times 10^1\text{ J}$$

Notice that the only way we could properly report $q_{calorimeter}$ was to use scientific notation because it must have 2 significant figures. Now we can use the calorimetery equation:

$$-q_{object} = q_{water} + q_{calorimeter} = 720\text{ J} + 2.0 \times 10^1\text{ J}$$

$$q_{glass} = -740\text{ J}$$

Now that we know the heat released by the glass, we can determine its mass:

$$q = m \times c \times \Delta T$$

$$-740\text{ J} = (m) \times \left(0.8372 \frac{\text{J}}{\text{g°C}}\right) \times (26.6 - 90.0\text{°C})$$

$$m = \frac{-740\text{ J}}{\left(0.8372 \frac{\text{J}}{\text{g°C}}\right) \times (-63.4\text{ °C})} = \underline{14\text{ g}}$$

QUARTER 3 TEST FOR MOD. 9-12

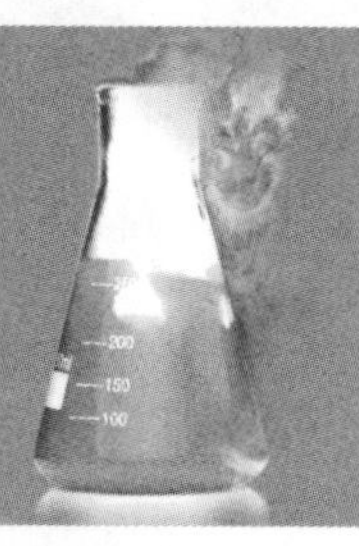

1. (2 pts) Identify the acid in the following reaction:

$$C_2H_6O + CH_5N \rightarrow C_2H_5O^- + CH_6N^+$$

   a. C_2H_6O
   b. CH_5N
   c. $C_2H_5O^-$
   d. CH_6N^+
   e. None of these

2. (2 pts) When 1 molecule of $Al_2(SO_4)_3$ dissolves in water, what ions does it form, and how many of each ion are present?
   a. 2 ions of Al^{3+} and 3 ions of SO_4^{2-}
   b. 3 ions of Al^{2+} and 2 ions of SO_4^{3-}
   c. 2 ions of Al^{2+} and 3 ions of SO_4^{3-}
   d. 3 ions of Al^{3+} and 2 ions of SO_4^{2-}
   e. None of the above

3. (4 pts) Give the balanced chemical equation for the reaction that occurs between nitric acid (HNO_3) and magnesium hydroxide.

4. (2 pts) Given that PH_3 is a base, determine the reaction that occurs between HNO_3 and PH_3 and give the balanced chemical equation.

5. (3 pts) What 2 things increase the solubility of a gas in a liquid?
   a. Increased temperature and decreased pressure
   b. Increased salt and increased pressure
   c. Decreased temperature and decreased pressure
   d. Decreased temperature and increased pressure
   e. Increased salt and STP

6. (2 pts) If you wanted to protect water from freezing, which compound would accomplish this best: $Al(NO_3)_3$, $Ca(NO_3)_2$, or KCl? Assume that the molality of the solution is the same in each case.
   a. $Al(NO_3)_3$
   b. $Ca(NO_3)_2$
   c. KCl
   d. Not enough information to answer the question

7. (3 pts) Which statement is *not* a true statement regarding an ideal gas?

a. The total volume available to the gas must be very large compared to the molecules (or atoms) that make up the gas.
b. There are no attractions or repulsions between the molecules (or atoms) of the gas because they are very far apart.
c. All collisions between molecules (or atoms) must be elastic (i.e., no energy lost or gained).
d. The pressure must be at or lower than 760 torr for a gas to behave ideally.
e. The temperature must be at 273 K for a gas to behave ideally.

8. (4 pts) A chemist collects 156 mL of N_2 gas at 25 °C and 7.9×10^2 torr. The volume of the gas at STP would be:
   a. 1.8×10^3 mL
   b. 1.5×10^2 mL
   c. 1.2×10^3 mL
   d. 6.7×10^{-3} mL
   e. 1.1×10^5 mL

9. (4 pts) A mixture of 1.2 g of N_2 and 1.5 g of O_2 has a pressure of 1.0 atm. The partial pressure of each gas in the mixture is:
   a. N_2 = 0.48 atm, O_2 = 0.52 atm
   b. N_2 = 0.957 atm, O_2 = 0.953 atm
   c. N_2 = 0.91 atm, O_2 = 1.1 atm
   d. The temperature must be given to calculate the answer.

10. (6 pts) What is the volume of 15.0 grams of carbon dioxide gas at STP?
    a. 7.64 mL
    b. 0.130 mL
    c. 7.64 L
    d. 0.130 L
    e. None of the above

11. (2 pts) Does a pile of firewood have potential energy, kinetic energy, or both?
    a. Potential energy
    b. Kinetic energy
    c. Both potential and kinetic energy

12. (2 pts) Does wind have potential energy, kinetic energy, or both?
    a. Potential energy
    b. Kinetic energy
    c. Both potential and kinetic energy

13. (2 pts) Does light have potential energy, kinetic energy, or both?
    a. Potential energy
    b. Kinetic energy
    c. Both potential and kinetic energy

14. (2 pts) Does a gallon of gasoline have potential energy, kinetic energy, or both?
    a. Potential energy
    b. Kinetic energy
    c. Both potential and kinetic energy

15. (2 pts) At what temperature does the following heating curve show as the melting point for this unknown substance?

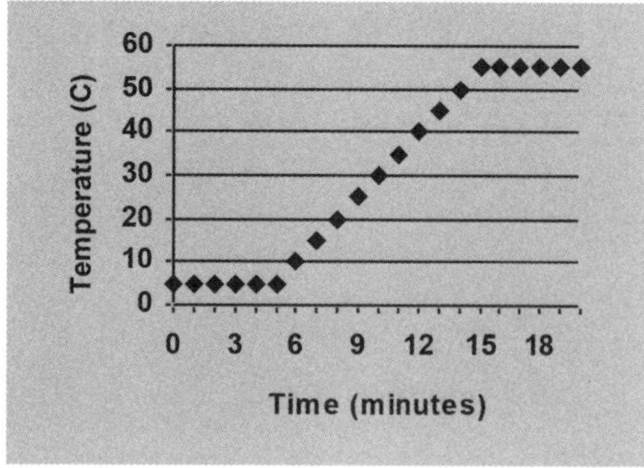

    a. 0 °C
    b. 5 °C
    c. 10 °C
    d. 55 °C
    e. None of the above

16. (8 pts) The following reaction is performed in a lab:

$$3Na_2SO_4\ (aq) + 2Al(NO_3)_3\ (aq) \rightarrow Al_2(SO_4)_3\ (s) + 6NaNO_3\ (aq)$$

    If 191 mL of 1.25 M aluminum nitrate is added to an excess of sodium sulfate, how many grams of aluminum sulfate will be produced?

17. (6 pts) A chemist makes a stock solution of KOH by dissolving 1,050.0 g in enough water to make 1.50 liters of solution. If he later wants to use this stock solution to make 200.0 mL of 0.10 M KOH, what would the chemist need to do?

18. (6 pts) A chemist needs to know the concentration of some KOH that is in the laboratory. To find this out, the chemist titrates a 50.0 mL sample of the solution with 2.5 M HCl. If it takes 14.7 mL of the HCl to reach the titration endpoint, what is the concentration of the KOH solution?

19. (6 pts) If you want to lower water's freezing point 11 °C by adding Na_2CO_3, what must be the molality of the salt solution? (K_f for water is 1.86 °C/m)
    a. 0.99 m
    b. 3.0 m
    c. 2.0 m
    d. 0.50 m
    e. 4.0 m

20. (6 pts) How many grams of Na_2CO_3 would you have to add to 500.0 g of water to make a solution with the molality you found in question 19 above?

21. (6 pts) What is the boiling point of a solution made by mixing 100.0 g NaCl with 1100.0 grams of water? (K_b for water is 0.512 °C/m)

22. (6 pts) A 25.0 g piece of copper (specific heat capacity = 0.385 J/g °C) at room temperature (25 °C) loses 856.7 J of heat. What is its new temperature?

23. (6 pts) A calorimeter is filled with 150.0 g of water at 22.1 °C. A 50.0 g sample of a metal at 100.0 °C is dropped in this calorimeter and causes the temperature to increase a total of 3.4 °C. What is the specific heat of the metal? Ignore the heat absorbed by the calorimeter.

24. (8 pts) A chemist performs the following reaction:

$$7H_2O_2\ (aq) + N_2H_4\ (g) \rightarrow 2HNO_3\ (g) + 8H_2O\ (g)$$

If the chemist starts with 110.0 grams of H_2O_2 and an excess of N_2H_4, what volume of water vapor will be produced at a temperature of 341°C and a pressure of 2.1 atm?

SOLUTIONS TO QUARTER 3 TEST FOR MOD. 9-12

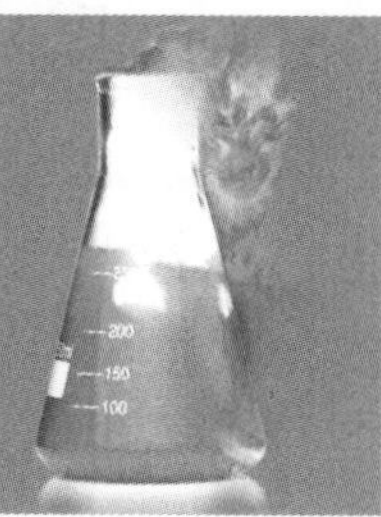

1. (2 pts) a. C_2H_6O
   Acids donate H+ ions. In this reaction, C_2H_6O becomes $C_2H_5O^-$. The only way that can happen is if it gives up an H^+. Thus, C_2H_6O is the acid.

2. (2 pts) a. 2 ions of Al^{3+} and 3 ions of SO_4^{2-}
   Looking at the chemical formula, you should immediately see the sulfate ion (SO_4^{2-}). The positive ion is the aluminum ion. Aluminum's position on the periodic table tells you it's a 3^+ ion. Thus, the molecule splits into 2 Al^{3+} ions and 3 SO_4^{2-} ions.

3. (4 pts : 2 pts for the unbalanced equation, and 2 pts for the balanced equation)
   $2HNO_3 + Mg(OH)_2 \rightarrow 2H_2O + Mg(NO_3)_2$
   Magnesium hydroxide is $Mg(OH)_2$. Acids and bases usually react to give a salt and water. The salt is made up of the positive ion from the base (Mg^{2+}) and the negative ion left over when the acid gets rid of its H^+ ions. In this case, that will be NO_3^-. These 2 ions form $Mg(NO_3)_2$. The unbalanced equation, then, is:

   $$HNO_3 + Mg(OH)_2 \rightarrow 2H_2O + Mg(NO_3)_2$$

   Now all we have to do is balance it:

   $$2HNO_3 + Mg(OH)_2 \rightarrow 2H_2O + Mg(NO_3)_2$$

4. (2 pts) $HNO_3 + PH_3 \rightarrow PH_4^+ + NO_3^-$
   In this case, the base does not contain an hydroxide ion. Thus, a salt and water are not formed in this problem. Here, we just rely on the definition of acids and bases. PH_3 will want to gain an H^+ to become PH_4^+, and the nitric acid will want to give up its H^+ ion to become NO_3^-.

5. (3 pts) d. Decreased temperature and increased pressure

6. (2 pts) a. $Al(NO_3)_3$
   The freezing point depression depends on the solvent (which is water in each case),

the molality (which is the same in each case), and the number of particles that the solute splits up into when it dissolves. In this problem, $Al(NO_3)_3$ splits into the most ions (4), so it will cause the greatest freezing point depression.

7. (3 pts) e. The temperature must be at 273 K for a gas to behave ideally.

8. (4 pts) b. 1.5×10^2 mL
This is obviously a combined gas law problem, with P_1 = 790 torr, V_1 = 156 mL, T_1 = 298 K, P_2 = 1.00 atm (standard pressure), and T_2 = 273 K (standard temperature). The problem asks us to determine the new volume, so we have to rearrange the combined gas law equation to solve for V_2:

$$\frac{P_1V_1T_2}{T_1P_2} = V_2$$

Before we can plug in the numbers, however, we need to convert T_1 to Kelvin. Additionally, we need to make the pressure units the same. We can do this by converting torr into atm or vice versa. We will do the latter:

$$P_2 = \frac{1.00\ \cancel{\text{atm}}}{1} \times \frac{760\ \text{torr}}{1\ \cancel{\text{atm}}} = 7.60 \times 10^2\ \text{torr}$$

Now we can plug in the numbers and cancel units:

$$V_2 = \frac{790\ \cancel{\text{torr}} \times 156\ \text{mL} \times 273\ \cancel{\text{K}}}{298\ \cancel{\text{K}} \times 7.60 \times 10^2\ \cancel{\text{torr}}} = \underline{150\ \text{mL}}$$

9. (4 pts) a. N_2 = 0.48 atm, O_2 = 0.52 atm
Remember, the partial pressure of the individual gases in a mixture depends on the mole fraction of each gas, according to Dalton's law. Mole fraction is defined as the number of *moles* of component divided by the total number of moles. Right now, the problem gives us *grams*, not moles. Thus, we must first convert from grams to moles:

$$\frac{1.2\ \cancel{\text{g N}_2}}{1} \times \frac{1\ \text{mole N}_2}{28.0\ \cancel{\text{g N}_2}} = 0.043\ \text{moles N}_2$$

$$\frac{1.5\ \cancel{\text{g O}_2}}{1} \times \frac{1\ \text{mole O}_2}{32.0\ \cancel{\text{g O}_2}} = 0.047\ \text{moles O}_2$$

Now that we have the number of moles of each component, we can calculate the total number of moles in the mixture:

Total number of moles = 0.043 moles + 0.047 moles = 0.090 moles

Plugging that into the mole fraction equation gives the mole fractions for each gas:

$$X_{N_2} = \frac{0.043 \cancel{\text{moles}}}{0.090 \cancel{\text{moles}}} = 0.48$$

$$X_{O_2} = \frac{0.047 \cancel{\text{moles}}}{0.090 \cancel{\text{moles}}} = 0.52$$

To get the partial pressure of each gas you need to multiply the mole fraction by the total pressure of 1 atm to give the partial pressure of each gas:

N_2 = 0.48 x 1 atm = <u>0.48 atm</u>, O_2 = 0.52 x 1 atm = <u>0.52 atm</u>

10. (6 pts) c. <u>7.64 L</u>
In this problem, we are given pressure and temperature and the mass (from which we can get moles). We are then asked to calculate V. We can do this by rearranging the ideal gas law:

$$PV = nRT \text{ becomes } V = \frac{nRT}{P}$$

In order for this to work, though, our temperature must be in Kelvin. Also, we do not have n yet. We do, however, have mass, so we can convert it into moles:

$$15.0 \cancel{\text{g } CO_2} \times \frac{1 \text{ mole } CO_2}{44.0 \cancel{\text{g } CO_2}} = 0.341 \text{ moles } CO_2$$

Now that we have all of the correct units, we can plug the numbers into the equation.

$$V = \frac{nRT}{P} = \frac{0.341 \cancel{\text{moles}} \times 0.0821 \text{ L} \cancel{\text{atm/mole K}} \times 273 \cancel{\text{K}}}{1.00 \cancel{\text{atm}}} = 7.64 \text{ L}$$

11. (2 pts) a. <u>Potential energy</u> A pile of firewood has <u>potential</u> energy in it because all matter has stored energy.

12. (2 pts) c. <u>Both potential and kinetic energy</u> Wind is moving air, so it has kinetic energy. Air also has mass, however, so it has stored energy as well. Thus, it has <u>both</u>.

13. (2 pts) b. Kinetic energy Light has no matter, but it does move, so it has kinetic energy.

14. (2 pts) a. Potential energy The gasoline is matter, so it has potential energy.

15. (2 pts) b. 5 °C We learned in our experiment that the heating curve for water has 2 flat regions. The first occurred when ice was melting, and the second occurred when water was boiling. Based on this fact, the unknown liquid must melt at 5 °C.

16. (8 pts: 3 pts for getting the moles of aluminum nitrate, 2 pts for getting the moles of aluminum sulfate, and 3 pts for getting the grams of aluminum sulfate)
$41.1 \text{ g } Al_2(SO_4)_3$
This is just a stoichiometry problem. We can tell this by the fact that we are being asked to determine the amount of one substance when we are given the amount of another substance. The only way to do that is by stoichiometry, so we must first get our amount in moles.

$$\frac{0.191 \cancel{\text{L}}}{1} \times \frac{1.25 \text{ moles } Al(NO_3)_3}{1 \cancel{\text{L}}} = 0.239 \text{ moles } Al(NO_3)_3$$

Now that we have moles, we can do stoichiometry:

$$\frac{0.239 \cancel{\text{moles } Al(NO_3)_3}}{1} \times \frac{1 \text{ mole } Al_2(SO_4)_3}{2 \cancel{\text{moles } Al(NO_3)_3}} = 0.120 \text{ moles } Al_2(SO_4)_3$$

Now, of course, this is not quite the answer we need. We were asked to figure out how many grams of aluminum sulfate were produced, so we have to convert from moles back to grams:

$$\frac{0.120 \cancel{\text{moles } Al_2(SO_4)_3}}{1} \times \frac{342.3 \text{ g } Al_2(SO_4)_3}{1 \cancel{\text{mole } Al_2(SO_4)_3}} = \underline{41.1 \text{ g } Al_2(SO_4)_3}$$

QT 3

17. (6 pts: 3 pts for the concentration of the stock KOH solution and 3 pts for the dilution instructions) The chemist needs to take 1.6 mL of the stock solution and mix it with enough water to make 200.0 mL of solution. The last part of this problem is a dilution problem, but in order to get the original concentration, we must deal with the first part of the problem, which is a concentration problem.

$$\frac{1050.0 \cancel{\text{g KOH}}}{1} \times \frac{1 \text{ mole KOH}}{56.1 \cancel{\text{g KOH}}} = 18.7 \text{ moles KOH}$$

$$\text{Concentration} = \frac{\text{\# moles solute}}{\text{\# liters solution}} = \frac{18.7 \text{ moles KOH}}{1.50 \text{ L}} = 12.5 \text{ M}$$

Now that we know the concentration of the stock solution, this is just a dilution problem:

$$M_1V_1 = M_2V_2$$

So rearranging the equation gives:

$$V_1 = \frac{M_2V_2}{M_1} = \frac{0.10 \not{M} \times 200.0 \text{ mL}}{12.5 \not{M}} = 1.6 \text{ mL}$$

18. (6 pts–2 pts for getting moles of HCl, 2 pts for converting to moles of KOH, and 2 pts for getting the concentration of KOH) 0.74 M
Remember, titrations are just stoichiometry problems, so first we have to come up with a balanced chemical equation:

$$HCl + KOH \rightarrow KCl + H_2O$$

Since the endpoint was reached, we know that exactly enough acid was added to eat up all of the base. First, then, we calculate how many moles of acid were added:

$$\frac{0.0147 \not{L}}{1} \times \frac{2.5 \text{ moles HCl}}{1 \not{L}} = 0.037 \text{ moles HCl}$$

We can now use the chemical equation to determine how many moles of base were present:

$$\frac{0.037 \cancel{\text{moles HCl}}}{1} \times \frac{1 \text{ mole KOH}}{1 \cancel{\text{mole HCl}}} = 0.037 \text{ moles KOH}$$

Now that we have the number of moles of base present, we simply divide by the volume of acid to get concentration:

$$\text{Concentration} = \frac{\text{\# moles solute}}{\text{\# liters solution}} = \frac{0.037 \text{ moles KOH}}{0.050 \text{ L}} = \underline{0.74 \text{ M of KOH}}$$

19. (6 pts) c. 2.0 m
Freezing point depression is determined by the equation $\Delta T = i\, K_f\, m$. We are already given 2 of the 4 variables in the equation (K_f, ΔT), and we can calculate a

third (i). Molality is the only unknown, so we can solve for it. Since Na_2CO_3 is ionic, it will split up into ions (2 sodium ions and 1 carbonate ion), so i = 3:

$\Delta T = i\,K_f\,m$ rearranges to solve for m (molal):

$$m = \frac{\Delta T}{-i\,K_f} = \frac{-11\ \cancel{^\circ C}}{-3 \times 1.86\ \cancel{^\circ C}/\text{molal}} = \underline{2.0 \text{ molal of } Na_2CO_3}$$

20. (6 pts: 3 pts for conversion to moles, 3 pts for conversion to grams)
<u>110 g Na_2CO_3</u>
Molality is defined as the number of moles of solute per kg of solvent. Thus, 2.0 m is 2.0 moles of Na_2CO_3 per 1.00 kg of solvent. We don't have 1.00 kg; we have 0.5000 kg, so we first need to calculate how many moles are required:

$$\frac{2.0 \text{ moles of } Na_2CO_3}{1.0\ \cancel{\text{kg water}}} \times 0.5000\ \cancel{\text{kg water}} = 1.0 \text{ mole } Na_2CO_3$$

That's how many moles are required, but we need to know grams. That's an easy conversion:

$$\frac{1.0\ \cancel{\text{moles } Na_2CO_3}}{1} \times \frac{106 \text{ g } Na_2CO_3}{1\ \cancel{\text{mole Na2CO3}}} = \underline{110 \text{ g } Na_2CO_3}$$

21. (6 pts: 3 pts for the molality, and 3 pts for the boiling point) <u>101.6 °C</u>
To calculate boiling points, we must use equation 11.3. To do that, however, we must know i and m. To calculate m:

$$\frac{100.0\ \cancel{\text{g NaCl}}}{1} \times \frac{1 \text{ mole NaCl}}{58.5\ \cancel{\text{g NaCl}}} = 1.71 \text{ moles NaCl}$$

$$\text{molality} = \frac{\#\text{ moles solute}}{\#\text{ kg solvent}} = \frac{1.71 \text{ moles NaCl}}{1.1000 \text{ kg water}} = 1.55 \text{ molal}$$

Since sodium chloride is an ionic compound, it dissolves by splitting up into 2 ions; thus, i = 2.

$$\Delta T = i\,K_b\,m = 2 \times 0.512\ ^\circ C/\cancel{m} \times 1.55\ \cancel{m} = 1.59\ ^\circ C$$

This means that the boiling point of the solution is 1.59 °C *higher* than that of pure water. The boiling point of pure water is 100.0 °C, so the boiling point of this solution is <u>101.6 °C</u>.

QT 3

22. (6 pts: 3pts for getting ΔT and 3 pts for getting T_{final}) $-64\ °C$
In order to get the copper's new temperature, we need to solve for ΔT in equation $q = m\ c\ \Delta T$. We can do this because we have the mass and heat given in the problem and the specific heat. Remember, though, since the copper lost heat, q is negative! So first we rearrange the equation to solve for ΔT:

$$q = m\ c\ \Delta T \quad \text{rearranging gives:}$$

$$\Delta T = \frac{q}{m\ c} = \frac{-856.7\ \cancel{J}}{25.0\ \cancel{g} \times 0.385\ \cancel{J}/\cancel{g}\ °C} = -89.0\ °C$$

Now that we have ΔT, we can rearrange $\Delta T = T_{final} - T_{initial}$ to solve for the final temperature:

$$T_{final} = \Delta T + T_{initial} = -89.0\ °C + 25\ °C = \underline{-64\ °C}$$

23. (6 pts: 3 pts for getting q_{water} and 3 pts for getting °C] $0.56\ J/g\ °C$
The problem says to ignore the heat absorbed by the calorimeter, so $q_{calorimeter} = 0$. We have enough information to calculate q_{water}, so we might as well start there:

$$q_{water} = m\ c\ \Delta T = 150.0\ \cancel{g} \times 4.184\ J/\cancel{g}\ \cancel{°C} \times 3.4\ \cancel{°C} = 2{,}100\ J$$

Now we can determine q_{metal}:

$$-q_{metal} = q_{water} + q_{calorimeter} = 2{,}100\ J + 0$$

$$q_{metal} = -2{,}100\ J$$

We can use that value of heat and the metal's change in temperature to calculate its specific heat. However, we have to figure out the ΔT. The metal started out at 100.0 °C and ended up with the same temperature as the water. What was the final temperature of the water? The water started out at 22.1 °C and its temperature rose 3.4 °C. Thus, its final temperature (which is also the metal's final temperature) is 25.5 °C.

$$\Delta T = T_{final} - T_{initial} = 25.5\ °C - 100.0\ °C = -74.5\ °C$$

$$c = \frac{q}{m\ \Delta T} = \frac{-2100\ J}{50.0\ g \times -74.5\ °C} = 0.56\ J/g\ °C$$

24. (8 pts: 3 pts for getting the moles of H_2O_2, 2 pts for getting the moles of water, and 3 pts for getting the volume of water) 89 L

In this stoichiometry problem, we are given the amount of limiting reactant and asked to calculate how much product will be made. We start by converting the amount of limiting reactant to moles:

$$\frac{110.0 \text{ \sout{g H}}_2\text{\sout{O}}_2}{1} \times \frac{1 \text{ mole } H_2O_2}{34.02 \text{ \sout{g H}}_2\text{\sout{O}}_2} = 3.24 \text{ moles } H_2O_2$$

We can then use stoichiometry to determine the number of moles of H_2O produced:

$$\frac{3.24 \text{ \sout{moles H}}_2\text{\sout{O}}_2}{1} \times \frac{8 \text{ moles } H_2O}{7 \text{ \sout{moles H}}_2\text{\sout{O}}_2} = 3.70 \text{ moles } H_2O$$

Now we need to use the ideal gas law solving for volume:

$$K = 341\ °C + 273 = 614\ K$$

$$V = \frac{nRT}{P} = \frac{3.70 \text{ \sout{moles}} \times 0.0821 \text{ L \sout{atm/mole K}} \times 614 \text{ \sout{K}}}{2.1 \text{ \sout{atm}}} = \underline{89 \text{ L}}$$

QT 3

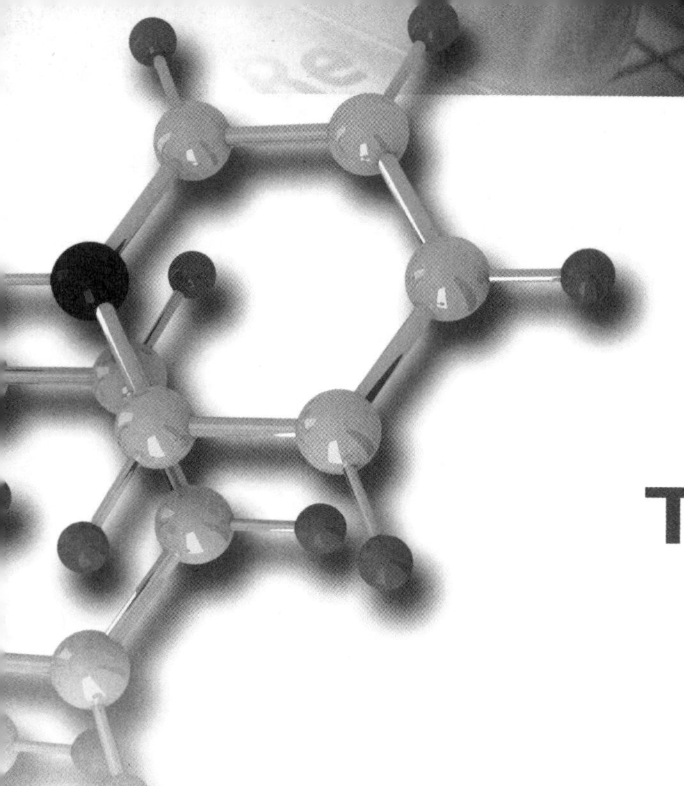

THERMODYNAMICS

SOLUTIONS TO THE MODULE 13 REVIEW QUESTIONS

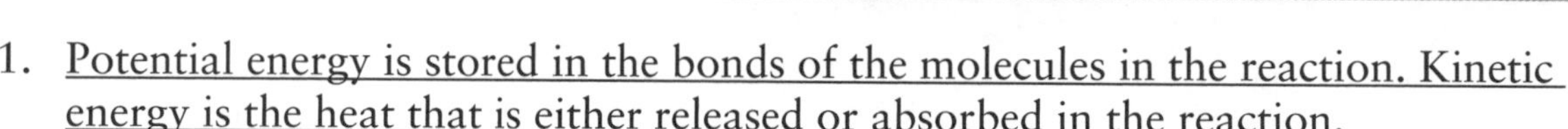

1. Potential energy is stored in the bonds of the molecules in the reaction. Kinetic energy is the heat that is either released or absorbed in the reaction.

2. A positive ΔH indicates an endothermic reaction. Endothermic reactions absorb heat from their surroundings. This leaves less energy for the surroundings. As a result, the beaker will feel cold.

3. Hess's law is more exact because it also takes into account the phases of each substance in the reaction.

4. A state function is one whose final value is independent of path. Enthalpy and Gibbs free energy are examples of state functions.

5. Only elements that are in their elemental form have a ΔH_f^o of zero. NaOH is not an element. Na^+ is not an element either; it is an ion. O is an element, but the elemental form of oxygen is gaseous O_2; thus, the ΔH_f^o for O is not zero. Finally, H_2 (l) is not the elemental form of hydrogen; H_2 (g) is. Thus, only O_2 (g) and Cl_2 (g) have ΔH_f^o of zero.

6. Endothermic reactions have their reactants at a lower energy than their products. Thus, diagram I is the endothermic reaction. Additionally, the ΔH of the reaction is just the energy of the products minus that of the reactants. Thus for Diagram I, the ΔH = 70 kJ – 18 kJ = 52 kJ. Since the answer is obtained by reading a graph, the answer can beanywhere from 52 kJ to 57 kJ. For Diagram II the ΔH = 60 kJ −90 kJ = −30 kJ. Since the answer is obtained by reading a graph, the answer can be anywhere from −25 kJ to 35 kJ.

7. If ΔH is zero, the reactant and products have the same potential energy. A large activation energy means a large hump at the intermediate state. The drawing below, then, represents a reaction in which the ΔH is zero and the activation energy is large.

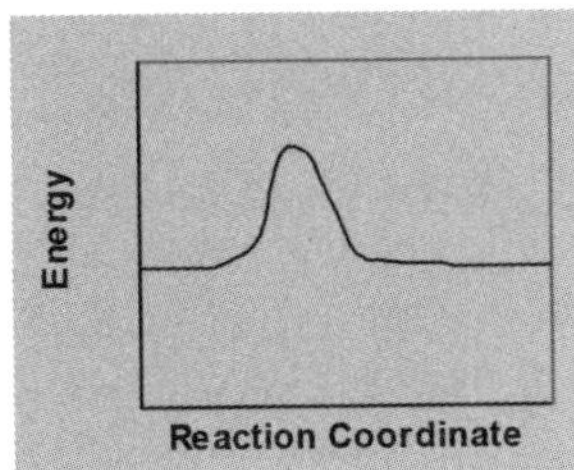

8. Increased temperature means increase molecular (or atomic) motion and thus more disorder. Therefore, the warmer block has a higher entropy.

9. In order to make a reaction spontaneous, ΔG must be negative. We remember that $\Delta G = \Delta H - T\Delta S$. If a reaction is exothermic, then the ΔH is negative. If ΔS is negative, then $T\Delta S$ is negative and result is a double negative or the product of $T\Delta S$ is added to the ΔH. To ensure that the result is negative (and thus the reaction is spontaneous), we must decrease the $T\Delta S$ result to be lower than the ΔH. The only way we can do that is to lower the temperature to make the $T\Delta S$ smaller.

SOLUTIONS TO THE PRACTICE PROBLEMS FOR MODULE 13

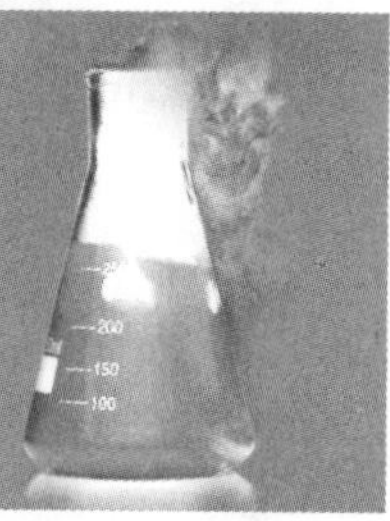

1. The chemical equation contains no phases, so we must use bond energies to solve this problem. This means we start with Lewis structures:

:Cl–Cl: + H–O–H + H–O–H → H–Cl: + H–Cl: + H–Cl: + H–Cl: + :O=O:
:Cl–Cl:

   Using this picture and table 13.2, we know that 2 Cl–Cl bonds (each worth 240 kJ/mole) and 4 H–O bonds (each worth 459 kJ/mole) must be broken while 4 H–Cl bonds (each worth 428 kJ/mole) and 1 O=O bond (worth 494 kJ/mole) must be formed. Equation 13.3 becomes:

$$\Delta H = \left(2\ \cancel{\text{moles}} \times 240\frac{\text{kJ}}{\cancel{\text{mole}}}\right) + \left(4\ \cancel{\text{moles}} \times 459\frac{\text{kJ}}{\cancel{\text{mole}}}\right) - \left(4\ \cancel{\text{moles}} \times 428\frac{\text{kJ}}{\cancel{\text{mole}}}\right) - \left(1\ \cancel{\text{mole}} \times 494\frac{\text{kJ}}{\cancel{\text{mole}}}\right)$$

$$\Delta H = \underline{110\ \text{kJ}}$$

   Since we are adding and subtracting here, we use the rule of addition and subtraction. That means we consider decimal place. The number 240 has its last significant figure in the tens place, so that's as precise as the answer can be.

2. Since we know the phases for the substances in a combustion reaction, we can use Hess's law here. The definition of combustion tells us that the reaction is:

$$2C_6H_6\ (l) + 15O_2\ (g) \rightarrow 12CO_2\ (g) + 6H_2O\ (g)$$

   The ΔH_f° of O_2 (g) is zero since it is oxygen's elemental form. The rest of the ΔH_f°'s are either given in the problem or are in the table 13.2, so we can apply equation 13.3 directly:

$$\Delta H° = \left(12 \text{ moles} \times -394 \frac{\text{kJ}}{\text{mole}}\right) + \left(6 \text{ moles} \times -242 \frac{\text{kJ}}{\text{mole}}\right) - \left(2 \text{ moles} \times 49.00 \frac{\text{kJ}}{\text{mole}}\right)$$

$$\Delta H° = \underline{-6{,}278 \text{ kJ}}$$

Using the rule of addition and subtraction, we can report our answer to the ones place, since the least precise bond energies have their last significant figure in the ones place.

3. In this problem, we are given the ΔH° of the reaction, and we are asked to calculate the $\Delta H_f°$ of one of the reactants. This isn't hard, however, because equation 13.3 relates the ΔH° of the equation to the $\Delta H_f°$'s of all of the substances in the equation. Since we know that the $\Delta H_f°$ of O_2 (g) is zero and the $\Delta H_f°$ of SO_3 (g) is in table 13.2, the $\Delta H_f°$ of SO_2 (g) is our only unknown in equation 13.3:

$$-198 \text{ kJ} = (2 \text{ moles}) \times \left(-396 \frac{\text{kJ}}{\text{mole}}\right) - (2 \text{ moles}) \times (\Delta H_f° \text{ of } SO_2)$$

Rearranging the equation gives us:

$$\Delta H_f° \text{ of } SO_2 = \frac{-198 \text{ kJ} - (2 \text{ moles}) \times \left(-396 \frac{\text{kJ}}{\text{mole}}\right)}{-2 \text{ moles}} = \underline{-297 \text{ kJ/mole}}$$

The standard enthalpy of formation for gaseous sulfur dioxide is <u>-297 kJ/mole</u>.

4. In problem 2, the answer was ΔH = –6,278 kJ/mole. This means that energy is a product in this reaction:

$$2C_6H_6 \text{ (l)} + 15O_2 \text{ (g)} \rightarrow 12CO_2 \text{ (g)} + 6H_2O \text{ (g)} + 6{,}278 \text{ kJ}$$

Now we can do stoichiometry:

$$\frac{250.0 \text{ g } C_6H_6}{1} \times \frac{1 \text{ mole } C_6H_6}{78.1 \text{ g } C_6H_6} = 3.20 \text{ moles } C_6H_6$$

$$\frac{3.20 \text{ moles } C_6H_6}{1} \times \frac{6{,}278 \text{ kJ}}{2 \text{ moles } C_6H_6} = \underline{1.00 \times 10^4 \text{ kJ}}$$

So <u>1.00×10^4 kJ</u> will be released when benzene is burned.

MOD 13

5. In order to answer any problem about the energy involved in a chemical reaction, we must first get ΔH. Since table 13.3 contains all the information we need for this problem, we will use Hess's law to do this calculation:

$$\Delta H^\circ = [(2\ \cancel{\text{moles}} \times -45.9\frac{\text{kJ}}{\cancel{\text{mole}}}) + (4\ \cancel{\text{moles}} \times -242\ \frac{\text{kJ}}{\cancel{\text{mole}}})] - (2\ \cancel{\text{moles}}) \times (33.2\frac{\text{kJ}}{\cancel{\text{mole}}})$$

$$\Delta H^\circ = -1{,}126\text{ kJ}$$

This means that energy is a product in the reaction:

$$2NO_2\ (g) + 7H_2\ (g) \rightarrow 2NH_3\ (g) + 4H_2O\ (g) + 1{,}126\text{ kJ}$$

Now we can do stoichiometry:

$$\frac{70.0\ \cancel{\text{g } NH_3}}{1} \times \frac{1\text{ mole } NH_3}{17.0\ \cancel{\text{g } NH_3}} = 4.12\text{ moles } NH_3$$

$$\frac{4.12\ \cancel{\text{moles } NH_3}}{1} \times \frac{1{,}126\text{ kJ}}{2\ \cancel{\text{moles } NH_3}} = \underline{2{,}320\text{ kJ}}$$

When 70.0 grams of ammonia are made this way, 2,320 kJ of energy are produced.

6. a. In this reaction, there is 1 molecule of gas on the reactants side and no molecules of gas on the products side. The reactants have a higher entropy. This means ΔS is negative.

   b. In this reaction, there are no molecules of gas on the reactants side and 2 molecules of gas on the products side. This means that the products are more disordered than the reactants, so ΔS is positive.

   c. In this reaction, there are 2 molecules of gas on the reactants side and 4 molecules of gas on the products side. This means that the products are more disordered than the reactants, so ΔS is positive.

7. Table 13.4 lists all of the substances in this reaction, so we can use it and equation 13.5 to solve this problem:

$$\Delta S^\circ = (1\ \cancel{\text{mole}} \times 76.1\frac{\text{J}}{\cancel{\text{mole}} \times \text{K}}) - [(1\ \cancel{\text{mole}} \times 69.9\ \frac{\text{J}}{\cancel{\text{mole}} \times \text{K}}) + (1\ \cancel{\text{mole}}) \times 38.2\frac{\text{J}}{\cancel{\text{mole}} \times \text{K}}\ )] = \underline{-32.0\frac{\text{J}}{\text{K}}}$$

8. This problem gives us ΔH and ΔS and asks us at what temperature the reaction is spontaneous. In other words, we need to see for what temperatures ΔG is negative. Thus:

$$\Delta H - T\Delta S < 0$$

In order to use this equation, though, we need to get our units consistent:

$$\frac{-324\text{ J}}{\text{mole} \times \text{K}} \times \frac{1\text{ kJ}}{1{,}000\text{ J}} = -0.324\ \frac{\text{kJ}}{\text{mole} \times \text{K}}$$

Now we can use the equation:

$$-1{,}023\ \frac{\text{kJ}}{\text{mole}} - T \times (-0.324\ \frac{\text{kJ}}{\text{mole} \times \text{K}}) < 0$$

We can solve this equation like any algebraic equation. We just need to remember that if we divide or multiply by a negative number, we must reverse the inequality sign:

$$T \times (0.324\ \frac{\text{kJ}}{\text{mole} \times \text{K}}) < 1{,}023\ \frac{\text{kJ}}{\text{mole}}$$

$$T < \frac{1023\ \frac{\cancel{\text{kJ}}}{\cancel{\text{mole}}}}{0.324\ \frac{\cancel{\text{kJ}}}{\cancel{\text{mole}} \times \text{K}}}$$

$$T < 3.16 \times 10^{3}\text{ K}$$

This reaction, then, is spontaneous for all temperatures lower than 3.16×10^{3} K.

9. The ΔH of a reaction is the difference in energy between the products and the reactants. According to this diagram, the products look to be at an energy of 200 kJ while the reactants look to be at an energy of 1200 kJ. This means that ΔH = 200 kJ - 1200 kJ = −1000 kJ. The activation energy is defined as the difference in energy between the intermediate phase and the reactants. Thus, the activation energy = 1500 kJ – 1200 kJ = 300 kJ. The reaction is exothermic.

10. This reaction is at 298 K, so we can use table 13.5 and equation 13.7 to calculate ΔG:

$$\Delta G^\circ = (6 \cancel{\text{moles}} \times -175 \frac{\text{kJ}}{\cancel{\text{mole}}}) - (2 \cancel{\text{moles}} \times 125 \frac{\text{kJ}}{\cancel{\text{mole}}}) = -1.300 \times 10^3 \text{ kJ}$$

Since ΔG is negative, the reaction is spontaneous at 298 K.

SAMPLE CALCULATIONS FOR EXPERIMENT 13.1

Mass of 10 Tablespoons of Lye: 212 g

Mass of 1 Teaspoon of Lye: $\frac{212 \text{ g}}{30} = 7.07 \text{ g}$

The 30 is exact, as it represents an integer number of teaspoons. You did not measure the mass of 9.9 tablespoons or 10.1 tablespoons of lye. You measured the mass of exactly 10 tablespoons.

Mass of the Lye Used in the Experiment: $\frac{7.07 \text{ g}}{2} = 3.54 \text{ g}$

Initial Temperature: 24.8 °C

Final temperature: 28.4 °C

Mass of Calorimeter Contents: $100.0 \cancel{\text{mL}} \times 0.99 \frac{\text{g}}{\cancel{\text{mL}}} + 3.54 \text{ g} = 103 \text{ g}$

When you take 100.0 times 0.99, your significant figures allow you to report the answer as 99 grams. When you add 3.54 g to that, the rule of addition and subtraction allows you to report your answer to the ones place.

Change in Temperature: $\Delta T = 28.4 \text{ °C} - 24.8 \text{ °C} = 3.6 \text{ °C}$

$$q = m \times c \times \Delta T = (103 \cancel{\text{g}}) \times \left(4.1 \frac{\text{J}}{\cancel{\text{g}}\cancel{\text{°C}}}\right) \times (3.6 \cancel{\text{°C}}) = 1{,}500 \text{ J}$$

One molecule of NaOH has a mass of 40.0 amu, which means 1 mole NaOH = 40.0 g NaOH:

$$\text{Moles NaOH} = \frac{3.54\ \cancel{\text{g NaOH}}}{1} \times \frac{1\ \text{mole NaOH}}{40.0\ \cancel{\text{g NaOH}}} = 0.0885\ \text{moles NaOH}$$

$$\Delta H = \frac{1{,}500\ \text{J}}{0.0885\ \text{moles}} = 17{,}000\ \frac{\text{J}}{\text{mole}}$$

NOTE: Your answer might be quite different from ours. That's fine. It depends a lot on the brand of lye that you used.

SOLUTIONS TO THE EXTRA PRACTICE PROBLEMS FOR MODULE 13

1. Elements in their elemental form have a $\Delta H_f°$ of zero. Only Cl_2 (g) and N_2 (g) fit the bill. Br- is an ion, Cl is a polyatomic so Cl (g) is not in its elemental form, and N_2 (l) naturally exists as a gas, which means it also isn't in its elemental form.

2. Endothermic reactions have products at a higher energy than reactants. Thus, diagram II represents an endothermic reaction. The ΔH is roughly 55 kcals, which is the difference between the energy of the products and that of the reactants. Your number can range from 50 to 60, since it is being read from a graph.

3. The activation energy is given by the difference in energy between the intermediate state and the reactants. Thus, diagram II represents the reaction with the highest activation energy.

4. Yes, it is possible for the reaction to occur. For the reaction to occur, however, heat must be released, and that must disorder the surroundings more than the chemicals become ordered.

5. a. There are no gas molecules at all, so we look at liquid and aqueous states. There are 3 aqueous molecules on the reactants side and 1 on the products side. ΔS is negative.

   b. There are 9 gas molecules on the reactants side and 10 on the products side. ΔS is positive.

   c. There are no gas molecules on the reactants side and one on the products side. ΔS is positive.

   d. There is one gas molecule on the reactants side and none on the products side. ΔS is negative.

6. To use bond energies, we have to draw the Lewis structures:

$$O{=}C{=}O + 4\ H{-}Cl \longrightarrow CCl_4 + 2\ H{-}O{-}H$$

Now we can see what bonds need to be broken and what ones need to be formed. We need to break 2 C=O bonds (each worth of 799 kJ/mole) and 4 H-Cl bonds (each worth 428 kJ/mole). In the process, 4 C-Cl bonds (worth 327 kJ/mole each) and 4 H-O bonds (worth 459 kJ/moles each) are formed. Equation 13.6, then, looks like this:

$$\Delta H = [(2\ \text{moles}) \times (799\ \frac{\text{kJ}}{\text{mole}}) + (4\ \text{moles}) \times (428\ \frac{\text{kJ}}{\text{mole}})] - [(4\ \text{moles}) \times (327\ \frac{\text{kJ}}{\text{mole}}) + (4\ \text{moles}) \times (459\ \frac{\text{kJ}}{\text{mole}})]$$

$$\Delta H = \underline{166\ \text{kJ}}$$

7. The $\Delta H_f°$ of O_2 (g) is zero. The rest are in table 13.3:

$$\Delta H° = [(4\ \text{moles} \times 90.3\ \frac{\text{kJ}}{\text{mole}}) + (6\ \text{moles} \times -242\ \frac{\text{kJ}}{\text{mole}})] - (4\ \text{moles} \times -45.9\ \frac{\text{kJ}}{\text{mole}})$$

$$\Delta H° = \underline{-907\ \text{kJ}}$$

8. We need to use table 13.4 to solve this:

$$\Delta S° = [(4\ \text{moles} \times 211\ \frac{\text{J}}{\text{mole} \times \text{K}}) + (6\ \text{moles} \times 189\ \frac{\text{J}}{\text{mole} \times \text{K}})] - [(4\ \text{moles} \times 193\ \frac{\text{J}}{\text{mole} \times \text{K}}) + (5\ \text{moles} \times 205.0\ \frac{\text{J}}{\text{mole} \times \text{K}})]$$

$$\Delta S° = \underline{181\ \frac{\text{J}}{\text{K}}}$$

9. We need to see for what temperatures ΔH is negative. Thus:

$$\Delta H - T\Delta S < 0$$

In order to use this equation, though, we need to get our units consistent:

$$\frac{-114\ \cancel{J}}{mole \times K} \times \frac{1\ kJ}{1{,}000\ \cancel{J}} = -0.114\ \frac{kJ}{mole \times K}$$

Now we can use the equation:

$$-623\ \frac{kJ}{mole} - T \times \left(-0.114\ \frac{kJ}{mole \times K}\right) < 0$$

We can solve this equation like any algebraic equation. We just need to remember that if we divide or multiply by a negative number, we must reverse the inequality sign:

$$T \times \left(0.114\ \frac{kJ}{mole \times K}\right) < 623\ \frac{kJ}{mole}$$

$$T < \frac{623\ \frac{\cancel{kJ}}{\cancel{mole}}}{0.114\ \frac{\cancel{kJ}}{\cancel{mole} \times K}}$$

$$\underline{T < 5.46 \times 10^3\ K}$$

TEST FOR MODULE 13

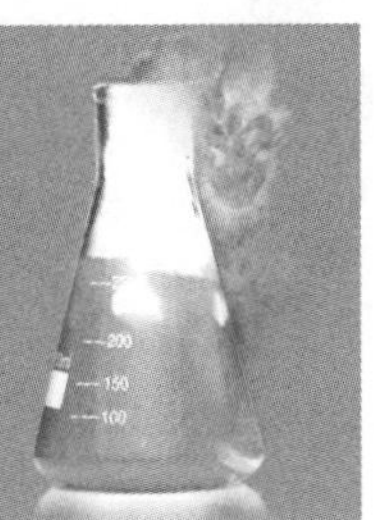

(Use tables at end of test to look up values for this test.)

1. (4 pts) True or False: Energy can be thought of as product in an exothermic reaction.

2. (4 pts) ΔH stands for:
   a. The potential energy associated with a substance
   b. The enthalpy of a molecule
   c. The potential energy change associated with a reaction
   d. None of the above

Questions 3–5 refer to the following energy diagrams:

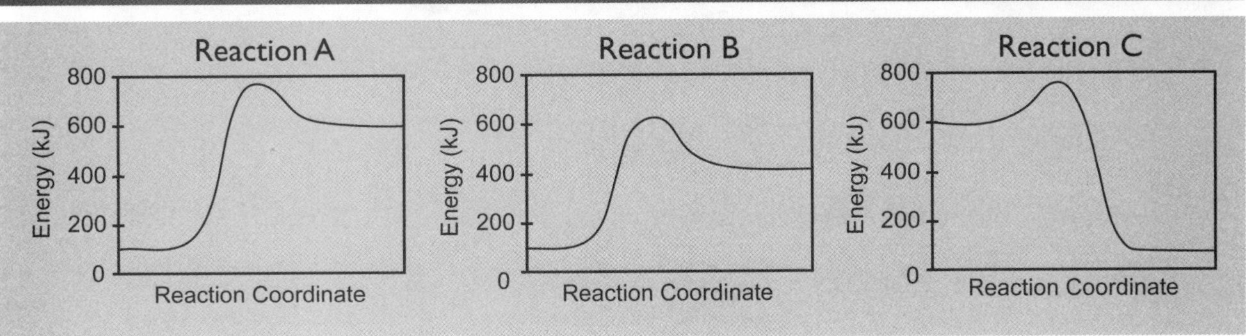

3. (4 pts) Which diagram(s) represent(s) an exothermic reaction?
   a. Reaction A
   b. Reaction B
   c. Reaction C
   d. None of the reactions

4. (4 pts) Which diagram represents the reaction that is easiest to start?
   a. Reaction A
   b. Reaction B
   c. Reaction C
   d. None of the reactions

5. (4 pts) Which reaction has a ΔH of 300 kJ?
   a. Reaction A
   b. Reaction B
   c. Reaction C
   d. None of the reactions

MOD 13

6. (4 pts) Which of the following is an accepted way of determining the ΔH of a reaction?
   a. Experimentally with calorimetery
   b. Mathematically using bond energies
   c. Mathematically using published ΔH_f values and Hess's law
   d. All of the above
   e. None of the above

7. (4 pts) What does a bond strength of 602 kJ/mol for a C=C bond mean?
   a. It tells the amount of energy required to break 1 mole of C=C bonds.
   b. It tells how much energy will be absorbed when 1 mole of C=C bonds are broken.
   c. It tells how much energy will be released when 1 mole of C=C bonds are formed.
   d. All of the above
   e. None of the above

8. (4 pts) A quantity that depends solely on the final destination and not on the way you get to the destination is called a(n) ________________.
   a. Inconclusive quantity
   b. State function
   c. Entropy
   d. Hess's law
   e. None of the above

9. (4 pts) What is the energy necessary to start a chemical reaction?
   a. ΔH
   b. ΔH_f
   c. ΔS
   d. Activation energy
   e. None of the above

10. (4 pts) Which of the following would definitely have a higher entropy than a 50.0 g sample of $CO_2(g)$ at 56 °C?
    a. 25.0 g $CO_2(g)$ at 60 °C
    b. 57.0 g $CO_2(l)$ at 56 °C
    c. 25.0 g $CO_2(l)$ at 50 °C
    d. 57.0 g $CO_2(g)$ at 60 °C
    e. There is not enough information to answer this question.

11. (4 pts) If a reaction is endothermic and has a positive ΔS, what should you do to the temperature in order to make sure the reaction will run spontaneously?
    a. Lower the temperature
    b. Raise the temperature
    c. Keep the temperature constant

12. (4 pts) Which of the following conditions ensures a spontaneous reaction?
    a. $\Delta H < 0$
    b. $\Delta S < 0$
    c. $\Delta G < 0$
    d. All of the above
    e. None of the above

13. (4 pts) If a reaction has a $\Delta H = 188$ kJ/mole and a $\Delta S = 3770$ J / (mole K), at what temperature range would this reaction be spontaneous?
    a. $T < 49.9$ K
    b. $T > 49.9$ K
    c. $T < 0.02$ K
    d. $T > 0.02$ K
    e. None of the above

14. (6 pts) Give the sign of ΔS in the following reactions:
    a. $CaSO_4$ (s) → CaO (s) + SO_3 (g)
    b. $2H_2$ (g) + O_2 (g) → $2H_2O$ (g)
    c. $2AgNO_3$ (aq) + $Mg(OH)_2$ (aq) → $2AgOH$ (s) + $Mg(NO_3)_2$ (aq)

For the following problems, please provide the correct answer and show the work that is needed to solve the problem.

15. (8 pts) Use bond energies to determine the ΔH for the combustion of methane (CH_4).

16. (8 pts) Use Hess's law to determine the ΔH for the combustion of liquid methanol (CH_3OH).

17. (8 pts) Using your answer from question 16, how much energy will you get from burning 245.0 g of methanol in excess oxygen?

18. (8 pts) The ΔS is 209.6 J/K for the following reaction:
    C_2H_4 (g) + $3O_2$ (g) → $2CO_2$ (g) + $2H_2O$ (g)

    What is the absolute entropy of O_2 (g)?

19. (4 pts) What is ΔG for the following reaction at 298 K?
    $2C_6H_6$ (l) + $15O_2$ (g) → $12CO_2$ (g) + $6H_2O$ (g)

20. (6 pts) If a reaction has a ΔH of –120.0 kJ/mole and is spontaneous for all temperatures less than 200.0 K, what is its ΔS?

TABLE 13.2 BOND ENERGIES

Chemical Bond	Bond Energy (kJ/mole)	Chemical Bond	Bond Energy (kJ/mole)
C-H	411	H-H	432
C-Cl	327	H-O	459
C-C	346	H-Cl	428
C-N	305	O=O	494
C-O	358	N≡N	942
C=C	602	N-H	386
C=O	799	Cl-Cl	240
C≡C	835	Br-Br	190

TABLE 13.3 STANDARD ENTHALPIES OF FORMATION IN kJ/mole

Substance	$\Delta H_f°$	Substance	$\Delta H_f°$	Substance	$\Delta H_f°$	Substance	$\Delta H_f°$
H_2O (g)	-242	NO_2 (g)	33.2	$Ca(OH)_2$ (s)	-987	C_2H_6O(l)	-278
H_2O (l)	-286	NH_3 (g)	-45.9	$CaCO_3$ (s)	-1207	C_2H_4 (g)	52.5
SO_3 (g)	-396	CO_2 (g)	-394	C_2H_6 (g)	-84.7	C_4H_{10} (g)	-126
NO (g)	90.3	CaO (s)	-635	CH_3OH (l)	-239	H_2SO_4 (l)	-814

TABLE 13.4 STANDARD ABSOLUTE ENTROPIES IN J/mole × K

Substance	S°	Substance	S°	Substance	S°	Substance	S°
H_2O (g)	189	NO_2 (g)	240	$Ca(OH)_2$ (s)	76.1	C_2H_6O(l)	161
H_2O (l)	69.9	NH_3 (g)	193	$CaCO_3$ (s)	92.9	C_2H_4 (g)	219
SO_3 (g)	257	CO_2 (g)	214	C_2H_6 (g)	230	C_4H_{10} (g)	260
NO (g)	211	CaO (s)	38.2	CH_3OH (l)	127	H_2SO_4 (l)	157

TABLE 13.5 STANDARD GIBBS FREE ENERGIES OF FORMATION IN kJ/mole

Substance	$\Delta G_f°$	Substance	$\Delta G_f°$	Substance	$\Delta G_f°$	Substance	$\Delta G_f°$
CH_4 (g)	-50.8	NO_2 (g)	240	$CaSO_4$ (s)	-1,320	C_2H_6O (l)	-175
C_6H_6 (l)	125	H_2O (l)	-237	$CaCO_3$ (s)	-1,129	$CaCl_2$ (s)	-750
CO (g)	-137	H_2O (g)	-229	H_2CO_3 (aq)	-623	HCl (aq)	-131
CO_2 (g)	-394	CaO (s)	38.2	CH_3OH (l)	-166	$Ca(OH)_2$ (s)	-897

SOLUTIONS TO THE TEST FOR MODULE 13

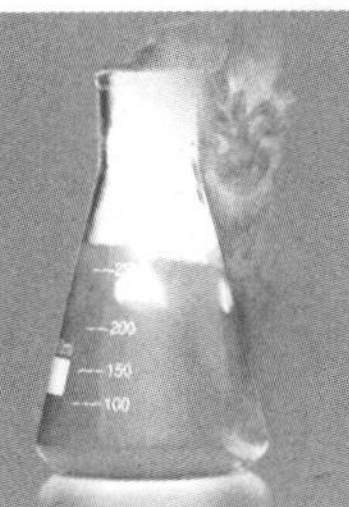

1. (4 pts) True
Energy can be thought of as product in an exothermic reaction.

2. (4 pts) c. The potential energy change associated with a reaction

3. (4 pts) c. Reaction C
The products have less energy than the reactants.

4. (4 pts) c. Reaction C
The hump is the smallest. The exothermic reaction requires less work.

5. (4 pts) b. Reaction B
The ending energy (400 kJ) minus the beginning energy (100 kJ) is around 300 kJ.

6. (4 pts) d. All of the above

7. (4 pts) d. All of the above

8. (4 pts) b. State function

9. (4 pts) d. Activation energy

10. (4 pts) d. 57.0 g $CO_2(g)$ at 60°C
The more molecules there are to keep track of, the more disordered the sample.

11. (4 pts) b. Raise the temperature
Remember, $\Delta G = \Delta H - T \times \Delta S$, and ΔG must be negative to make a reaction spontaneous. For endothermic reactions, ΔH is positive. If ΔS is also positive, then

the only way to make ΔG negative is to have a large value for T. That way, a large number will be subtracted from the ΔH. If the number is large enough, ΔG will be negative.

12. (4 pts) c. $\Delta G < 0$

13. (4 pts) b. $T > 49.9$ K
To make the reaction spontaneous, ΔG must be negative or T × ΔS > ΔH.
The energy units must be the same, ΔS = 3770 J / (mole K) = 3.770 kJ/mol K.

$$\text{Solving for T} = \Delta H / \Delta S = \frac{188 \cancel{\text{kJ/mol}}}{3.770 \cancel{\text{kj/mol}}\ \text{K}} = 49.9\ \text{K}$$

So any $T > 49.9$ K will make the reaction spontaneous.

14. (6 pts)
    a. (2 pts) Positive
    There are more gas molecules on the products side.

    b. (2 pts) Negative
    There are more gas molecules on the reactants side.

    c. (2 pts) Negative
    There are more aqueous molecules on the reactants side.

15. (8 pts: 4 pts for the Lewis structures, and 4 pts for the answer) – 802 kJ
The ideal way to calculate ΔH is with Hess's law. However, table 13.2 does not list methane. Thus, we cannot use Hess's law. We must therefore use bond energies.

$$CH_4 + O{=}O + O{=}O \longrightarrow O{=}C{=}O + H{-}O{-}H + H{-}O{-}H$$

$$\Delta H = [(4 \cancel{\text{moles}} \times 411 \frac{\text{kJ}}{\cancel{\text{mole}}}) + (2 \cancel{\text{moles}} \times 494 \frac{\text{kJ}}{\cancel{\text{mole}}})] - [(2 \cancel{\text{moles}} \times 799 \frac{\text{kJ}}{\cancel{\text{mole}}}) + (4 \cancel{\text{moles}} \times 459 \frac{\text{kJ}}{\cancel{\text{mole}}})]$$

$$\Delta H = \underline{-802\ \text{kJ}}$$

16. (8 pts: 4 pts for the balanced equation, and 4 pts for the answer) $\underline{-1{,}278 \text{ kJ}}$
The combustion of CH_3OH (l) is given by:

$$2CH_3OH\ (l) + 3O_2\ (g) \rightarrow 2CO_2\ (g) + 4H_2O\ (g)$$

Since all of the compounds in this equation are in table 13.2, we can use Hess's law. Remember that the ΔH_f of O_2 (g) is zero because it is an element in its elemental form!

$$\Delta H° = [(2\ \cancel{\text{moles}} \times -394 \frac{\text{kJ}}{\cancel{\text{mole}}}) + (4\ \cancel{\text{moles}} \times -242 \frac{\text{kJ}}{\cancel{\text{mole}}})] - (2\ \cancel{\text{moles}} \times -239 \frac{\text{kJ}}{\cancel{\text{mole}}})$$

$$\Delta H° = \underline{-1{,}278 \text{ kJ}}$$

17. (8 pts: 4 pts for each step If the answer to question 16 was wrong, give the student full credit as long as he used it properly in this question.) $\underline{4{,}890 \text{ kJ}}$
The answer to question 16 tells us that this reaction has 1,278 kJ as a product. Thus, we can use it in stoichiometry:

$$\frac{245.0\ \cancel{\text{g } CH_3OH}}{1} \times \frac{1 \text{ mole } CH_3OH}{32.0\ \cancel{\text{g } CH_3OH}} = 7.66 \text{ moles } CH_3OH$$

$$\frac{7.66\ \cancel{\text{moles } CH_3OH}}{1} \times \frac{1{,}278 \text{ kJ}}{2\ \cancel{\text{moles } CH_3OH}} = 4{,}890 \text{ kJ}$$

18. (8 pts: 4 pts for setting up the equation, and 4 pts for the answer) $\underline{126 \frac{\text{J}}{\text{mole} \times \text{K}}}$
Remember, only enthalpies of formation of elements in their natural form are zero. Thus, O_2 (g) does have an absolute entropy. To get it, we will use equation 13.5. The only unknown will be the ΔS of O_2, so we can solve for it:

$$209.6 \frac{\text{J}}{\text{K}} = [(2\ \cancel{\text{moles}} \times 189 \frac{\text{J}}{\cancel{\text{mole}} \times \text{K}}) + (2\ \cancel{\text{moles}} \times 214 \frac{\text{J}}{\cancel{\text{mole}} \times \text{K}})]$$

$$- [(1\ \cancel{\text{mole}} \times 219 \frac{\text{J}}{\cancel{\text{mole}} \times \text{K}}) + (3 \text{ moles} \times \Delta S_{O_2})$$

$$\Delta S_{O_2} = \frac{2 \times (189 \frac{\text{J}}{\text{K}}) + 2 \times (214 \frac{\text{J}}{\text{K}}) - 219 \frac{\text{J}}{\text{K}} - 209.6}{3 \text{ moles}} = \underline{126 \frac{\text{J}}{\text{mole} \times \text{K}}}$$

MOD 13

19. (4 pts) <u>– 6.352 kJ</u>
This is also a Hess's law problem. Remember, ΔG_f of an element in its natural form is zero!

$$\Delta G° = [(12 \cancel{\text{moles}} \times -394 \frac{\text{kJ}}{\cancel{\text{mole}}}) + (6 \cancel{\text{moles}} \times -229 \frac{\text{kJ}}{\cancel{\text{mole}}})] - (2 \cancel{\text{moles}} \times 125 \frac{\text{kJ}}{\cancel{\text{mole}}})$$

$$\Delta G° = \underline{-6{,}352 \text{ kJ}}$$

20. (6 pts) $\underline{-0.6000 \frac{\text{kJ}}{\text{mole} \times \text{K}}}$

To be spontaneous, $\Delta G < 0$. It if it spontaneous for all temperatures less than 200 K, then ΔG must equal 0 at 200 K. Thus, $\Delta H - T \times \Delta S = 0$

$$-120.0 \frac{\text{kJ}}{\text{mole}} - 200.0 \text{ K} \times (\Delta S) = 0$$

$$\Delta S = \frac{-120.0 \frac{\text{kJ}}{\text{mole}}}{200.0\text{K}} = \underline{-0.6000 \frac{\text{kJ}}{\text{mole} \times \text{K}}} \text{ or } -600.0 \frac{\text{J}}{\text{mole} \times \text{K}}$$

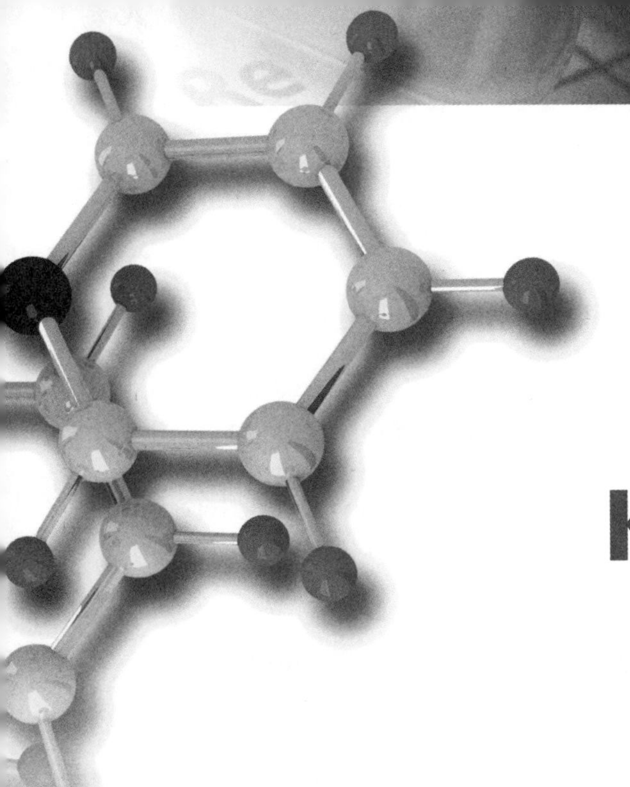

KINETICS

SOLUTIONS TO THE MODULE 14 REVIEW QUESTIONS

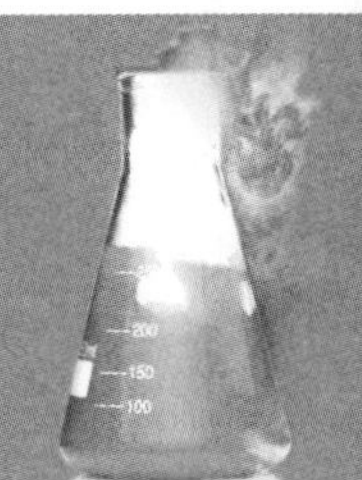

1. In order for molecules to react, they must collide with each other so that they are close enough to exchange or transfer electrons.

2. Since rate increases with increasing temperature, the reaction at higher temperature will run faster.

3. In order for reactants to react, they must first collide. The more likely collisions are, the faster the reaction will go. When reactants get more concentrated, the vessel that contains them gets more crowded, increasing the chance for collisions between reactants.

4. The units of rate constant depend on the overall order of the reaction. Thus, since the units are different, the overall order must be different as well. The second reaction will be faster than the first because the rate constant is part of the rate equation. Based on the rate equation, if the rate constant is larger, the rate should be larger.

5. When the order of a chemical reaction is zero with respect to one of its reactants, the reaction rate is independent of the concentration of that reactant. Therefore, doubling the concentration of that reactant will not affect the rate at all. This means that the rate will stay the same.

6. The student is not correct. Although temperature is not directly in the rate equation, the value for the rate constant changes with temperature. Thus, since the rate constant is in the rate equation, and since the rate constant depends on temperature, the rate must also depend on temperature.

7. Chemicals that increase reaction rate without getting used up in the process are called catalysts.

8. The higher the activation energy, the lower the reaction rate. Thus, reaction 2 is the fastest.

9. Heterogeneous catalysts are in a different phase from any of the reactants in the chemical equation. Homogeneous catalysts, however, are in the same phase as the reactants. This is the main difference between them. They also use different means to reduce the activation energy of a reaction, so that is an acceptable answer as well.

10. A catalytic converter speeds up the conversion of poisonous carbon monoxide from car exhaust into nonpoisonous carbon dioxide.

SOLUTIONS TO THE PRACTICE PROBLEMS FOR MODULE 14

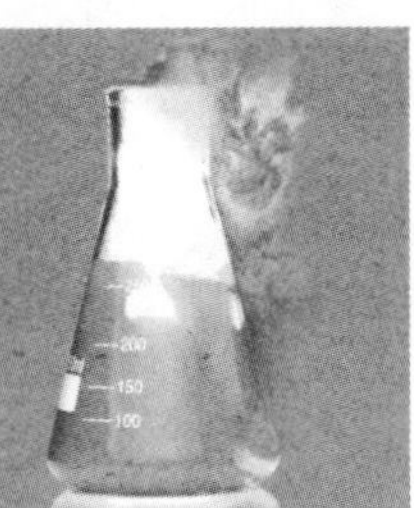

1. Since the souring of milk is governed by a chemical reaction, storing the milk in the refrigerator will cause the reaction to run at a lower temperature. A lower temperature slows down the reaction that causes souring, making the milk last longer.

2. The rate equation for this reaction will look like this:

$$R = k[NO]^x[O_2]^y$$

To figure out k, x, and y, we have to look at the data from the experiment. The value for x can be determined by comparing 2 trials in which the concentration of NO changes, but the concentration of O_2 stays the same. This would correspond to trials 1 and 2. In these 2 trials, the concentration of NO doubled, and the rate went up by a factor of 4. This means that x = 2 because the only way we can get a 4-fold increase in rate from a doubling of the concentration is by squaring the concentration. The value for y can be determined by looking at trials 1 and 3, where the concentration of NO stayed the same but the concentration of O_2 doubled. When that happened, the rate increased by a factor of 2. Since rate doubled when concentration doubled, that means y = 1. Thus, the rate equation becomes:

$$R = k[NO]^2[O_2]$$

Now that we have x and y, we only need to find out the value for k. We can do this by using any one of the trials in the experiment and plugging the data into the equation. The only unknown will be k, and we can therefore solve for it:

$$R = k[NO]^2[O_2]$$

$$0.0281\ \frac{M}{s} = k \times (0.0250\ M)^2 \times (0.0253\ M)$$

$$k = \frac{0.0281\ \frac{\cancel{M}}{s}}{(0.0250\ M)^2 \times (0.0253\ \cancel{M})} = 1.78 \times 10^3\ \frac{1}{M^2\,s}$$

Thus, the final rate equation is:

$$R = (1.78 \times 10^3 \frac{1}{M^2\,s}) \times [NO]^2[O_2]$$

3. The rate equation will take on the form:

$$R = k[C_4Cl_9OH]^x[F^-]^y$$

To determine x and y, we look at trials where the concentration of one reactant stayed the same and the concentration of the other reactant changed. In trials 1 and 2, the concentration of C_4Cl_9OH remained the same but the concentration of F^- doubled. When that happened, the rate stayed the same. This means that y = 0 because the rate is not affected by the change in concentration of F^-. In the same way, between trials 2 and 3, the F^- concentration remained constant, but the C_4Cl_9OH concentration doubled. When that happened, the rate doubled. This means x = 1. The rate equation, then, looks like:

$$R = k[C_4Cl_9OH][F^-]^0 \text{ or } R = k[C_4Cl_9OH]$$

To solve for k, we can use the data from any trial and plug it into our rate equation. We can then solve for k:

$$R = k[C_4Cl_9OH]$$

$$0.0202 \frac{M}{s} = k \times (0.25\ M)$$

$$k = \frac{0.0202 \frac{\cancel{M}}{s}}{(0.25\ \cancel{M})} = 0.081 \frac{1}{s}$$

The overall rate equation, then is

$$R = (0.081 \frac{1}{s}) \times [C_4Cl_9OH]$$

4. Second order with respect to I_2 means that the exponent in the rate equation that is attached to I_2 equals 2. In the same way, first order in Br_2 means that the exponent tied to that reactant is 1. The overall order, therefore is 3. Since the rate constant is given, we can say that the rate equation is:

$$R = (1.1 \times 10^{-3} \frac{1}{M^2\,s}) \times [I_2]^2[Br_2]$$

To determine the rate, then, we just need to plug the concentrations into the equation:

$$R = (1.1 \times 10^{-3} \frac{1}{\cancel{M^2}\ s}) \times (1.0\ \cancel{M})^2(1.0\ M) = \underline{1.1 \times 10^{-3} \frac{M}{s}}$$

5. The rate of a chemical reaction doubles for every 10 °C that the temperature is raised. Alternatively, the rate decreases by a factor of 2 for every 10 °C that the temperature is lowered. In this problem, the temperature is lowered for 6 ten-degree increments. This means that the old rate must be divided by 2 for a total of 6 times:

$$R = 0.0167 \frac{M}{s} \div 2 \div 2 \div 2 \div 2 \div 2 \div 2 = \underline{0.000261 \frac{M}{s}}$$

The rate at the lower temperature is <u>0.000261 M/s</u>.

6. Since chemical reaction rate doubles for every 10 °C increment, to increase the rate of the reaction by a factor of 32, we just need to raise the temperature by 5 ten-degree increments. That way, we will multiply the old rate by 2×2×2×2×2, which equals 32. To increase the reaction rate by a factor of 32, we just raise the temperature by 50 degrees. Therefore, the new temperature should be 30 °C + 50°C = <u>80 °C</u>.

7. The rate constant increases with increasing temperature, so that fact alone rules out graphs I and II. We also know, however, that the rate constant increases dramatically with temperature. This rules out graph IV. <u>Graph III</u> looks like the one presented in the module, so it is the correct answer.

8. This is a <u>heterogeneous catalyst</u> because it is in a different phase than the reactants.

9. A catalyst lowers the activation energy, which increases the rate of the reaction. The better the catalyst, the lower the activation energy and hence the faster the reaction. Thus, the diagram with the largest activation energy would correspond to the reaction without a catalyst; the one with the lowest activation energy would correspond to the reaction with the best catalyst, and the one with a medium activation energy would correspond to the reaction with the other catalyst. Thus, <u>III represents the reaction with no catalyst, I represents the reaction with the catalyst that speeds up the rate 3x, and II represents the reaction with the catalyst that speeds up rate 10x</u>.

10. A catalyst is a substance that does not get used up in the reaction. Thus, in a reaction mechanism, a catalyst must be a reactant in the first step of the mechanism and a product in the last step. Thus, Cl is the catalyst here. Since it is in the same phase as the reactants, it is a homogeneous catalyst.

SOLUTIONS TO THE EXTRA PRACTICE PROBLEMS FOR MODULE 14

1. Reaction rate has units of M/s. When solving for the rate constant, we divide by the concentrations of the reactants raised to their orders. To get these units for the rate constant, then, the rate must be divided by M^2. That means the overall order is 2.

2. If the order is 3, then we must raise the concentration to the third power. If we quadruple the concentration, that would be like raising 4 to the third power, which is 64. Thus, the rate increases by a factor of 64.

3. The rate equation for this reaction will look like:

$$R = k[NO]^x[Cl_2]^y$$

To figure out k, x, and y, we have to look at the data from the experiment. The value for x can be determined by comparing 2 trials in which the concentration of NO changes, but the concentration of Cl_2 stays the same. This would correspond to trials 1 and 2. In these 2 trials, the concentration of NO doubled, and the rate went up by a factor of 4. This means that x = 2 because the only way we can get a 4-fold increase in rate from a doubling of the concentration is by squaring the concentration. The value for y can be determined by looking at trials 2 and 3, where the concentration of NO stayed the same but the concentration of O_2 doubled. When that happened, the rate increased by a factor of 2. Since rate doubled when concentration doubled, that means y = 1. Thus, the rate equation becomes:

$$R = k[NO]^2[Cl_2]$$

Now that we have x and y, we only need to find out the value for k. We can do this by using any one of the trials in the experiment and plugging the data into the equation. The only unknown will be k, and we can therefore solve for it:

$$R = k[NO]^2[Cl_2]$$

$$0.113\,\frac{M}{s} = k \times (0.100\ M)^2 \times (0.050\ M)$$

$$k = \frac{0.113\,\frac{\cancel{M}}{s}}{(0.0100\ M^2) \times (0.050\ \cancel{M})} = 230\ \frac{1}{M^2\,s}$$

Thus, the final rate equation is:

$$R = (230 \frac{1}{M^2 s}) \times [NO]^2[Cl]_2$$

4. The rate equation will take on the form:

$$R = k[C_3H_6Br_2]^x[I^-]^y$$

To determine x and y, we look at trials where the concentration of one reactant stayed the same and the concentration of the other reactant changed. In trials 1 and 2, the concentration of I^- remained the same but the concentration of $C_3H_6Br_2$ doubled. When that happened, the rate doubled. This means that x = 1. In trials 1 and 3, the $C_3H_6Br_2$ concentration remained constant, but the I^- concentration doubled. When that happened, the rate doubled. This means y = 1. The rate equation, then, looks like:

$$R = k[C_3H_6Br_2][I^-]$$

To solve for k, we can use the data from any trial and plug it into our rate equation. We can then solve for k:

$$R = k[C_3H_6Br_2][I^-]$$

$$0.234 \frac{M}{s} = k \times (0.100\ M) \times (0.200\ M)$$

$$k = \frac{0.234 \frac{\cancel{M}}{s}}{(0.100\ \cancel{M})\ (0.200\ M)} = 11.7 \frac{1}{M \times s}$$

The overall rate equation, then is

$$R = (11.7 \frac{1}{M s}) \times [C_3H_6Br_2][I^-]$$

5. Since chemical reaction rate doubles for every 10 °C increment, then to increase the rate of the reaction by a factor of 16, we just need to raise the temperature by 4 ten-degree increments. That way, we will multiply the old rate by 2×2×2×2, which equals 16. To increase the reaction rate by a factor of 16, we just raise the temperature by 40 degrees. Therefore, the new temperature should be 25 °C + 40 °C = 65 °C.

6. A catalyst is used up in an early step and remade in a later step so that its concentration does not change. This is happening with Cl_2. It is a homogeneous catalyst, as it is in the same phase as the reactants.

7. It lowers the size of the hill.

TEST FOR MODULE 14

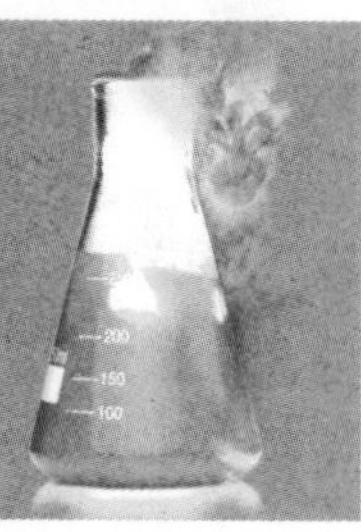

1. (4 pts) A chemist performs a reaction by adding 50 g of NaOH pellets to 500 mL of a 3.0 M HCl solution. What could the chemist do to increase the rate of the reaction?
   a. Crush the pellets into a powder increasing the surface area.
   b. Increase the concentration of HCl to 5.0 M.
   c. Add heat to the reaction.
   d. All of the above
   e. None of the above

2. (4 pts) A test done under standard conditions is referred to as the:
   a. STP
   b. Control
   c. Rate constant
   d. Kinetics
   e. None of the above

Use this general rate equation for questions 3–6: $R = k [A]^x [B]^y$

3. (4 pts) Which is the rate constant?
   a. R
   b. k
   c. [A]
   d. x + y
   e. None of the above

4. (4 pts) Which one is a molarity?
   a. R
   b. k
   c. [A]
   d. x + y
   e. None of the above

5. (4 pts) What is the overall order of the reaction?
   a. R
   b. k
   c. [A]
   d. x + y
   e. None of the above

6. (4 pts) Which is dependent on the temperature?
   a. R
   b. $[A]^x$
   c. [A]
   d. x + y
   e. None of the above

Use the following data table and chemical equation for questions 7–11.

The reaction is: $C_3H_6Cl_2 + 3Br^- \rightarrow C_3H_6 + 2Cl^- + 3Br^-$
Which gives the following data:

Trial	Initial Concentration of $C_3H_6Cl_2$(M)	Initial Concentration of Br^-(M)	Instantaneous Reaction Rate(M/s)
1	0.080	0.080	0.116
2	0.160	0.080	0.232
3	0.160	0.160	0.232

7. (4 pts) What is the generalized rate equation for this reaction?
   a. $R = k\,[C_3H_6Cl_2]\,[Br^-]^3$
   b. $R = k\,[C_3H_6Cl_2]^3\,[Br^-]$
   c. $R = k\,[C_3H_6Cl_2]\,[Br^-]$
   d. $R = k\,[C_3H_6Cl_2]^x\,[Br^-]^y$

8. (4 pts) What would be the order of this reaction with respect to $C_3H_6Cl_2$?
   a. 0
   b. 1
   c. 2
   d. 4

9. (4 pts) What would be the order of this reaction with respect to Br^-?
   a. 0
   b. 1
   c. 2
   d. 4
   e. None of the above

10. (4 pts) What would the value for k be? (Do not include the units.)
   a. 3.0
   b. 1.5
   c. 0.69
   d. 18
   e. None of the above

11. (4 pts) What would the units on k be?
    a. 1/s
    b. M/s
    c. 1 / (M × s)
    d. 1 / (M^2 × s)
    e. None of the above

12. (4 pts) True or False: Sometimes the rate of a chemical reaction can be unaffected by the increase of concentration of one of the reactants.

13. (4 pts) A certain chemical reaction has 3 reactants. According to experiment, it is first order with respect to one of the reactants and second order with respect to each of the other 2 reactants. What is the overall order of the reaction?
    a. 3
    b. 4
    c. 5
    d. 6
    e. Cannot determine from the information given

14. (4 pts) Identify the catalyst in the following mechanism:
    Step 1. Ce^{4+} + Mn^{2+} → Ce^{3+} + Mn^{3+}
    Step 2. Ce^{4+} + Mn^{3+} → Ce^{3+} + Mn^{4+}
    Step 3. Mn^{4+} + Tl^{+} → Tl^{3+} + Mn^{2+}
    a. Ce^{4+}
    b. Mn^{2+}
    c. Mn^{3+}
    d. Mn^{4+}
    e. None of the above

Use the following diagrams to answer questions 15 and 16.

Reaction A

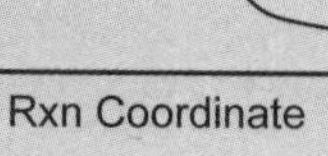

Reaction B

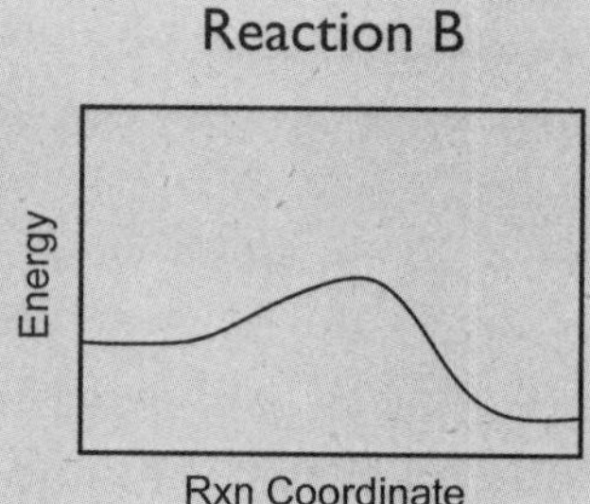

Reaction C

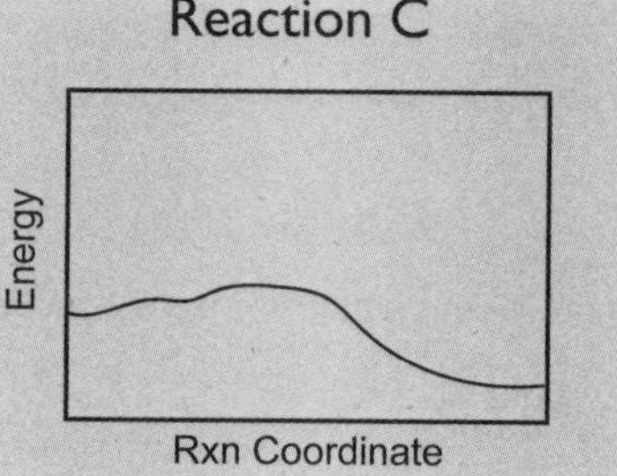

15. (4 pts) Which reaction has the fastest rate?
    a. Reaction A
    b. Reaction B
    c. Reaction C
    d. All of the reactions have the same rate.

16. (4 pts) If these are the same reaction, which reaction does not have a catalyst?
    a. Reaction A
    b. Reaction B
    c. Reaction C
    d. All of the reactions have a catalyst.

17. (4 pts) Two different reactions have exactly the same activation energy. What can you say about their reaction rates? Assume that temperature, reactant concentration, and order are the same in both reactions.

18. (4 pts) Give the definitions for heterogeneous and homogeneous catalysts.

19. (4 pts) A student is studying the rate of the following chemical reaction:

$$C_2H_4O + NaOH \rightarrow H_2O + NaC_2H_3O$$

Knowing that this is an exothermic reaction, he is measuring the rate of the reaction by timing how quickly the reaction vessel heats up. He notices that if he adds HCl to this reaction, the rate increases dramatically. He also determines that the HCl is being used up during the reaction. Is the HCl a catalyst for this reaction?

For the following questions, please provide the correct answer and show all the work that is needed to solve the problem.

20. (12 pts) A chemist does a rate analysis on the following reaction:

$$2NO + I_2 \rightarrow 2NOI$$

He gets the following data:

Trial	Initial Concentration of NO (M)	Initial Concentration of I_2 (M)	Instantaneous Reaction Rate(M/s)
1	1.5	1.0	1.25
2	1.5	2.0	2.50
3	3.0	2.0	10.0

What is the rate equation for this reaction?

21. (4 pts) Experiment tells us that the following reaction:

$$CH_3OH + KF \rightarrow KOH + CH_3F$$

is first order with respect to each of its reactants. We also know that the rate constant for this reaction is equal to 0.0123 1/Ms at 10 °C. What is the instantaneous rate for this reaction at 10 °C if the initial concentration of CH_3OH is 0.59 M and the initial concentration of KF is 1.22 M?

22. (4 pts) A chemist runs a reaction at 50 °C and determines its rate to be 0.00451 M/s. If she increases the temperature to 80 °C, what will the rate of the reaction be?

23. (4 pts) A chemist runs a reaction at 25 °C and determines that the reaction proceeds too quickly. He decides that the reaction needs to be slowed down by a factor of 4. At what temperature should he run the reaction?

SOLUTIONS TO THE TEST FOR MODULE 14

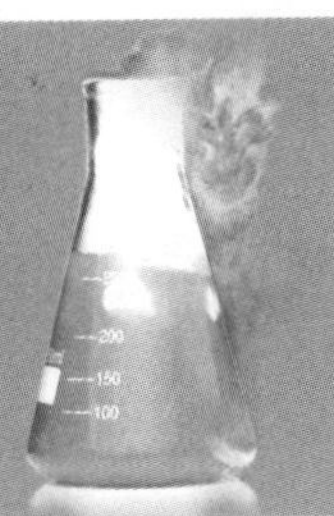

1. (4 pts) d. All of the above

2. (4 pts) b. Control

3. (4 pts) b. k

4. (4 pts) c. [A]

5. (4 pts) d. x + y

6. (4 pts) a. R

7. (4 pts) d. $R = k\,[C_3H_6Cl_2]^x\,[Br^-]^y$

8. (4 pts) b. 1
   In trials 1 and 2, the concentration of Br^- stayed the same, but the concentration of $C_3H_6Cl_2$ doubled. This resulted in a doubling of the reaction rate, thus x = 1.

9. (4 pts) a. 0
   In trials 2 and 3, the concentration of $C_3H_6Cl_2$ stayed the same, but the concentration of Br^- doubled. This resulted in no change in the rate, thus y = 0.

10. (4 pts) b. 1.5

$$R = k[C_3H_6Cl_2]$$

$$0.116\,\frac{M}{s} = k \times (0.080\ M)$$

$$k = \frac{0.116 \frac{\cancel{M}}{s}}{(0.080 \cancel{M})} = 1.5 \frac{1}{s}$$

11. (4 pts) a. 1/s

12. (4 pts) True
Sometimes the rate of a chemical reaction can be unaffected by the increase of concentration of one of the reactants if that reactant is a zero order reactant.

13. (4 pts) c. 5
The overall order is the sum of the individual orders, which is 5.

14. (4 pts) b. Mn^{2+}
It is not used up in the reaction. It is consumed in step 1 but produced in step 3.

15. (4 pts) c. Reaction C
The only thing that changes from diagram to diagram is the height of the hump. The faster the rate, the lower the height of the hump.

16. (4 pts) a. Reaction A

17. (4 pts) Their rates should be the same.

18. (4 pts) Homogeneous catalysts are catalysts that have the same phase as the reactants. Heterogeneous catalysts have a different phase than the reactants.

19. (4 pts) HCl is not a catalyst
It gets used up. Catalysts are never used up in the reaction.

20. (12 pts: 4 pts for each order, 4 pts for k) $R = (0.56 \frac{1}{M^2 s}) \times [NO]^2[I_2]$

The rate equation will have the form:

$$R = k\,[NO]^x[I_2]^y$$

In trials 1 and 2, the concentration of NO stayed the same but the concentration of I_2 doubled. This resulted in a doubling of the reaction rate, thus y = 1. In trials 2 and 3, the concentration of I_2 stayed the same, but the concentration of NO doubled. This resulted in a quadrupling of the reaction rate, thus x = 2.

$$R = k[NO]^2[I_2]$$

$$1.25\,\frac{M}{s} = k \times (1.5\ M)^2 \times (1.0\ M)$$

$$k = \frac{1.25\,\frac{\not{M}}{s}}{(1.5\ M)^2 \times (1.0\ \not{M})} = 0.56\,\frac{1}{M^2\,s}$$

The rate equation is

$$R = \left(0.56\,\frac{1}{M^2 s}\right) \times [NO]^2[I_2]$$

21. (4 pts) $\underline{0.0089\,\frac{M}{s}}$

We do not need the temperature to solve this problem. That was put there to fool you. This is simply an application of the rate equation. The problem tells us:

$$R = \left(0.0123\,\frac{1}{M\,s}\right) \times [CH_3OH] \times [KF]$$

$$R = \left(0.0123\,\frac{1}{\not{M}\,s}\right) \times (0.59\ \not{M}) \times (1.22\ M) = \underline{0.0089\,\frac{M}{s}}$$

22. (4 pts) 0.0361 M/s
The rate should double for every 10 °C increase. This rate, then, should go up by 2x2x2 = 8.

23. (4 pts) 5 °C
The rate will decrease by a factor of 2 for every 10 °C the temperature is lowered. To slow down by a factor of 4, the temperature must be dropped 20 °C.

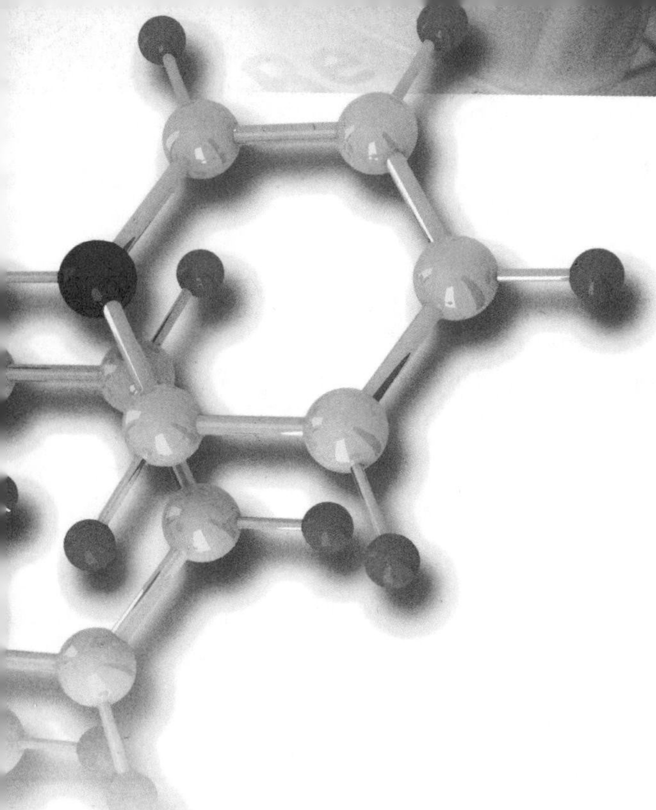

CHEMICAL EQUILIBRIUM

SOLUTIONS TO THE MODULE 15 REVIEW QUESTIONS

1. Chemical equilibrium is the point at which the rate of the forward reaction equals the rate of the reverse reaction.

2. Chemical reactions never stop, even when equilibrium is reached. Even though the concentrations of the substances involved do not change, the forward and reverse reactions are still going.

3. The larger the equilibrium constant, the more weighted the reaction is toward products. Thus, the first one will make more products.

4. The student is wrong because all chemical reactions are, in fact, equilibria. We just write those reactions with enormous Ks as reactions with only one direction because there are virtually no reactants left when those reactions reach equilibrium.

5. The concentrations of solids remain constant despite what happens in a chemical reaction. Make sure you understand that *concentration* and *amount* are 2 different things. Even if we change the amount of a solid, the concentration remains constant.

6. They are important because they determine the strength of an acid.

7. The pH scale ranges from 0 to 14.

8. Solution A is the acidic one. Any solution with pH below 7 is acidic.

9. All of these solutions are acids, so we are really asking which is the weakest because a low ionization constant means weak acid. Solution C has the highest

pH and therefore would be considered the weakest acid and have the lowest ionization constant.

10. Acid rain comes from pollutants like sulfur trioxide and nitrogen dioxide that react with water to form acids.

SOLUTIONS TO THE PRACTICE PROBLEMS FOR MODULE 15

1. According to equation 15.2, the equilibrium constant for this reaction is:

$$K = \frac{[N_2]_{eq}[H_2]^3_{eq}}{[NH_3]_{eq}{}^2}$$

Plugging those equilibrium concentrations into the equation:

$$K = \frac{(0.90\ M) \times (1.26\ M)^3}{(0.48\ M)^2} = 7.8\ M^2$$

The equilibrium constant is $\underline{7.8\ M^2}$.

2. To get the equation for the equilibrium constant, we have to realize that we ignore both $Pb(NO_3)_2$ and PbO because they are solids. Thus, equation 15.2 becomes:

$$K = [NO_2]^4_{eq}[O_2]_{eq}$$

Since we ignore solids, we ignore the amounts of both given in the problem. We only use the equilibrium concentrations of the gases. Plugging those equilibrium concentrations into the equation:

$$K = (0.36\ M)^4\ (0.090\ M) = \underline{1.5 \times 10^{-3}\ M^5}$$

The equilibrium is $\underline{1.5 \times 10^{-3}\ M^5}$.

3. a. When the equilibrium constant is very small, only reactants are present at any significant concentration once equilibrium is achieved. Thus, this reaction can be written as its reverse:

$$2NOCl\ (g) + O_2\ (g) \leftarrow 2NO_2\ (g) + Cl_2\ (g)$$

To make it a bit easier to read, we usually turn it around:

$$\underline{2NO_2\ (g) + Cl_2\ (g) \rightarrow 2NOCl\ (g) + O_2\ (g)}$$

b. This equilibrium constant is neither large nor small, so we cannot replace the double arrow with a single arrow.

c. When the equilibrium constant is very large, product is present in significant amounts only when the reaction reaches equilibrium. Thus, this reaction can be written with a single arrow:

$$2NO_2 \rightarrow N_2O_4$$

4. In this reaction, we must ignore water because it is a liquid. The equation for the equilibrium constant, then, is:

$$K = \frac{[CO_2]_{eq}}{[H_2CO_3]_{eq}}$$

If the concentrations are, in fact, equilibrium concentrations, then the equation should equal the value given for K.

$$K = \frac{(7.0 \cancel{M})}{(4.6 \cancel{M})} = 1.5$$

This is nowhere near the value of 2.3×10^4. Since our calculated value is too low, K must get bigger; thus, the reaction must shift toward products.

5. The equation for the equilibrium constant here is:

$$K = \frac{[SO_3]_{eq}^2}{[SO_2]_{eq}^2[O_2]_{eq}}$$

If the concentrations are, in fact, equilibrium concentrations, then the equation should equal the value given for K.

$$K = \frac{(0.560 \cancel{M})^2}{(0.170 \cancel{M})^2(0.087\ M)} = 120\ \frac{1}{M}$$

This is not equal to the value for K, so the reaction is not at equilibrium. Since this value is greater than K then this reaction will need to shift toward the reactants.

6. a. We ignore solids as a source of stress on the equilibrium, so nothing will happen.

   b. We also ignore liquids a source of stress on the equilibrium, so nothing will happen.

   c. When H_2CO_3 is removed, the reverse reaction will slow down. This will make the forward reaction faster than the reverse, causing a shift toward the products. Thus, more H_2CO_3 and CaO will be made and there will be less $CaCO_3$. Remember, solids and liquids are not sources of stress because their *concentrations* do not change. However, if we stress the equilibrium by varying the amount of another substance in the equation, the *amounts* of liquids and solids can change.

7. a. The reaction is exothermic, which means energy is a product. If the temperature is raised, the equilibrium shifts away from the side with the energy, so the H_2 and F_2 concentration will go down while the concentration of HF will go up.

   b. When temperature is lowered, the reaction shifts toward the side with energy. Thus, the concentration of HF will lower and the concentrations of H_2 and F_2 will increase.

8. a. This is an endothermic reaction, so energy is a reactant. When the temperature is raised, the reaction shifts away from the side with the energy, so the concentration of H_2 and N_2 will increase and the concentration of NH_3 will decrease.

   b. When pressure is raised, the reaction shifts away from the side with the most gas molecules. There are 4 gas molecules on the reactants side and only 2 on the products side. Thus, the reaction will shift away from reactants, causing the concentrations of N_2 and H_2 to decrease while the concentration of NH_3 to rise.

   c. When pressure is lowered, the reaction shifts toward the side with more gas molecules, making the concentrations of N_2 and H_2 increase and NH_3 decrease.

9. The ionization constant is simply the equilibrium constant for the acid ionization reaction. In order to determine the ionization reaction, you simply take the acid in its aqueous phase and remove an H^+. When we remove an H^+ ion from $HC_2H_3O_2$, we are left with $C_2H_3O_2^-$. In the end, then, the aqueous acid is the reactant, and the H^+ ion and $C_2H_3O_2^-$ (both in aqueous phase) will be the products:

   $$HC_2H_3O_2\ (aq) \rightleftharpoons H^+\ (aq) + C_2H_3O_2^-\ (aq)$$

   The equilibrium constant for this reaction is the ionization constant, K_a:

   $$K_a = \frac{[H^+][C_2H_3O_2^-]}{[HC_2H_3O_2]}$$

10. The base ionization reaction involves having the base accept an H^+ ion from water. If PO_4^{3-} accepts an H^+, it becomes HPO_4^{2-}. When water gives up that H^+, it becomes OH^-. All of this takes place in water, so the water phase is liquid and everything else is aqueous:

$$PO_4^{3-}\ (aq) + H_2O\ (l) \rightleftharpoons HPO_4^{2-}\ (aq) + OH^-\ (aq)$$

The ionization constant, then, is just the equilibrium constant of this reaction:

$$K_b = \frac{[OH^-][HPO_4^{2-}]}{[PO_4^{3-}]}$$

SOLUTIONS TO THE EXTRA PRACTICE PROBLEMS FOR MODULE 15

1. Acidic solutions have pH levels under 7. Thus, solutions A and B are acidic.

2. The largest ionization constant corresponds to the strongest acid, which would produce the lowest pH. Thus, solution C is made from the acid with the largest ionization constant.

3. According to equation 15.2, the equilibrium constant for this reaction is:

$$K = \frac{[NH_3]_{eq}[HCO_3]_{eq}}{[NH_4^+]_{eq}[CO_3^{2-}]_{eq}}$$

Plugging those equilibrium concentrations into the equation:

$$K = \frac{(2.4\ \cancel{M})(2.4\ \cancel{M})}{(1.60\ \cancel{M})\ (1.60\ \cancel{M})} = \underline{2.3}$$

4. The equation for the equilibrium constant here is:

$$K = \frac{[SO_3]_{eq}{}^2}{[SO_2]_{eq}{}^2[O_2]_{eq}}$$

If the concentrations are, in fact, equilibrium concentrations, then the equation should equal the value given for K.

$$K = \frac{(0.280\ \cancel{M})^2}{(0.140\ \cancel{M})^2\ (0.147\ M)} = 27.2\ \frac{1}{M}$$

If the reaction were at equilibrium, the value we just calculated would be equal to K. It is not, so the reaction is not at equilibrium. The calculated value is larger than K, so the value needs to decrease. This will happen if the reaction shifts toward the reactants.

5. a. Since this is an endothermic reaction, energy is a reactant. Lowering the

temperature, then, is like removing a reactant. So the equilibrium will shift toward the reactants. This will <u>decrease</u> the concentration of H_2.

b. When pressure is lowered, the equilibrium shifts to the side with the most gas molecules. In this case, that's the product side. The concentration of NH_3 will <u>decrease</u>.

c. If the concentration of NH_3 is raised, the forward reaction rate will increase, making the forward reaction faster in comparison. This will cause a shift toward the products, making the concentration of N_2 <u>increase</u>.

6. a. Since this is an exothermic reaction, energy is a product. Lowering the temperature, then, is like removing a product. Therefore, the equilibrium will shift toward the products. This will <u>decrease</u> the concentration of CO.

b. When pressure is lowered, the equilibrium shifts to the side with the most gas molecules. In this case, that's the reactant side. This means the concentration of CO will <u>increase</u>.

c. If carbon is removed, <u>nothing will happen</u> because changing the amount of solid will not stress the equilibrium.

d. If more CO is added, that will increase the rate of the forward reaction, making more products. Thus, the amount of carbon will <u>increase</u>. Its concentration will not change, but the amount will increase.

7. The ionization constant is simply the equilibrium constant for the acid ionization reaction. In order to determine the ionization reaction, we simply take the acid in its aqueous phase and remove an H^+. When we remove an H^+ ion from NH_4^+, we are left with NH_3. In the end, then, the aqueous acid is the reactant, and the H^+ ion and NH_3 (both in aqueous phase) will be the products:

$$NH_4^+ (aq) \rightleftharpoons H^+ (aq) + NH_3 (aq)$$

The equilibrium constant for this reaction is the ionization constant, K_a:

$$K_a = \frac{[H^+][NH_3]}{[NH_4^+]}$$

MOD 15

TEST FOR MODULE 15

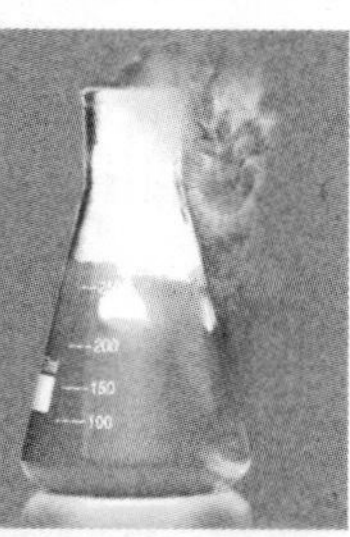

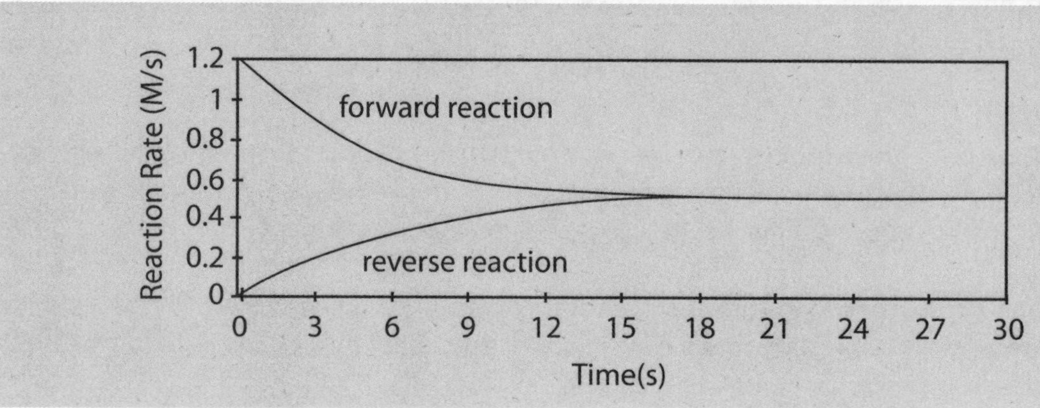

1. (4 pts) At which time is this reaction not in equilibrium?
   a. 0 to 18 seconds
   b. 18 second mark
   c. 18 to 30 seconds
   d. This reaction is not at equilibrium.

2. (4 pts) At which time is this reaction at equilibrium?
   a. 0 to 18 seconds
   b. 18 second mark
   c. 18 to 30 seconds
   d. This reaction is not at equilibrium.

3. (4 pts) What does the down-sloping solid line represent?
   a. The equilibrium rate
   b. The forward reaction rate
   c. The reverse reaction rate
   d. All of the above
   e. None of the above

4. (4 pts) True or False: All reactions are in essence equilibrium reactions.

5. (4 pts) Which arrow would be present in a reaction where $K = 4.65 \times 10^{15}$?
   a. $\rightarrow$
   b. $\leftarrow$
   c. $\rightleftharpoons$
   d. None of the above

6. (4 pts) Which arrow would be present in a reaction where K = 4.65×10^{-15}?
   a. →
   b. ←
   c. ⇌
   d. None of the above

Use the following graph to answer questions 7–9.

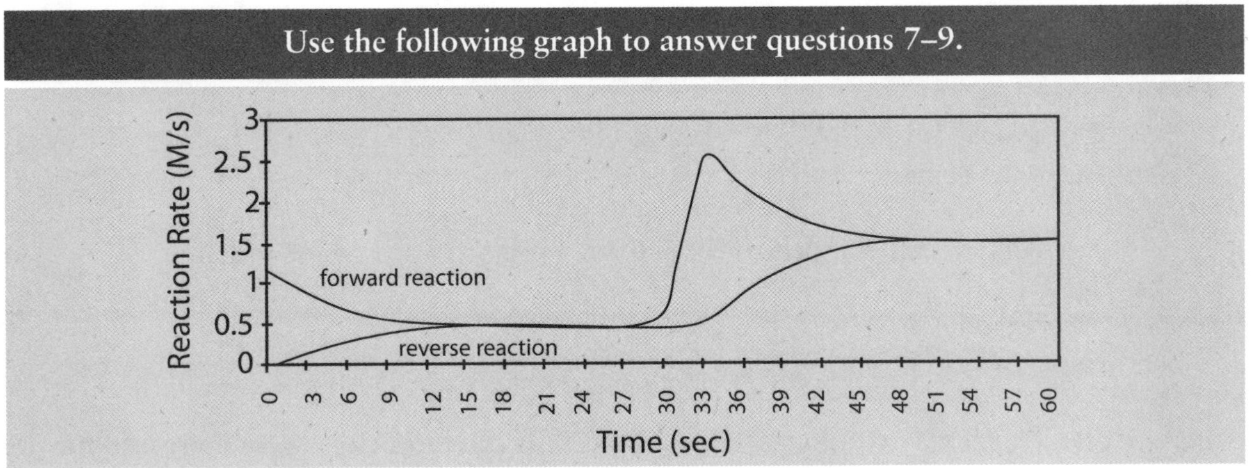

7. (4 pts) At what time was a stress applied to this system?
   a. 10 seconds
   b. 29 seconds
   c. 45 seconds
   d. 60 seconds

8. (4 pts) At what time is Le Chatelier's principle at work?
   a. 0 to 15 seconds
   b. 15 to 29 seconds
   c. 29 to 50 seconds
   d. 50 to 60 seconds

9. (4 pts) True or False: This chemical reaction reaches equilibrium only from 50 to 60 seconds.

10. (4 pts) What would be the equilibrium constant equation for the following reaction? $2NaOH(aq) + MgCl_2(aq) \rightleftharpoons Mg(OH)_2(s) + 2NaCl(aq)$

    a. K = $[Mg(OH)_2][NaCl]^2 / [NaOH][MgCl_2]$
    b. K = $[NaCl]^2 / [NaOH]^2[MgCl_2]$
    c. K = $[NaOH][MgCl_2] / [Mg(OH)_2][NaCl]$
    d. K = $[NaOH]^2[MgCl_2] / [Mg(OH)_2][NaCl]^2$
    e. None of the above

Answer questions 11–13 using the following chemical reaction:
$Ca^{2+}_{(aq)} + 2\ HCO_3^-{}_{(aq)} \rightleftharpoons CaCO_{3\,(s)} + CO_{2\,(g)} + H_2O_{(l)}$

11. (4 pts) What would happen to the $[Ca^{2+}]$ if the $[CO_2]$ were increased?
    a. Increases
    b. Decreases
    c. Stays the same

12. (4 pts) What would happen to the $[HCO_3^-]$ if $CaCO_3$ were removed?
    a. Increases
    b. Decreases
    c. Stays the same

13. (4 pts) What would happen to the $[HCO_3^-]$ if more water were added?
    a. Increases
    b. Decreases
    c. Stays the same

14. (4 pts) Which way would the equilibrium shift if the pressure were increased for this reaction? $4NH_3\ (g) + 5O_2\ (g) \rightleftharpoons 4NO\ (g) + 6H_2O\ (g)$

    a. Shift toward reactants
    b. Shift toward products
    c. Remain the same
    d. None of the above

15. (4 pts) Which way would the equilibrium shift if the temperature were increased for this reaction? $N_2\ (g) + 2O_2\ (g) \rightleftharpoons 2NO_2\ (g)\ \Delta H = 52.2\ kJ$

    a. Shift toward reactants
    b. Shift toward products
    c. Remain the same
    d. None of the above

Please use the following 5 solutions to answer questions 16 and 17.
Solution A: pH = 7.0
Solution B: pH = 14.0
Solution C: pH = 9.1
Solution D: pH = 5.5
Solution E: pH = 1.2

16. (4 pts) Which solution contains the strongest acid?
    a. Solution A
    b. Solution B
    c. Solution C
    d. Solution D
    e. Solution E

17. (4 pts) Which contains the strongest base?
    a. Solution A
    b. Solution B
    c. Solution C
    d. Solution D
    e. Solution E

18. (4 pts) Five acids have the following pH in equal concentrations:
    Acid A: pH = 6.8 Acid C: pH = 1.1 Acid E: pH = 2.1
    Acid B: pH = 5.0 Acid D: pH = 4.5

    Order the acids in terms of increasing ionization constants.
    a. A < B < D < E < C
    b. C< E < D < E < A
    c. A < B < C < D < E
    d. These solutions are acids, so they do not have ionization constants.

19. (4 pts) True or False: Rain is naturally acidic.

20. (4 pts) What does the pH scale measure?

For the following questions, please provide a correct answer and show the work that is needed to solve the problem.

21. (4 pts) What is the acid ionization reaction for HNO_3?

22. (4 pts) The following reaction: $2NOBr\ (g) \rightleftharpoons 2NO\ (g) + Br_2\ (g)$ reached equilibrium when the concentrations were: [NOBr] = 0.10 M, [NO] = 0.010 M, and $[Br_2]$ = 0.0050 M. What is the equilibrium constant for this reaction?

23. (4 pts) A chemist knows that the equilibrium constant is 0.345 M for the following reaction: $BaSO_3\ (s) \rightleftharpoons BaO\ (s) + SO_2\ (g)$

    What is the concentration of SO_2 when the reaction reaches equilibrium?

24. (8 pts) A chemist is studying the following reaction:
    $SO_2\ (g) + H_2O\ (l) \rightleftharpoons H_2SO_3\ (aq)$ $K = 2.1 \times 10^{-3}$

    She measures the concentrations of H_2SO_3 and SO_2, and their concentrations are 0.23 M and 0.35 M, respectively. Is the reaction at equilibrium? If not, which way must the reaction shift to attain equilibrium?

SOLUTIONS TO THE TEST FOR MODULE 15

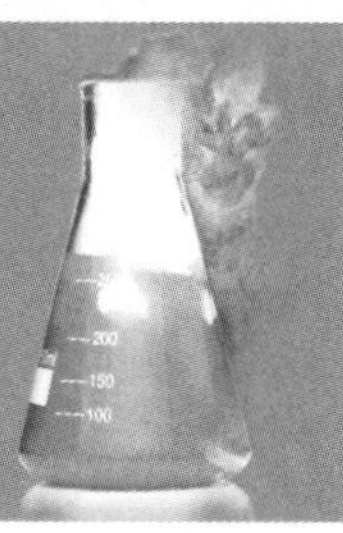

1. (4 pts) a. 0 to 18 seconds
   Equilibrium occurs when the rates of the forward and reverse reactions are equal. This occurs at about 18 seconds, according to the graph.

2. (4 pts) c. 18 to 30 seconds

3. (4 pts) b. The forward reaction rate

4. (4 pts) True
   All reactions are in essence equilibrium reactions.

5. (4 pts) a. $\rightarrow$
   When K is very large, it means the reaction gives high concentrations of products.

6. (4 pts) b. $\leftarrow$
   When K is very small, it means the reaction gives high concentrations of reactants.

7. (4 pts) b. 29 seconds
   When an equilibrium is stressed, one of the rates (forward or reverse) changes dramatically. On the graph, this seems to occur at about 29 seconds.

8. (4 pts) c. 29 to 50 seconds

9. (4 pts) False
   This chemical reaction is in equilibrium from 15 to 29 seconds and again from 50 to 60 seconds.

10. (4 pts) b. $K = [NaCl]^2 / [NaOH]^2[MgCl_2]$

11. (4 pts) a. Increases
Increasing $[CO_2]$ pushes the reaction to the toward reactants, which increases $[Ca^{2+}]$.

12. (4 pts) c. Stays the same
Solids are ignored in the equation for the equilibrium.

13. (4 pts) c. Stays the same
Liquids are ignored.

14. (4 pts) a. Shift toward reactants
Raising pressure shifts the equilibrium to the side with the least molecules of gas.

15. (4 pts) b. Shift toward products
The ΔH tells us that energy is a reactant. When we raise temperature, we are therefore adding a reactant, shifting the equilibrium to the products side.

16. (4 pts) e. Solution E

17. (4 pts) b. Solution B

18. (4 pts) a. $A < B < D < E < C$
The higher the pH, the weaker the acid. The weaker the acid, the smaller the ionization constant. Thus, high pH means low ionization constant.

19. (4 pts) True
Rain is naturally acidic.

20. (4 pts) The acidity or basicity of a solution

21. (4 pts) $HNO_3\ (aq) \rightarrow H^+\ (aq) + NO_3^-\ (aq)$

22. (4 pts) 5.0×10^{-5} M

We take the concentrations and equilibrium and plug them into the equation:

$$K = \frac{[NO]^2 \times [Br_2]}{[NOBr]^2} = \frac{(0.010\ \cancel{M})^2 \times (0.0050\ M)}{(0.10\ \cancel{M})^2} = \underline{5.0 \times 10^{-5}\ M}$$

23. (4 pts) <u>0.345 M</u>
Since $BaSO_3$ and BaO are both solids, they are ignored in the equation for the equilibrium constant. Thus, K = $[SO_2]$. This means that at equilibrium, the concentration of SO_2 is the same as K.

24. (8 pts: 4 pts for working out the equation, 4 pts for determining the direction of the shift) <u>0.66</u>, <u>This reaction is not at equilibrium. The reaction must shift toward the reactants in order to reach equilibrium.</u>
To test and see if the reaction is at equilibrium, we evaluate the equation for K. Remember, we ignore liquids!

$$K = \frac{[H_2SO_3]}{[SO_2]} = \frac{0.23\ \cancel{M}}{0.35\ \cancel{M}} = 0.66$$

<u>At this point, K is too large compared to its correct value. To reduce the number, we must get fewer products and more reactants.</u>

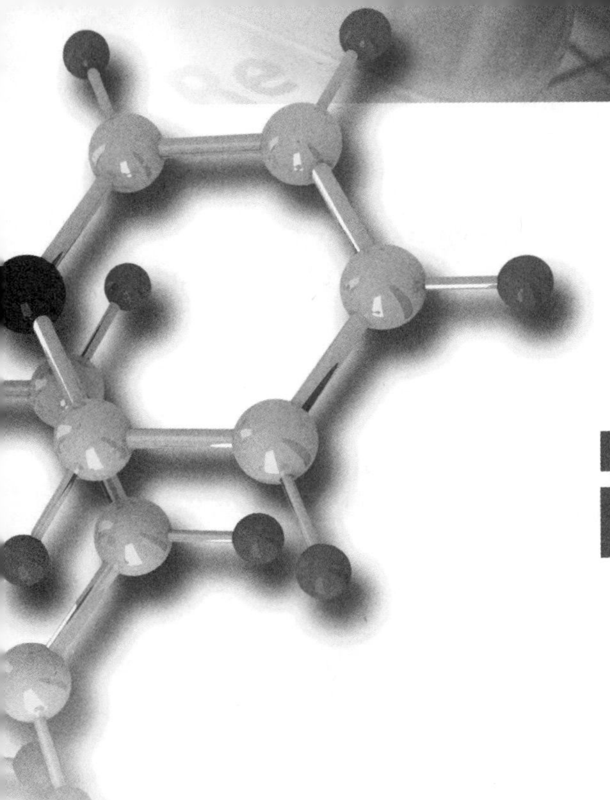

REDUCTION-OXIDATION REACTIONS

SOLUTIONS TO THE MODULE 16 REVIEW QUESTIONS

1. The oxidation number is the charge that an atom in a molecule would develop if the most electronegative atoms in the molecule took the shared electrons from the less electronegative atoms.

2. Since the oxidation number tells us the charge that the atom would have if the more electronegative atoms took the shared electrons from the less electronegative atoms, we can conclude that the atom in question was more electronegative than the other atoms in the first molecule because a negative charge indicates that it took electrons. The positive oxidation number in the second molecule, however, tells us that it lost electrons to the other atoms in that molecule, indicating that it was less electronegative. Thus, the electronegativities of the other atoms in molecule 1 were lower than the atom in question, while the electronegativities of the atoms in molecule 2 were greater.

3. The sum of all oxidation numbers must equal the charge of the molecule.

4. Oxidation - The process by which an atom loses electrons
   Reduction - The process by which an atom gains electrons

5. No, oxidation can never happen without reduction because a substance cannot lose an electron unless there is something around that can gain it.

6. According to the definition, the anode is where oxidation occurs. In oxidation, a substance loses (gives up) electrons. Thus, the anode is a *source* of electrons. Reduction occurs at the cathode. This means that electrons flow to the cathode so that the substance there can take them. Electrons, then, flow from the anode to the cathode. Thus, anodes are negative and cathodes are positive.

7. If all else fails, assume that the atom's oxidation number is the same as what it would take on in an ionic compound. The atoms that are most likely to follow this rule are in groups 3A, 6A, and 7A. This must be used as a last resort because there are many exceptions to it.

8. A lead-acid battery requires PbO_2, Pb, and H_2SO_4.

9. The internal structure of most batteries gets destroyed as the reaction proceeds. There is no way to reverse the destruction, so the battery is not rechargeable.

10. The alkaline cell has no aqueous solutions, but the lead-acid battery does. The lead-acid battery can be recharged; the alkaline cell cannot be recharged.

SOLUTIONS TO THE PRACTICE PROBLEMS FOR MODULE 16

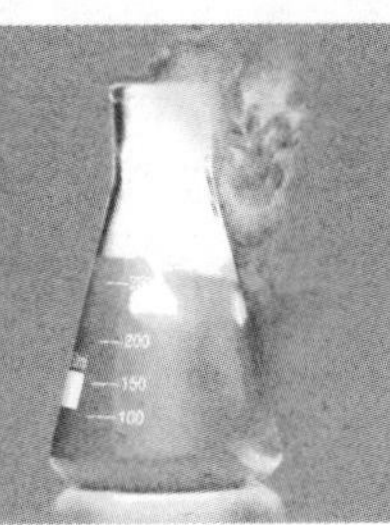

1. When a substance is made up of only one type of atom, the oxidation number of the atom is the charge of the substance divided by the number of atoms in the substance.
   a. 0 b. 0 c. –2 d. 0 e. +2

2. a. Rule 3 tells us that Mg is +2. This makes Cl –1. The oxidation numbers are: Mg: +2, Cl: –1

   b. We cannot predict the charge of V because it is not in groups 1–8 A. However, S is in group 6A, so the last resort rule says it will have a –2 oxidation number. Thus, S is –2 and V is +2.

   c. Rule 4 tells us that F is –1. That makes S +6. The oxidation numbers, then, are: S: +6, F: –1

   d. Rule 6 tells us that O is –2 here. Since the sum of all oxidation numbers must equal the overall charge (–2), C must be +4. The oxidation numbers, then, are: C: +4, O: –2

   e. Rule 6 says that O will have an oxidation number of –2. Since all of the oxidation numbers must add up to the overall charge, the Mn is +4. The oxidation numbers, then, are: Mn: +4, O: –2

   f. Rule 2 tells us that K is +1. Rule 6 tells us that O is –2. This makes N +5. The oxidation numbers, then, are: K: +1, N: +5, O: –2

   g. Rule 5 tells us that H is +1 here. Rule 6 tells us that O is –2. From H and O, we have a sum of –6. In order for the sum of all oxidation numbers to equal the overall charge (0), S must be +6. The oxidation numbers, then, are: H: +1, S: +6, O: –2

   h. We have to use the last resort rule here. Since Ir is not in groups 1–8 A, we cannot predict its charge in an ionic compound. However, we know that Cl is –1 in an ionic compound. This means Cl has an oxidation number of –1, making Ir +3. The oxidation numbers, then, are: Ir: +3, Cl –1

3. To go from +5 to +1, you must gain negatives. This means the atom gained electrons, indicating that it was reduced. To go from +5 to +1, we must gain 4 electrons.

4. To go from 0 to +2, we must lose negatives. This means the atom lost electrons, indicating that it was oxidized. To go from 0 to +2, we must lose 2 electrons.

5. To go from –3 to 0, we must lose negatives. This means the atom lost electrons, indicating that it was oxidized. To go from –3 to 0, we must lose 3 electrons.

6. To go from –2 to –4, we must gain negatives. This means the atom gained electrons, indicating that it was reduced. To go from –2 to –4, we must gain 2 electrons.

7. a. This is a redox reaction because Cl went from 0 to –1, indicating that Cl was reduced. At the same time, Na went from 0 to +1, indicating that Na was oxidized.

   b. This is a redox reaction because Ni went from +2 to 0, indicating that Ni was reduced. At the same time, Cd went from 0 to +2, indicating that Cd was oxidized.

   c. In this reaction, Mg stayed at +2, O stayed at –2, and N stayed at +5, Na stayed at +1 and H stayed at +1. Thus, this is not a redox reaction.

   d. In this reaction, H stayed at +1, S stayed at +6, O stayed at –2, and N stayed at –3. Thus, this is not a redox reaction.

   e. This is a redox reaction because V went from +5 to +4, indicating that V was reduced. At the same time, Zn went from 0 to +2, indicating that Zn was oxidized.

8. In this reaction, Cu^{2+} is going from an oxidation number of +2 to an oxidation number of 0. This indicates that it is gaining electrons. Thus, the solution holding aqueous Cu^{2+} will have electrons flowing into it. Electrons flow toward the Cu^{2+}, so that container is positive (it attracts electrons) and thus will be the cathode. The Co is going from an oxidation number of 0 to an oxidation number of +2. This means it loses electrons. Since it is losing electrons, the electrons are flowing away from the container holding the solid Co. This makes that container the negative side of the battery (it repels electrons), and it is thus the anode. The picture, then, looks

like this:

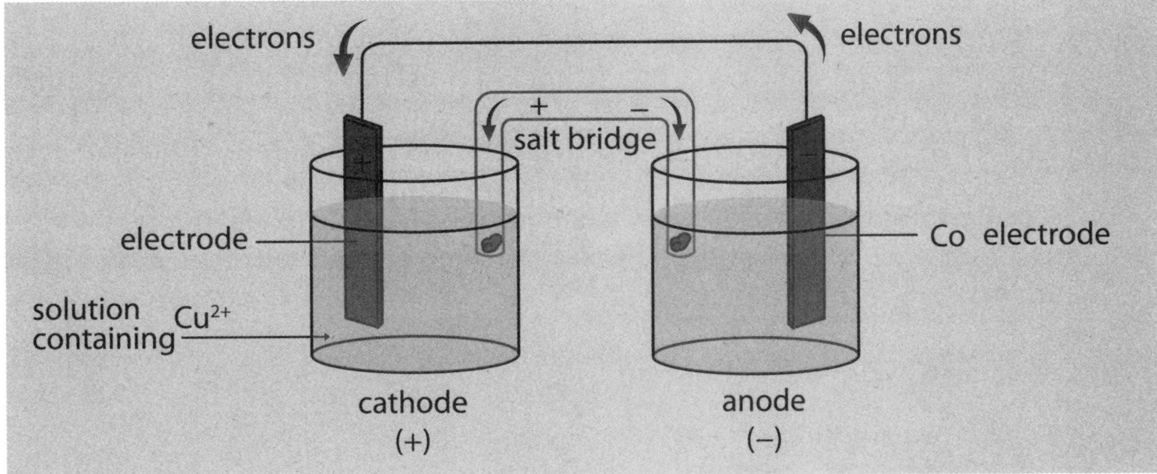

9. The first thing that we have to do is look at the reactants and see which is being oxidized and which is being reduced. Since aluminum goes from an oxidation number of 0 to an oxidation number of +3, it must be losing electrons, so it is oxidized. This means that the container that holds it will be the anode. The Fe^{3+}, on the other hand, gains electrons because it goes from an oxidation number of +3 to an oxidation number of 0. This means that Fe^{3+} is reduced, and the container that holds it will be the cathode.

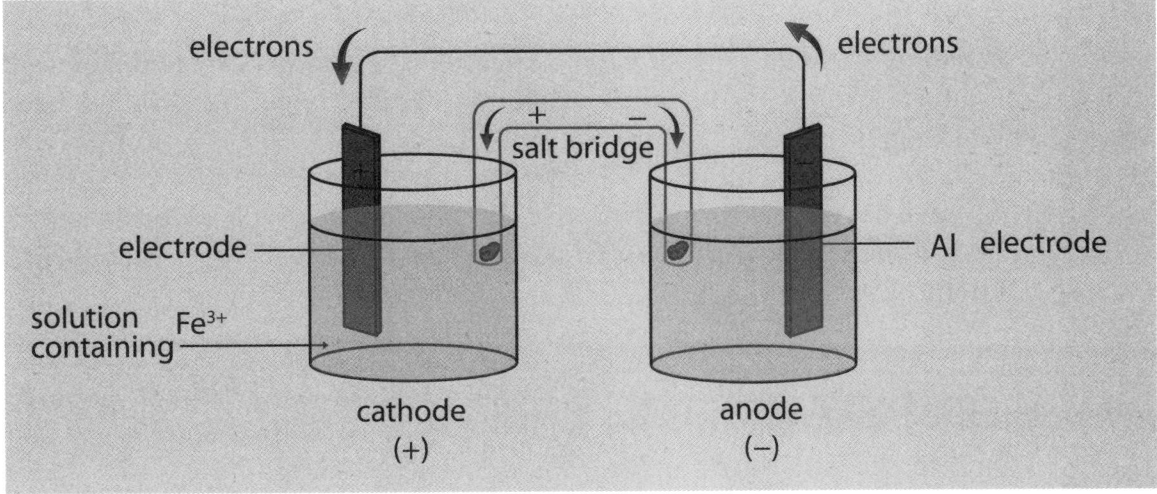

SOLUTIONS TO THE EXTRA PRACTICE PROBLEMS FOR MODULE 16

1. When a substance is made up of only one type of atom, the oxidation number of the atom is the charge of the substance divided by the number of atoms in the substance.

   a. 0 b. +1 c. 0 d. 0

2. a. Rule 2 says that K will have an oxidation number of +1, and rule 6 says that O will have an oxidation number of –2. Since all of the oxidation numbers must add up to the overall charge, the Mn is +7. The oxidation numbers, then, are: K: +1, Mn: +7, O: –2

   b. Rule 2 tells us that Na is +1 here. Rule 5 tells us that H is also +1 here. Rule number 6 tells us that O is –2. In order for the sum of all oxidation numbers to equal the overall charge (0), C must be +2. The oxidation numbers, then, are: Na: +1, C: +2, H: +1,O: –2

   c. Rule 6 tells us that O is –2 here. Rule 5 tells us that H is +1 here. Since the sum of all oxidation numbers must equal the overall charge (0), Zn must be +2. The oxidation numbers, then, are: Zn: +2, O: –2, H: +1

   d. Here we use the last resort rule. We should always start with group 7A atoms when using the last resort, so Cl is –1. That makes S +2. The oxidation numbers, then, are: S: +2, Cl: –1

3. This atom lost 3 electrons, so it was oxidized.

4. This atom gained 4 electrons, so it was reduced.

5. a. This is a redox reaction because Mg went from 0 to +2 and O went from 0 to –2.

   b. This is a redox reaction because H went from +1 to 0 and Cl went from –1 to 0.

   c. This is not a redox reaction because the oxidation numbers did not change.

   d. This is not a redox reaction because the oxidation numbers did not change.

6. In 5a, <u>Mg was oxidized</u> because it lost electrons, and <u>O was reduced</u> because it gained electrons.

   In 5b, <u>H was reduced</u> because it gained electrons, and <u>Cl was oxidized</u> because it lost electrons.

7. In 5(a), <u>2 electrons were transferred</u> because the charges changed by 2.

   In 5(b), <u>1 electron was transferred</u> because the charges changed by 1.

8. In this reaction, Al^{3+} is going from an oxidation number of +3 to an oxidation number of 0. This indicates that it is gaining electrons. Thus, the solution holding aqueous Al^{3+} will have electrons flowing into it. Electrons flow toward the Al^{3+}, so that container is positive (it attracts electrons) and thus will be the cathode. The Mg is going from an oxidation number of 0 to an oxidation number of +2. This means it loses electrons. Since it is losing electrons, the electrons are flowing away from the container holding the solid Mg. This makes that container the negative side of the battery (it repels electrons), and it is thus the anode. The picture, then, looks like this:

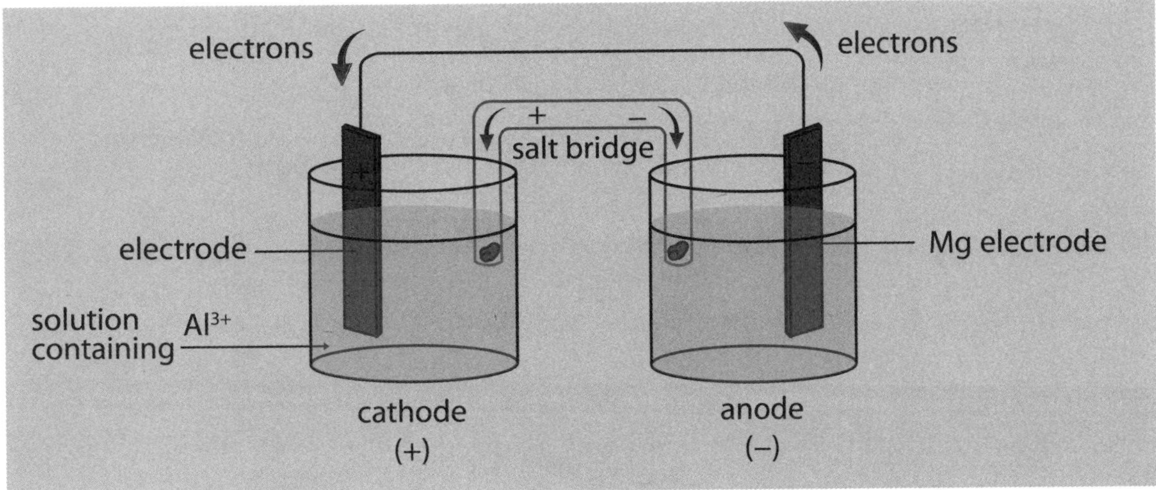

9. In this reaction, F_2 is going from an oxidation number of 0 to an oxidation number of –1. This indicates that it is gaining electrons. Thus, the solution holding aqueous F_2 will have electrons flowing into it. Electrons flow toward the F_2, so that container is positive (it attracts electrons) and thus will be the cathode. The Sn is going from an oxidation number of 0 to an oxidation number of +2. This means it loses electrons. Since it is losing electrons, the electrons are flowing away from the container holding the solid Sn. This makes that container the negative side of the battery (it repels electrons), and it is thus the anode. The picture, then, looks like this:

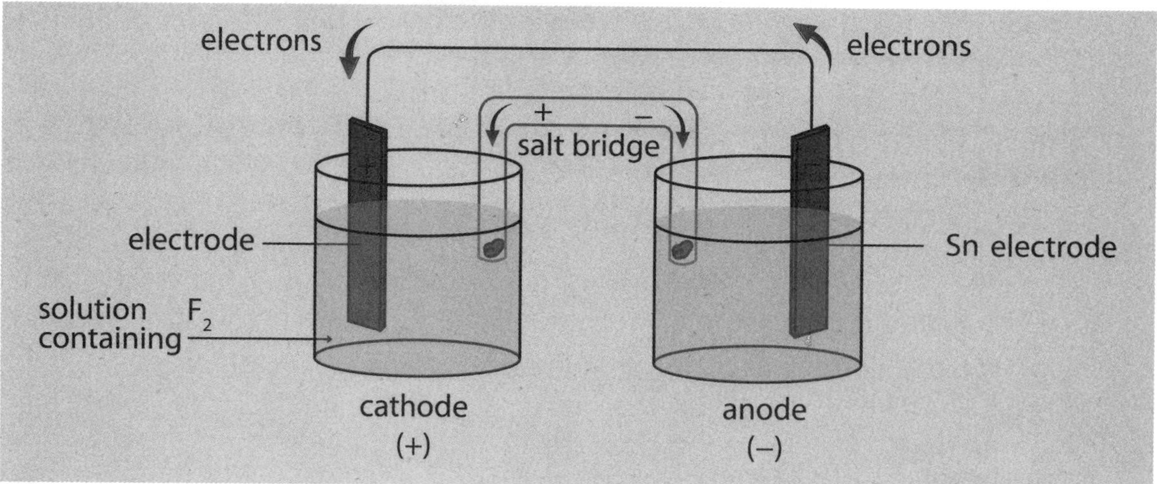

10. In this reaction, Cu^{2+} is going from an oxidation number of +2 to an oxidation number of 0. This indicates that it is gaining electrons. Thus, the solution holding aqueous Cu^{2+} will have electrons flowing into it. Electrons flow toward the Cu^{2+}, so that container is positive (it attracts electrons) and thus will be the cathode. The Cr is going from an oxidation number of 0 to an oxidation number of +3. This means it loses electrons. Since it is losing electrons, the electrons are flowing away from the container holding the solid Cr. This makes that container the negative side of the battery (it repels electrons), and it is thus the anode. The picture, then, looks like this:

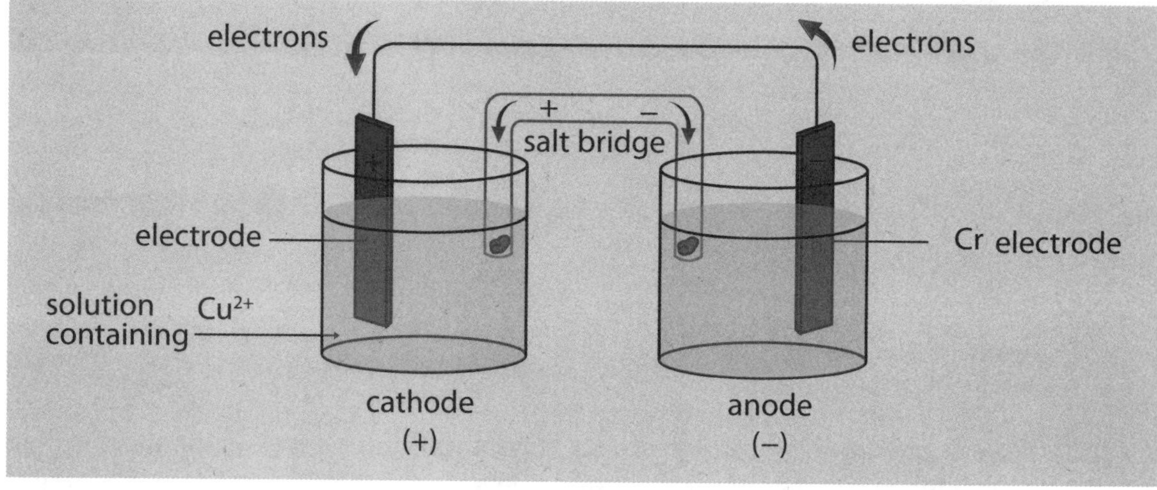

TEST FOR MODULE 16

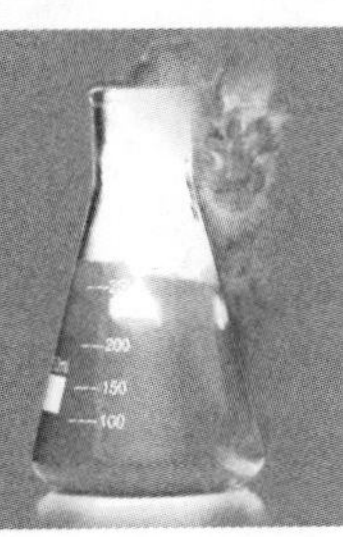

1. (4 pts) True or False: Oxidation numbers are the charges on atoms if all the bonds in an ionic compound were assumed to be covalent.

2. (4 pts) An atom has an oxidation number of –3 in a molecule. If it is placed in another molecule whose other atoms are significantly less electronegative than the atoms in the first molecule, what will the oxidation number most likely do?
   a. Increase
   b. Decrease
   c. Stay the same
   d. It will not have an oxidation number.

3. (4 pts) True or False: The sum of all of the oxidation numbers in a molecule or ion must equal zero.

4. (4 pts) True or False: In the molecule, MnO_2, the oxidation number of Mn is +4.

5. (4 pts) What is the oxidation number of O in PO_4^{3-}?
   a. –1
   b. –2
   c. +2
   d. 0
   e. None of the above

6. (4 pts) What are the oxidation numbers of all atoms in PH_4^+?
   a. P = –3, H = +4
   b. P = +5, H = –1
   c. P = +3, H = +1
   d. P = –3, H = +1
   e. None of the above

7. (4 pts) An atom changes its oxidation number from +3 to –1. Is it oxidized or reduced?
   a. Oxidized
   b. Reduced
   c. Neither

8. (4 pts) An oxidation number changes from –2 to 0. Does it gain or lose electrons?
   a. Gains electrons
   b. Loses electrons
   c. Neither

9. (4 pts) True or False: The following reaction is a redox reaction.
   $2H_3O^+ (aq) + Cu (s) + 2HNO_3 (aq) \rightarrow Cu^{2+} (aq) + 2NO_2 (g) + 4H_2O (l)$

10. (4 pts) True or False: The following reaction is a redox reaction.
    $Al_2O_3 (aq) + 6NaOH (aq) \rightarrow 2Al(OH)_3 (s) + 3Na_2O (aq)$

11. (4 pts) What is the purpose of the salt bridge in a galvanic cell?
    a. It allows the reaction to keep running.
    b. It neutralizes the charge buildup at the cathode and anode.
    c. Both A and B
    d. Neither A nor B

12. (4 pts) True or False: A cell is labeled *dry* because no water is involved in the reaction.

13. (4 pts) What makes a rechargeable battery different from an alkaline battery?
    a. Rechargeable batteries run a reversible redox reaction.
    b. A rechargeable battery's salt bridge will not degrade significantly when used.
    c. Both A and B
    d. Neither A nor B

14. (4 pts) Which of the following is *not* a difference between an automobile battery and an alkaline battery?
    a. The automobile battery is rechargeable.
    b. The automobile battery uses aqueous compounds.
    c. The automobile battery is made of several battery cells connected together.
    d. The automobile battery uses an acid as one of the reactants.
    e. None of the above

15. (4 pts) You hook a wire to the anode and cathode of a battery. Which way do the electrons flow?
    a. Cathode to anode
    b. Anode to cathode
    c. Neither

16. (4 pts) When a metal corrodes:
    a. It undergoes oxidation.
    b. Its oxidation number goes from 0 to negative.
    c. It is a useful reaction.
    d. None of the above

17. (4 pts) Why must reduction always accompany oxidation?

18. (16 pts) Give the oxidation numbers of all atoms in the following compounds:
 a. SO_2
 b. $KClO_3$
 c. $PtCl_4^{2-}$
 d. N_2

19. (4 pts) Determine whether or not the following is a redox reaction. If it is, determine which atom is being reduced and which is being oxidized.
O_2 (g) + Cl_2 (g) → 2OCl (g)

20. (4 pts) Determine whether or not the following is a redox reaction. If it is, determine which atom is being reduced and which is being oxidized.
$5HSO_3^-$ (aq) + $2IO_3^-$ (aq) → I_2 (aq) + $5SO_4^{2-}$ (aq) + $3H^+$ (aq) + H_2O (l)

21. (4 pts) A Galvanic cell runs on the following reaction:
3Ba (s) + $2Al^{3+}$ (aq) → $3Ba^{2+}$ (aq) + 2Al (s)

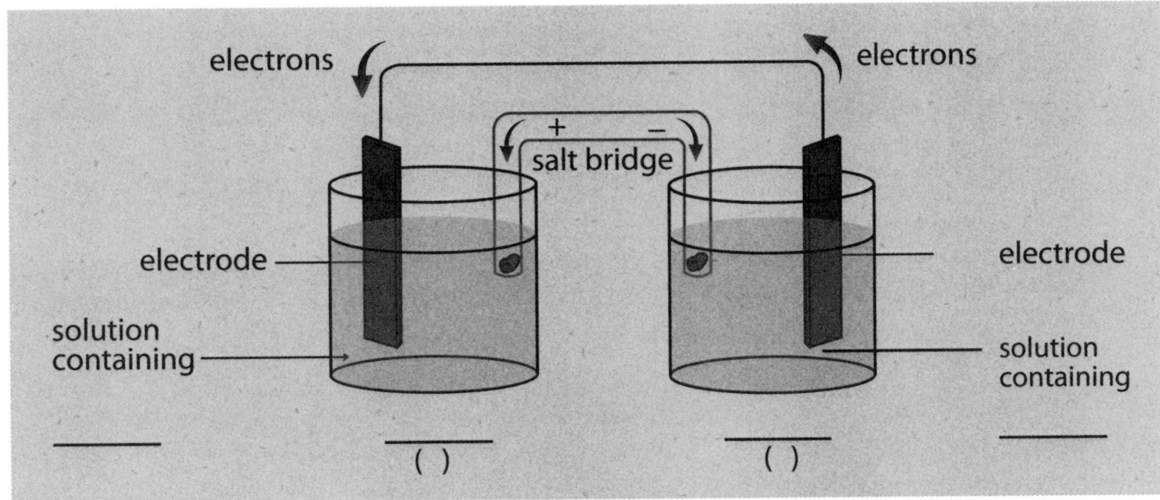

Given this Galvanic cell with the electron flow, label the anode, cathode, location of all reactants and products, and positive and negative side of the battery.

22. (4 pts) A Galvanic cell runs on the following reaction:
$8H_2S$ (aq) + $8F_2$ (aq) → $16H^+$ + $16F^-$(aq) + S_8 (s)

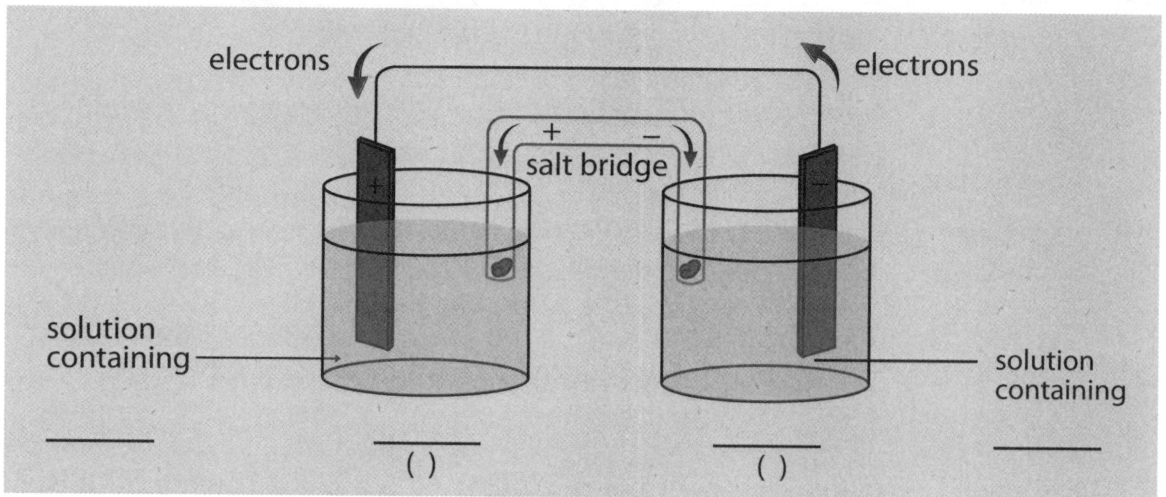

Given this Galvanic cell with the electron flow, label the anode, cathode, location of each reactant, and positive and negative side of the battery.

SOLUTIONS TO THE TEST FOR MODULE 16

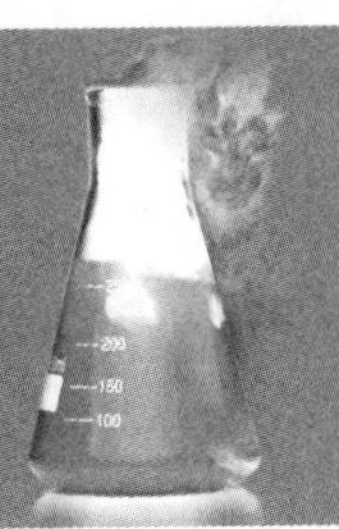

1. (4 pts) False

2. (4 pts) b. Decrease
If the other atoms are less electronegative, they will pull away fewer electrons, allowing the atom in question to get more. More electrons mean a more negative charge.

3. (4 pts) False
The sum of all of the oxidation numbers in a molecule or ion does not have to equal zero.

4. (4 pts) True
In the molecule, MnO_2, the oxidation number of Mn is +4.

5. (4 pts) b. –2

6. (4 pts) d. P = –3, H = +1

7. (4 pts) b. Reduced

8. (4 pts) b. Loses electrons

9. (4 pts) True
It is a redox reaction.

10. (4 pts) False
It is *not* a redox reaction.

11. (4 pts) c. Both a and b

12. (4 pts) False. Dry cells contain no liquid.

13. (4 pts) c. Both a and b

14. (4 pts) e. None of the above

15. (4 pts) b. Anode to cathode
The anode is the negative side of the battery (a source of anions), and the cathode is the positive side of the battery (a source of cations). Thus, electrons will flow from the anode to the cathode.

16. (4 pts) a. It undergoes oxidation.

17. (4 pts) Reduction must always accompany oxidation because electrons cannot simply appear or disappear. If one substance is going to lose electrons, another substance must be there to gain them.

18. (16 pts: 4 pts for each part)
   a. S: +4, O: –2
   b. K: +1, Cl: +5, O: –2
   c. Pt:+2, Cl: –1
   d. N: 0

19. (4 pts) Redox: O is reduced; Cl is oxidized.

20. (4 pts) Redox: S is oxidized; I is reduced.

21. (4 pts)

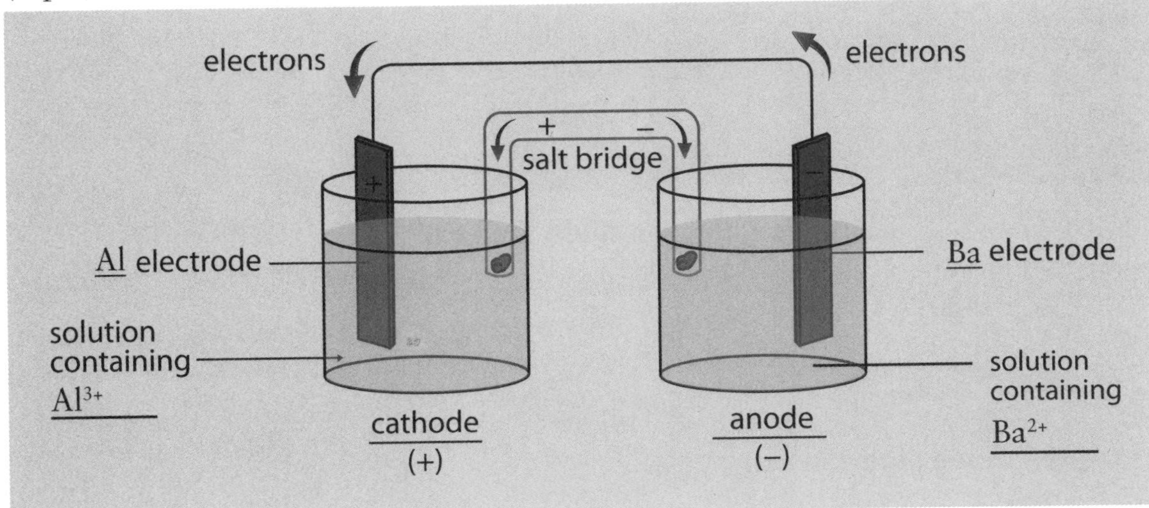

22. (4 pts)

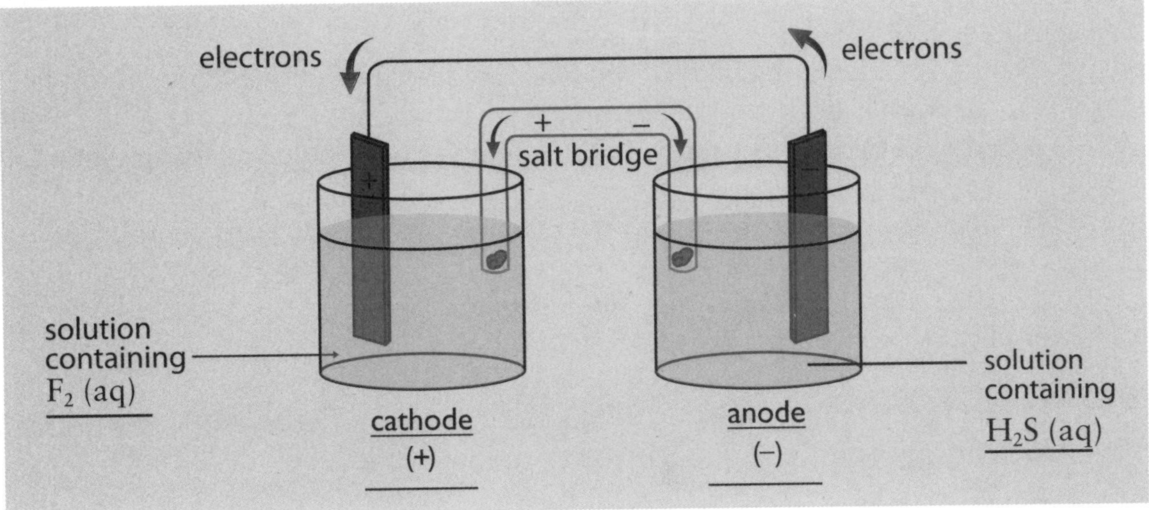

QUARTERLY 4 TEST FOR MOD. 13-16

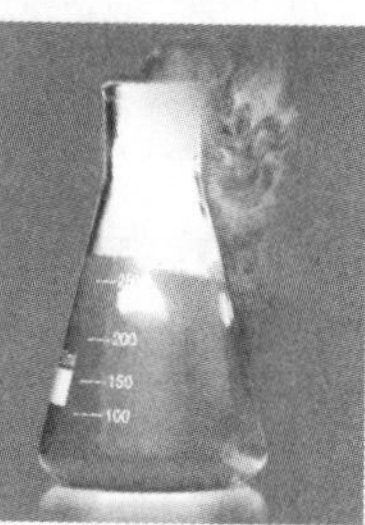

1. (3 pts) Which of the following substances will have a ΔH_f of zero?
   KOH (aq), N_2 (g), Cl^- (aq), O_2 (l)
   a. N_2 (g) and O_2 (l)
   b. N_2 (g)
   c. Cl^- (aq)
   d. O_2 (l)
   e. None of the above

2. (9 pts) Draw an energy diagram for a reaction that starts with reactants whose energy is 20.0 kJ and has a ΔH of 20.0 kJ. The activation energy for the reaction is 35.0 kJ.

3. (3 pts) An energy diagram of the reaction described in question 2 is drawn, but the diagram is drawn taking into account the effect of a catalyst. What would be different between this energy diagram and the one you drew for question 2?
   a. The ΔH is lower.
   b. The catalyst gets used up as the reaction proceeds toward completion.
   c. The reaction becomes exothermic.
   d. The reaction becomes more endothermic.
   e. The activation energy is lower.

4. (3 pts) Is it possible for a reaction to occur if the reaction results in a decrease in the entropy of the chemicals involved in the reaction?
   a. Yes
   b. No
   c. Unable to determine from the information given

5. (3 pts) What is the sign of ΔS for the following reaction?
   $NaHCO_3$ (aq) + HCl (aq) → NaCl (aq) + H_2O (l) + CO_2 (g)
   a. Positive
   b. Negative
   c. Zero
   d. Unable to determine from the information given

6. (6 pts) If the ΔH of a certain reaction is 423 kJ/mole and the ΔS is 194 J/mole K, what is the temperature range for which this reaction is spontaneous?

7. (3 pts) A chemistry book lists the rate constant for a reaction as $186.1 \frac{1}{M^3\ s}$.
What is the overall order of the reaction?
   a. 1
   b. 2
   c. 3
   d. 4
   e. None of the above

8. (3 pts) The order of a chemical reaction with respect to one of its reactants is zero. If you double the concentration of that reactant, what happens to the rate?
   a. Remains the same
   b. Doubles
   c. Decreases by half
   d. Quadruples
   e. None of the above

9. (6 pts) A chemist does a reaction rate analysis on the following reaction:

$$2CO\ (g) + O_2\ (g) \rightarrow 2CO_2\ (g)$$

She collects the following data:

Trial	Initial Concentration of CO (M)	Initial Concentration of O_2 (M)	Instantaneous Reaction Rate(M/s)
1	0.150	0.150	0.113
2	0.300	0.150	0.226
3	0.300	0.300	0.904

What is the rate equation for this reaction?

10. (3 pts) A chemist runs a chemical reaction at 25 °C and decides that it proceeds far too rapidly. As a result, he decides that the reaction rate must be decreased by a factor of 4. At what temperature should the chemist run the reaction to achieve this goal?
   a. 20 °C
   b. 15 °C
   c. 10 °C
   d. 5 °C
   e. None of the above

11. (3 pts) In the reaction mechanism below, indicate what substance is acting like a catalyst.
Step 1: H_2O_2 (aq) + I^- (aq) → H_2O (l) + IO^- (aq)
Step 2: H_2O_2 (aq) + IO^- (aq) → H_2O (l) + I^- (aq)
   a. H_2O_2 (aq)
   b. I^- (aq)
   c. IO^- (aq)
   d. H_2O (l)
   e. None of the above

12. (3 pts) Is the catalyst in question 11 a heterogeneous or a homogeneous catalyst?
   a. Heterogeneous
   b. Homogeneous
   c. There was no catalyst in the reaction.
   d. Unable to determine with the information given

13. (3 pts) Write the balanced chemical equation for the reaction of hydrochloric acid (HCl) with magnesium hydroxide. The stoichiometric ratio of the acid to the salt is:
   a. 1:2
   b. 1:1
   c. 2:1
   d. 2:2

14. (3 pts) Which of the following solutions are acidic?
Solution A: pH = 11 Solution B: pH = 5 Solution C: pH = 2
   a. A
   b. B
   c. C
   d. B and C
   e. None of the above

15. (3 pts) Which solution is made with the acid that has the *smallest* ionization constant for the following three solutions have the following pH:
Solution A: pH = 2 Solution B: pH = 5 Solution C: pH = 3
   a. A
   b. B
   c. C
   d. Unable to determine with the information given

16. (4 pts) A chemist is studying the following equilibrium:

$$2Pb(NO_3)_2\ (s) \rightleftharpoons 2PbO\ (s) + 4NO_2\ (g) + O_2\ (g)$$

He starts out with 10 g of $Pb(NO_3)_2$ and, at equilibrium, has 2.02 g of PbO. The concentrations of NO_2 and O_2 at equilibrium are 0.25 M and 0.019 M, respectively. What is the value of the equilibrium constant?

17. (4 pts) The equilibrium constant is equal to 0.23 M for the following reaction:

$$2SO_3\ (g) \rightleftharpoons 2SO_2\ (g) + O_2\ (g)$$

If the following concentrations are present: $[SO_2]$ = 0.480 M, $[O_2]$ = 0.561 M, $[SO_3]$ = 0.220 M, which statement is true?
   a. The reaction is at equilibrium.
   b. The reaction is not at equilibrium and will shift toward products.
   c. The reaction is not at equilibrium and will shift toward reactants.
   d. The reaction is not at equilibrium but will shift only when stressed by an outside force.

18. (4 pts) What is the equation for the acid ionization constant of HI?

19. (6 pts) Give the oxidation numbers of all atoms in $NaMnO_4$.

For questions 20 and 21, consider the following reaction that has reached equilibrium:

$$NH_3\ (aq) + C_2H_4O_2\ (aq) \rightleftharpoons NH_4^+\ (aq) + C_2H_3O_2^-\ (aq) \quad \Delta H = -102.1\ kJ$$

20. (3 pts) What will happen to the concentration of NH_4^+ (aq) if the temperature is raised?
   a. Increase
   b. Decrease
   c. Stay the same
   d. Unable to determine with information given

21. (3 pts) What will happen to the concentration of NH_4^+ (aq) if the concentration of NH_3 is lowered?
   a. Increase
   b. Decrease
   c. Stay the same
   d. Unable to determine with information given

22. (4 pts) An atom changes its oxidation number from –2 to –5. Is it oxidized or reduced, and how many electrons did it take to do this?
   a. Oxidized, 3 electrons
   b. Reduced, 3 electrons
   c. Oxidized, 2 electrons
   d. Reduced, 4 electrons
   e. None of the above

23. (4 pts) An atom changes its oxidation number from 0 to +2. Is it oxidized or reduced, and how many electrons did it take to do this?
   a. Oxidized, 3 electrons
   b. Reduced, 3 electrons
   c. Oxidized, 2 electrons
   d. Reduced, 2 electrons
   e. None of the above

24. (3 pts) Which of the following choices best describes this reaction:

$$2VO_3^- (aq) + Zn (s) + 8H^+ (aq) \rightarrow 2VO^2+ (aq) + Zn^{2+} (aq) + 4H_2O (l)$$

   a. This is not a redox reaction. It is an acid-base reaction.
   b. This is a redox reaction. V is oxidized at the cathode, and Zn is reduced at the anode.
   c. This is a redox reaction. O is oxidized at the anode, and Zn is reduced at the cathode.
   d. This is a redox reaction. Zn is oxidized at the anode, and V is reduced at the cathode.

25. (8 pts) A Galvanic cell runs on the following reaction:

$$Co (s) + Cu^{2+} (aq) \rightarrow Co^{2+} (aq) + Cu (s)$$

Draw a diagram for this Galvanic cell, labeling the electron flow, the anode and cathode, and the positive and negative sides of the Galvanic cell.

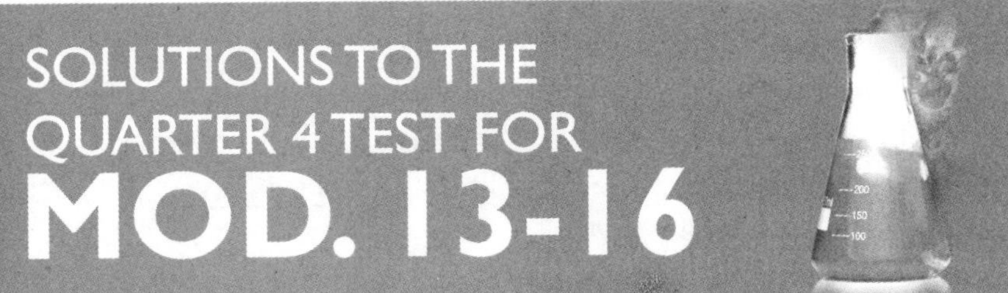

SOLUTIONS TO THE QUARTER 4 TEST FOR MOD. 13-16

1. (3 pts) b. $N_2(g)$
   Elements in their natural form have ΔH_f^o of zero. The only substance that is an element in its natural form is $N_2(g)$. The natural form of O_2 is in the gas phase, not the liquid phase.

2. (9 pts: 3 pts for the position of the reactants, 3 pts for the height of the hump, and 3 pts for the position of the products) If the reactants have an energy of 20.0 kJ, the graph must start at 20.0 kJ. If the ΔH is 20.0 kJ, then the graph must end 20.0 kJ higher than it started, so it must end at 40.0 kJ. If the activation energy is 35.0 kJ, then the hump in the middle must be 35.0 kJ higher than the reactants, so it must be at an energy of 55.0 kJ:

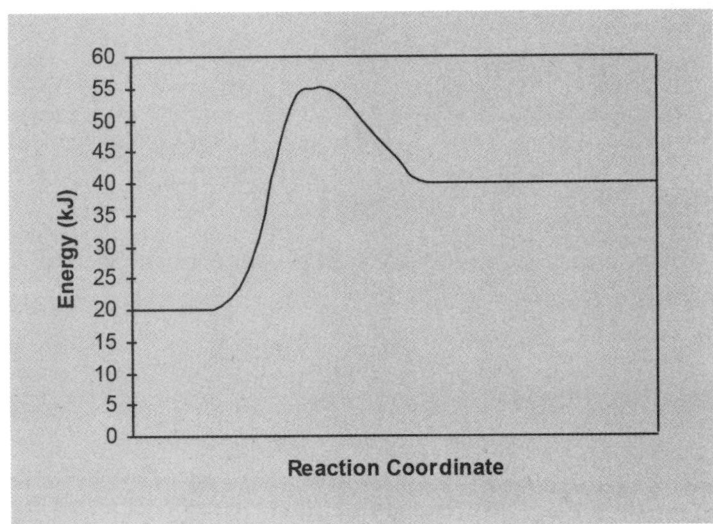

3. (3 pts) e. The activation energy is lower
   The only difference would be that the hump in the reaction with the catalyst would be smaller. That's what a catalyst does to the energy diagram: It lowers the activation energy.

4. (3 pts) a. Yes
   For a reaction to be spontaneous, its ΔG must be negative. If the chemicals decrease in disorder, this just means ΔS is negative. A negative ΔS tends to make ΔG positive, but if ΔH is negative enough, ΔG can still be negative.

5. (3 pts) a. Positive
Notice that there is a gas on the products side of the equation and no gases on the reactants side. Since the gas phase is by far the most disordered, this reaction results in an increase in the disorder of the chemicals. Thus, ΔS is positive.

6. (6 pts: 3 pts for setting up the equation with consistent units and 3 pts for solving it properly) T > 2180 K
This problem gives us ΔH and ΔS and asks us at what temperature the reaction is spontaneous. In other words, we need to see for what temperatures ΔG is negative. Thus:

$$\Delta H - T\Delta S < 0$$

To use this equation, though, we need to get our units consistent and convert the J to kJ:

$$\Delta S = 194 \cancel{J}/\text{mole K} \times \frac{1\text{ kJ}}{1000\cancel{J}} = 0.194\text{ kJ/mole K}$$

Now we can rearrange and use the equation:

$$T > \frac{\Delta H}{\Delta S}$$

Notice that the direction of the inequality sign switched when multiplying both sides by a negative number. That's a rule when doing algebra on equations with inequality signs.

$$T > \frac{423\ \cancel{\text{kJ/mole}}}{0.194\ \cancel{\text{kJ/mole}}\text{ K}}$$

$$\underline{T > 2180\text{ K}}$$

7. (3 pts) d. 4
The rate of a chemical reaction must be M/s. Since the rate constant multiplies the concentrations of the reactants raised to their orders, the overall order can be determined by figuring out what unit must be multiplied by $1/M^3s$ to get M/s. To do this, we would have to multiply by M^4. Thus concentration must be raised to the fourth power in the rate equation. This means that the overall order must be 4.

8. (3 pts) a. Remains the same
If the order of the reaction with respect to a reactant is zero, then the reaction rate does not depend on the concentration of that reactant. Thus, nothing would happen to the rate.

9. (6 pts: 3 pts for each order, and 3 pts for k) $R = (33.5\ 1/M^2\,s)\ [CO][O_2]^2$
The rate equation for this reaction will look like:

$$R = k[CO]^x[O^2]^y$$

To figure out k, x, and y, we have to look at the data from the experiment. The value for × can be determined by comparing 2 trials in which the concentration of CO changes but the concentration of O_2 stays the same. This would correspond to trials 1 and 2. In these 2 trials, the concentration of CO doubled, and the rate doubled. This means that × = 1. The value for y can be determined by looking at trials 2 and 3, where the concentration of CO stayed the same but the concentration of O2 doubled. When that happened, the rate increased by a factor of 4. This means y = 2 because the only way we can get a 4-fold increase in rate from a doubling of the concentration is by squaring the concentration. Thus, the rate equation becomes:

$$R = k[CO][O_2]^2$$

Now that we have × and y, we only need to find out the value for k. We can do this by using any one of the trials in the experiment and plugging the data into the equation. The only unknown will be k, and we can rearrange the equations and solve for it:

$$k = \frac{R}{[CO][O_2]^2} = \frac{0.113\ \cancel{M}/s}{0.150\ \cancel{M} \times 0.0225\ M^2} = 33.5\ \frac{1}{M^2\ s}$$

Thus, the final rate equation is:

$$R = (33.5\ 1/M^2\,s)\ [CO][O_2]^2$$

10. (3 pts) d. 5 °C
Since chemical reaction rate doubles for every 10 °C increment, it falls by a factor of 2 if you lower the temperature by 10 °C. If the temperature is lowered another 10 °C, it would drop by another factor of 2, making the total decrease factor of 4. Thus, to decrease the reaction rate by a factor of 4, we just lower the temperature by 20 degrees. Therefore, the new temperature is 5 °C.

11. (3 pts) b. I^- (aq)
I^- is used up in the first reaction and remade in the second reaction. Thus, it is the catalyst.

12. (3 pts) b. Homogeneous
It is a homogeneous catalyst because it has the same phase as the reactants.

13. (3 pts) c. 2:1
The balanced chemical equation is: 2HCl (aq) + $Mg(OH)_2$(aq) → $2H_2O$(aq) + $MgCl_2$ (aq) The ratio of acid to salt is 2 HCl to 1 $MgCl_2$.

14. (3 pts) d. B and C
Acidic solutions have pH under 7. Thus, B and C are acidic.

15. (3 pts) b. B
A small acid ionization constant indicates a weak acid. The higher the pH (below 7), the weaker the acid. Thus, solution B has the acid with the smallest ionization constant.

16. (4 pts: count off 1 if the student did not ignore the solids) $7.4 \times 10^{-5}\ M^5$
To get the equation for the equilibrium constant, we have to ignore both $Pb(NO_3)_2$ and PbO because they are solids. Thus, the equilibrium constant is:

$$K = [NO_2]^4_{eq}[O_2]_{eq}$$

Since we ignore solids, we ignore the amounts of both given in the problem. We use only the equilibrium concentrations of the gases. Plugging those equilibrium concentrations into the equation:

$$K = (0.25\ M)^4\ (0.019\ M) = \underline{7.4 \times 10^{-5}\ M^5}$$

17. (4 pts) c. The reaction is not at equilibrium and will shift toward reactants.
The equation for the equilibrium constant here is:

$$K = \frac{[SO_2]^2_{eq}[O_2]_{eq}}{[SO_3]^2_{eq}}$$

If the concentrations are equilibrium concentrations, then the equation should equal the value given for K.

$$K = \frac{(0.480\ \cancel{M})^2 \times (0.561\ M)}{(0.220\ \cancel{M})^2} = 2.67\ M$$

This is larger than the equilibrium constant. To get the results of the equation to equal the equilibrium point, the reaction will have to get rid of products and increase the concentration of reactants. Thus, the reaction is *not* at equilibrium and will shift toward the reactants.

18. (4 pts: 2 pts for the reaction equation, 2 pts for the ionization constant) The ionization constant is simply the equilibrium constant for the acid ionization reaction. To determine the ionization reaction, we simply take the acid in its aqueous phase and remove an H^+ ion. When we remove an H^+ ion from HI, we are left with an I– ion. In the end, then, the aqueous acid is the reactant, and the H^+ and I^- ions (both in aqueous phase) will be the products:

$$HI\ (aq) \rightleftharpoons H^+\ (aq) + I^-\ (aq)$$

The equilibrium constant for this reaction is the ionization constant, K_a:

$$K_a = \frac{[H^+]\,[I^-]}{[HI]}$$

19. (6 pts: 2 pts for each) Na: +1, Mn: +7, O: –2
Na is in group 1A, so its oxidation number is always +1. We have no rule for Mn. Oxygen is almost always –2, so that's a safe bet here. That means Mn must be +7 in order for the oxidation numbers to add to zero. Thus, the oxidation numbers are: Na: +1, Mn: +7, O: –2.

20. (3 pts) b. Decrease
The reaction is exothermic because ΔH is negative. This tells us that energy is a product. Raising the temperature, then, will be like increasing the amount of product. This will shift the equilibrium to the reactants, consuming products. Thus, the concentration of NH_4^+ will decrease.

21. (3 pts) b. Decrease
Decreasing the NH_3 concentration will shift the reaction toward the reactants. Thus, the concentration of NH_4^+ will decrease.

22. (4 pts) b. Reduced, 3 electrons

To go from −2 to −5, we must gain negatives. This means the atom gained electrons, indicating that it was reduced. To go from −2 to −5, we must gain 3 electrons.

23. (4 pts) c. Oxidized, 2 electrons
To go from 0 to +2, we must lose negatives. This means the atom lost electrons, indicating that it was oxidized. To go from 0 to +2, we must lose 2 electrons.

24. (3 pts) d. This is a redox reaction. Zn is oxidized at the anode, and V is reduced at the cathode.
Since V went from +5 to +4, it gained a negative. This means it gained an electron and thus V was reduced. Since Zn went from 0 to +2, it lost negatives. This means it lost electrons and thus Zn was oxidized.

25. (8 pts: 2 pts for the diagram, 2 pts for the anode labeling, 2 pts for cathode labeling, and 2 pts for the electron labeling)
In this reaction, Cu^{2+} is going from an oxidation number of +2 to an oxidation number of 0. This indicates that it is gaining electrons. Thus, the solution holding aqueous Cu^{2+} will have electrons flowing into it. Electrons flow toward the Cu^{2+}, so that container is positive (it attracts electrons) and thus will be the cathode. The Co is going from an oxidation number of 0 to an oxidation number of +2. This means it loses electrons. Since it is losing electrons, the electrons are flowing away from the container holding the solid Co. This makes that container the negative side of the battery (it repels electrons), and it is thus the anode. The picture, then, looks like this:

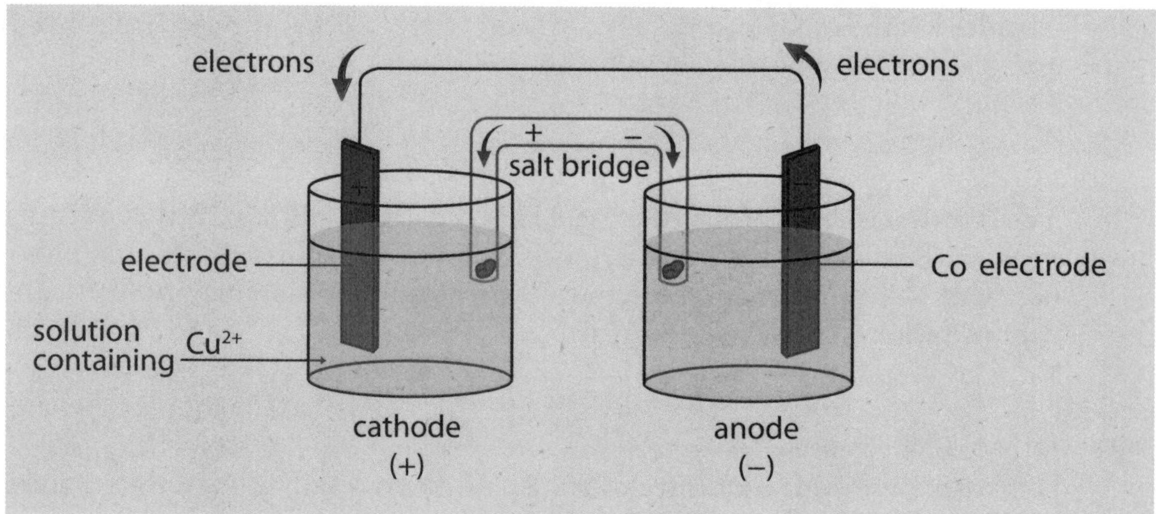